CONNECT
WITH MATHS
INTRODUCTION TO JUNIOR CYCLE

ORDINARY AND HIGHER LEVEL

Revised and fully in line with the NEW JUNIOR CYCLE SPECIFICATION

This book is complemented by:

- Free **Student Workbook**
- Extensive **Teacher's Resource Book**
- A full suite of easy-to-use and stimulating **Digital Resources** for teachers at **www.edcolearning.ie**

Edco

John McKeon   Michelle Kelly   Gillian Russell

First published 2018

The Educational Company of Ireland

Ballymount Road

Walkinstown

Dublin 12

www.edco.ie

A member of the Smurfit Kappa Group plc

ISBN 978-1-84536-819-7

The paper used in this book comes from Managed Forests in Northern Europe For every tree felled, at least one new tree is planted

Editor and proofreader: Eric Pradel

Design and layout: Compuscript, Liz White

Cover: emc design, Getty Images: Digital Vision

Photos and artwork: Compuscript, Shutterstock, Getty Images

05M21

Contents

Authors

John McKeon
Member of the PM Development Team from 2008 to 2012
Member of NCCA Mathematics Course Committee for many years
Advising Examiner for State Exams
Authors of SEC Exam Papers
Teacher of Maths and Applied Maths at Maynooth Post-Primary School
Master's Degree in Education

Gillian Russell
Teacher of Maths and Applied Maths at Maynooth Post-Primary School
First Class Honours degree in Mathematics and Maths Physics with a Postgraduate
Degree in Education from NUI Maynooth

Michelle Kelly
Teacher of Maths and Applied Maths at Maynooth Post-Primary School
Member of the IMTA and IAMTA
Winner of Industry Award for Teaching Excellence
BEng (Honours) in Mechanical Engineering and Masters in Education
Higher Diploma (Honours) in Mathematics and First Class Honours Postgraduate Degree in
Education from NUI Maynooth

Introduction

Connect With Maths – Introduction to Junior Cycle is a complete **first year** course for aspiring Higher level and Ordinary level students. On its completion, students can then choose to complete their Junior Cycle studies using either

Connect With Maths – Junior Cycle Ordinary Level or
Connect With Maths – Junior Cycle Higher Level.

Teachers can access a full suite of **digital activities** at **www.edcolearning.ie**.
Further information is available in the **Teacher Resource Book**.

The Connect With Maths series of books follows the aims and objectives of the new specification and associated assessment with an emphasis on:

- Teaching and learning for understanding by investigation and discussion
- Developing problem-solving skills
- Making connections between the five strands of the syllabus so that students are able to transfer their skills from one topic to other seemingly unrelated topics.
- Making mathematics relevant to everyday life
- Making the learning of mathematics as enjoyable as possible given that some students find the subject challenging.

Connect With Maths has the following features:

- A learning outcomes section at the start of each chapter
- Connection boxes where feasible linking the topic to other strands
- Plenty of well constructed graded activities so that students of different ability levels are challenged
- Class activity boxes to encourage class discussion
- Blue definition boxes to highlight key points
- Key information boxes to emphasise important information
- Revision activities for each chapter
- Exam-style questions at the end of each chapter
- A Key words section at the end of each chapter

A Student Activity Book comes free with *Connect With Maths – Introducton to Junior Cycle*. This has activities related to each chapter and can be used independently of the main book for revision, class tests or extra class work. The Activity Book can be used at any stage in the three years of the Junior Cycle once the relevant chapter in *Connect With Maths* has been studied.

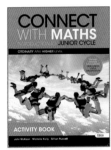

A separate **Teacher's Resource book** is provided for teachers and contains chapter notes and fully worked out solutions for every activity in *Connect With Maths – Introduction To Junior Cycle*.

Additional teacher resources, including a full suite of digital activities, are available at **www.edcolearning.ie**.

Many years of teaching experience and a lot of effort and consultation has gone into the writing of this book. We hope that students and teachers enjoy working with it together.

John McKeon, Gillian Russell, Michelle Kelly

Note from the authors

The authors would like to thank Lucy Taylor, Emer Ryan, Meike Sommer, Declan Dempsey, Martina Harford, Julie Glennon and all at Edco whose endless patience, support and expertise was so important in bringing this work to fruition. Thanks also to Eric Pradel for his painstaking proof-reading.

A special word of thanks to the students and staff of Maynooth Post Primary School, past and present. Many happy hours of teaching there have contributed hugely to this book.

Dedications

To Emily, my wife and best friend down all the years and to our wonderful sons, Robert, Barry, Stephen and Kevin. For Adi, Isla, Cora, Sean, Doug and Frank and remembering little Charlie. – John

To my family, especially my husband Oscar, thank you all for your support and guidance through this process. – Gillian

To my family and friends who have been very patient and supportive, in particular David, Jack, Katie and Conor. – Michelle

Digital Resources

The *Connect with Maths – Introduction to Junior Cycle* digital resources will enhance classroom learning by encouraging student participation and engagement. They support the New Junior Cycle Specification's emphasis on the use of modern technology in the classroom and are designed to cater for different learning styles.

To provide guidance for the integration of digital resources in the classroom and to aid lesson planning, they are **referenced throughout the textbook** using the following icons:

 Highly adaptable **Interactive Tools** that allow students to create their own activities

 A series of stimulating **videos**, covering a variety of different topics, allowing students to observe maths in action

 Editable **PowerPoint** presentations providing step-by-step solutions to a selection activity questions

 Dynamic curriculum based **Animated Constructions**.

Teachers can access the *Connect with Maths* digital resources, including **digital activity suggestions, weblinks** and **team projects** via the *Connect with Maths* interactive e-book, which is available online at **www.edcolearning.ie**.

Learning Objectives

Number strand

Students should be able to:

N.1   investigate the representation of numbers and arithmetic operations so that they can:

    a. represent the operations of addition, subtraction, multiplication, and division in $\mathbb{N}$, $\mathbb{Z}$, and $\mathbb{Q}$ using models including the number line, decomposition, and accumulating groups of equal size

    b. perform the operations of addition, subtraction, multiplication, and division and understand the relationship between these operations and the properties: commutative, associative and distributive in $\mathbb{N}$, $\mathbb{Z}$, and $\mathbb{Q}$ **and in $\mathbb{R}\backslash\mathbb{Q}$, including operating on surds**

    c. explore numbers written as a^b (in index form) so that they can:

        I.   flexibly translate between whole numbers and index representation of numbers

        II.   use and apply generalisations such as $a^p\, a^q = a^{p+q}$; $(a^p)/(a^q) = a^{p-q}$; $(a^p)^q = a^{pq}$; and $n^{1/2} = \sqrt{n}$, for $a \in \mathbb{Z}$, and $p, q, p-q, \sqrt{n} \in \mathbb{N}$ **and for $a, b, \sqrt{n} \in \mathbb{R}$, and $p, q \in \mathbb{Q}$**

        III.   use and apply generalisations such as $a^0 = 1$; $a^{p/q} = \sqrt[q]{a^p} = (\sqrt[q]{a})^p$; $a^r = 1/(a^r)$; $(ab)^r = a^r\, b^r$; and $(a/b)^r = (a^r)/(b^r)$, for $a, b \in \mathbb{R}$; $p, q \in \mathbb{Z}$; and $r \in \mathbb{Q}$

        IV.   generalise numerical relationships involving operations involving numbers written in index form

        V.   correctly use the order of arithmetic and index operations including the use of brackets

    d. calculate and interpret factors (including the highest common factor), multiples (including the lowest common multiple), and prime numbers

    e. present numerical answers to the degree of accuracy specified, for example, correct to the nearest hundred, to two decimal places, or to three significant figures

    f. convert the number p in decimal form to the form $a \times 10^n$, where $1 \le a < 10$, $n \in \mathbb{Z}$, $p \in \mathbb{Q}$, and $p \ge 1$ **and $0 < p < 1$**

N.2   investigate equivalent representations of rational numbers so that they can:

    a. flexibly convert between fractions, decimals, and percentages

    b. use and understand ratio and proportion

    c. solve money-related problems including those involving bills, VAT, profit or loss, % profit or loss (on the cost price), cost price, selling price, compound interest for not more than 3 years, income tax (standard rate only), net pay (including other deductions of specified amounts), value for money calculations and judgements, **mark up (profit as a % of cost price), margin (profit as a % of selling price), compound interest, income tax and net pay (including other deductions)**

N.3 investigate situations involving proportionality so that they can:

    a. use absolute and relative comparison where appropriate

    b. solve problems involving proportionality including those involving currency conversion and those involving average speed, distance, and time

N.4 analyse numerical patterns in different ways, including making out tables and graphs, and continue such patterns

N.5 explore the concept of a set so that they can:

    a. understand the concept of a set as a well-defined collection of elements, and that set equality is a relationship where two sets have the same elements

    b. define sets by listing their elements, if finite (including in a 2-set or **3-set** Venn diagram), or by generating rules that define them

    c. use and understand suitable set notation and terminology, including null set, Ø, subset, $\subset$, complement, element, $\in$, universal set, cardinal number, #, intersection, $\cap$, union, $\cup$, set difference, \, $\mathbb{N}$, $\mathbb{Z}$, $\mathbb{Q}$, $\mathbb{R}$, and $\mathbb{R}\backslash\mathbb{Q}$

    d. perform the operations of intersection and union on 2 sets **and on 3 sets**, set difference, and complement, including the use of brackets to define the order of operations

    e. **investigate whether the set operations of intersection, union, and difference are commutative and/or associative**

Geometry and trigonometry strand

Students should be able to:

GT.1 calculate, interpret, and apply units of measure and time

GT.2 investigate 2D shapes and 3D solids so that they can:

    a. draw and interpret scaled diagrams

    b. draw and interpret nets of rectangular solids, **prisms (polygonal bases), cylinders**

    c. find the perimeter and area of plane figures made from combinations of discs, triangles, and rectangles, including relevant operations involving pi

    d. find the volume of rectangular solids, cylinders, **triangular-based prisms, spheres,** and combinations of these, including relevant operations involving pi

    e. find the surface area and **curved surface area (as appropriate)** of rectangular solids, **cylinders, triangular-based prisms, spheres,** and combinations of these

GT.3 investigate the concept of proof through their engagement with geometry so that they can:

    a. perform constructions 1 to 15 in *Geometry for Post-Primary School Mathematics* **(constructions 3 and 7 at HL only)**

    b. recall and use the concepts, axioms, theorems, corollaries and converses, specified in *Geometry for Post-Primary School Mathematics* (section 9 for OL **and section 10 for HL**)

       I. axioms 1, 2, 3, 4 and 5

       II. theorems 1, 2, 3, 4, 5, 6, 9, 10, 13, 14, 15 **and 11, 12, 19**, and appropriate converses, including relevant operations involving square roots

       III. corollaries 3, 4 **and 1, 2, 5** and appropriate converses

c. use **and explain** the terms: theorem, proof, axiom, corollary, converse, and implies

d. create and evaluate proofs of geometrical propositions

e. display understanding of the proofs of theorems 1, 2, 3, 4, 5, 6, 9, 10, 14, 15, **and 13, 19**; and of corollaries 3, 4, **and 1, 2, 5** (full formal proofs are not examinable)

GT.4 evaluate and use trigonometric ratios (sin, cos, and tan, defined in terms of right-angled triangles) and their inverses, involving angles between 0° and 90° at integer values **and in decimal form**

GT.5 investigate properties of points, lines and line segments in the co-ordinate plane so that they can:

a. find and interpret: distance, midpoint, slope, point of intersection, and slopes of parallel **and perpendicular** lines

b. draw graphs of line segments and interpret such graphs in context, including discussing the rate of change (slope) and the y intercept

c. find and interpret the equation of a line in the form $y = mx + c$; $y - y_1 = m(x - x_1)$; **and $ax + by + c = 0$** (for a, b, c, m, x_1, $y_1 \in \mathbb{Q}$); including finding the slope, the y intercept, and other points on the line

GT.6 investigate transformations of simple objects so that they can:

a. recognise and draw the image of points and objects under translation, central symmetry, axial symmetry, and rotation

b. draw the axes of symmetry in shapes

Algebra and functions strand

Students should be able to:

AF.1 investigate patterns and relationships (linear, quadratic, doubling and tripling) in number, spatial patterns and real-world phenomena involving change so that they can:

a. represent these patterns and relationships in tables and graphs

b. generate a generalised expression for linear **and quadratic** patterns in words and algebraic expressions and fluently convert between each representation

c. categorise patterns as linear, non-linear, **quadratic, and exponential (doubling and tripling)** using their defining characteristics as they appear in the different representations

AF.2 investigate situations in which letters stand for quantities that are variable so that they can:

a. generate and interpret expressions in which letters stand for numbers

b. find the value of expressions given the value of the variables

c. use the concept of equality to generate and interpret equations

AF.3 apply the properties of arithmetic operations and factorisation to generate equivalent expressions so that they can develop and use appropriate strategies to:

a. add, subtract and simplify

    I. linear expressions in one or more variables with coefficients in $\mathbb{Q}$

    II. quadratic expressions in one variable with coefficients in $\mathbb{Z}$

    III. expressions of the form $\dfrac{a}{(bx + c)}$, where a, b, $c \in \mathbb{Z}$

b. multiply expressions of the form

 I. $a(bx + cy + d)$; $a(bx^2 + cx + d)$; and $ax(bx^2 + cx + d)$, where $a, b, c, d \in \mathbb{Z}$

 II. **$(ax + b)(cx + d)$ and $(ax + b)(cx^2 + dx + e)$,** where $a, b, c, d, e \in \mathbb{Z}$

c. divide quadratic **and cubic expressions** by linear expressions, where all coefficients are integers and there is no remainder

d. flexibly convert between the factorised and expanded forms of algebraic expressions of the form:

 I. axy, where $a \in \mathbb{Z}$

 II. $axy + byz$, where $a, b \in \mathbb{Z}$

 III. $sx - ty + tx - sy$, where $s, t \in \mathbb{Z}$

 IV. $dx^2 + bx$; $x^2 + bx + c$; **and $ax^2 + bx + c$,** where $b, c, d \in \mathbb{Z}$ **and $a \in \mathbb{N}$**

 V. $x^2 - a^2$ **and $a^2 x^2 - b^2 y^2$,** where $a, b \in \mathbb{Z}$

AF.4 select and use suitable strategies (graphic, numeric, algebraic, trial and improvement, working backwards) for finding solutions to:

a. linear equations in one variable with coefficients in $\mathbb{Q}$ and solutions in $\mathbb{Z}$ **or in $\mathbb{Q}$**

b. quadratic equations in one variable with coefficients and solutions in $\mathbb{Z}$ **or coefficients in $\mathbb{Q}$ and solutions in $\mathbb{R}$**

c. simultaneous linear equations in two variables with coefficients and solutions in $\mathbb{Z}$ **or in $\mathbb{Q}$**

d. linear inequalities in one variable of the form $g(x) < k$, and graph the solution sets on the number line for $x \in \mathbb{N}$, $\mathbb{Z}$, and $\mathbb{R}$

AF.5 generate quadratic equations given integer roots

AF.6 apply the relationship between operations and an understanding of the order of operations including brackets and exponents to change the subject of a formula

AF.7 investigate functions so that they can:

a. demonstrate understanding of the concept of a function

b. represent and interpret functions in different ways—graphically (for $x \in \mathbb{N}$, $\mathbb{Z}$, and $\mathbb{R}$, [continuous functions only], as appropriate), diagrammatically, in words, and algebraically — using the language and notation of functions (domain, range, co-domain, $f(x) =$, $f{:}x \mapsto$, and $y =$) (drawing the graph of a function given its algebraic expression is limited to linear and quadratic functions at *OL*)

c. use graphical methods to find and interpret approximate solutions of equations such as $f(x) = g(x)$

 and approximate solution sets of inequalities such as $f(x) < g(x)$

d. make connections between the shape of a graph and the story of a phenomenon, including identifying and interpreting maximum and minimum points

Statistics and probability strand

Students should be able to:

SP.1   investigate the outcomes of experiments so that they can:

    a. generate a sample space for an experiment in a systematic way, including tree diagrams for successive events and two-way tables for independent events

    b. use the fundamental principle of counting to solve authentic problems

SP.2   investigate random events so that they can:

    a. demonstrate understanding that probability is a measure on a scale of 0–1 of how likely an event (including an everyday event) is to occur

    b. use the principle that, in the case of equally likely outcomes, the probability of an event is given by the number of outcomes of interest divided by the total number of outcomes

    c. use relative frequency as an estimate of the probability of an event, given experimental data, and recognise that increasing the number of times an experiment is repeated generally leads to progressively better estimates of its theoretical probability

SP.3   carry out a statistical investigation which includes the ability to:

    a. generate a statistical question

    b. plan and implement a method to generate and/or source unbiased, representative data, and present this data in a frequency table

    c. classify data (categorical, numerical)

    d. select, draw and interpret appropriate graphical displays of univariate data, including pie charts, bar charts, line plots, histograms (equal intervals), ordered stem and leaf plots, **and ordered back-to-back stem and leaf plots**

    e. select, calculate and interpret appropriate summary statistics to describe aspects of univariate data. Central tendency: mean **(including of a grouped frequency distribution),** median, mode. Variability: range

    f. evaluate the effectiveness of different graphical displays in representing data

    g. discuss misconceptions and misuses of statistics

    h. discuss the assumptions and limitations of conclusions drawn from sample data or graphical/numerical summaries of data

Unifying strand

Elements		Students should be able to:
Building blocks	U.1	recall and demonstrate understanding of the fundamental concepts and procedures that underpin each strand
	U.2	apply the procedures associated with each strand accurately, effectively, and appropriately
	U.3	recognise that equality is a relationship in which two mathematical expressions have the same value

Representation	U.4	represent a mathematical situation in a variety of different ways, including: numerically, algebraically, graphically, physically, in words; and to interpret, analyse, and compare such representations
Connections	U.5	make connections within and between strands
	U.6	make connections between mathematics and the real world
Problem solving	U.7	make sense of a given problem, and if necessary mathematise a situation
	U.8	apply their knowledge and skills to solve a problem, including decomposing it into manageable parts and/or simplifying it using appropriate assumptions
	U.9	interpret their solution to a problem in terms of the original question
	U.10	evaluate different possible solutions to a problem, including evaluating the reasonableness of the solutions, and exploring possible improvements and/or limitations of the solutions (if any)
Generalisation and proof	U.11	generate general mathematical statements or conjectures based on specific instances
	U.12	generate and evaluate mathematical arguments and proofs
Communication	U.13	communicate mathematics effectively: justify their reasoning, interpret their results, explain their conclusions, and use the language and notation of mathematics to express mathematical ideas precisely

Sets

Chapter 1

Learning Intentions

In this chapter, you will learn about:

- The concept of a set as a collection of well-defined objects
- Listing elements of a set
- Describing a set
- The cardinal number of a set
- Venn diagrams, the universal set, the null set and subsets
- Performing the operations of union and intersection on two sets
- Solving problems involving sets

LO: N.5(a-b), U.5, U.6, U.13

Section 1A Introduction to Sets

Class Discussion

Where have you met the word 'set' before, apart from mathematics?
Can you think of examples of sets that you have at home? Could you say
in a few words what a set is?

In mathematics we need to say precisely what we mean when we use a word or a phrase.

When we say exactly what something is, we are giving a **definition** of it. We might also say
that we are **defining** it.

Let's define what we mean by a set:

A **set** is a well-defined collection of objects.

The objects which make up
a set can be anything:
numbers, people, items,
words, etc.

By well-defined we mean that it must be clear which objects are in the set and which are not.

Class Activity

Count the number of students with fair-coloured hair in your class.

■ Will everyone in the class get the same answer?

■ Does this group form a set?

What about the number of tall students in the room? Does this group form a set? Explain your answer.

If it is not clear which objects should be included, then it is not a set. 'Fair hair' is not well-defined and different people will see this differently. The word 'tall' is not clear either – you might not think you are tall, but everyone is tall when compared to something very small, like an insect.

Good examples of sets would be 'names beginning with the letter A', 'letters in a word' or 'odd numbers'. Can you think of any others?

The objects which make up a set are called **elements** or **members** of the set.

We name a set by a capital letter: A, B, C, etc.

There are different ways to identify a set:

1. Write out the set in words:

   For example: A is the set of odd numbers greater than 5 but less than 20.

2. The **list method**:

   For example: $A = \{7, 9, 11, 13, 15, 17, 19\}$

Key Points

In the list method, we:
- separate the elements by commas
- enclose the set in chain (curly) brackets { }
- list each element **once only**.

Example 1

Write D, the set of letters in the word 'happy' using the list method.

Solution

$D = \{h, a, p, y\}$

In mathematics, we like to write sentences as efficiently as we can. We often use symbols to do this.

If we want to say '11 is an element of set A' we simply write **'11 ∈ A'**.

The statement '12 is not an element of set A' is written as **'12 ∉ A'**.

Note that the symbol for 'is not an element of' is similar to a No Parking sign as it also has a diagonal line through it.

No Parking

For example:

| ∈ | means 'is an element of': e.g. u ∈ {a, e, i, o, u} |
| ∉ | means 'is not an element of': e.g. John ∉ {Andrew, Anthony, Alan} |

Example 2

(i) List the elements of the set W, the days of the week.

(ii) If set B = {Monday, Tuesday, Friday, Saturday, Sunday}

   (a) Which of the elements of the set B belong to the set W?

   (b) Which of the elements of set W do not belong to set B?

Solution

(i) W = {Monday, Tuesday, Wednesday, Thursday, Friday, Saturday, Sunday}

(ii) (a) {Monday, Tuesday, Friday, Saturday, Sunday} ∈ W

(b) {Wednesday, Thursday} ∉ B

Cardinal Number (#)

The **cardinal number** of a set is the number of elements or members in the given set.

The symbol for the cardinal number is: #.

For example: If set P = {a, b, c, d, e, f}, then #P = 6, as there are 6 elements in set P.

Example 3

(i) List the elements of the set A, the days of the week beginning with the letter T.

(ii) What is the cardinal number of the set A?

Solution

(i) A = {Tuesday, Thursday} as there are only two days of the week beginning with the letter T.

(ii) #A = 2, as there are 2 elements in the set.

Example 4

(i) List the members of the following set.
C = {the even numbers between 25 and 35}

(ii) What is #C, the cardinal number of C?

Solution

(i) C = {26, 28, 30, 32, 34}

(ii) #C = 5 as there are 5 elements in the set.

Example 5

Describe in words the following set:
B = {a, b, c, d}

Solution

The set B contains the first four letters of the alphabet.

Activity 1.1

1 Which of the following lists are mathematical sets?

(i) The even numbers between 20 and 40

(ii) The small animals on a farm

(iii) The students in your maths class

(iv) The members of the school basketball team

(v) The good movies out this year.

Sets

2 List the elements in each of the following sets and state the cardinal number of each set.

  (i) A = {the days of the week}

  (ii) B = {the odd numbers between 0 and 20}

  (iii) C = {the months of the year beginning with the letter S}

  (iv) D = {the first six letters of the alphabet}

  (v) E = {the vowels in the word 'suspicious'}

3 List the elements of the following sets and state the cardinal number of each.

  (i) A = {the letters in the word 'mathematics'}

  (ii) B = {the last six letters of the alphabet}

  (iii) C = {the counties in Connacht}

  (iv) D = {the days of the week beginning with the letter S}

  (v) E = {the digits in the number 12 385}

4 The sets Q, R and S are as follows:

Q = {a, e, i, o, u}, R = {1, 2, 3, 4, 5} and S = {2, 4, 6, 8, 10}.

Write out the following statements, putting in the correct symbol ($\in$ or $\notin$):

  (i) 1 ___ Q (vi) u ___ Q

  (ii) 2 ___ R (vii) w ___ Q

  (iii) 10 ___ S (viii) 3 ___ R

  (iv) 9 ___ S (ix) 2 ___ S

  (v) 0 ___ R (x) 3 ___ Q

5 State whether the following statements are true or false.

  (i) 3 $\notin$ {1, 2, 3, 4}

  (ii) f $\in$ {g, h, i, j, k}

  (iii) 9 $\in$ {1, 2, 3, ... , 10}

  (iv) Saturday $\in$ {days of the week beginning with the letter S}

  (v) c $\notin$ {the letters of the alphabet}

  (vi) d $\in$ {vowels in the alphabet}

  (vii) 10 $\notin$ {even numbers between 5 and 25}

  (viii) s $\in$ {letters in the word 'surprise'}

  (ix) 31 $\notin$ {odd numbers between 5 and 25}

  (x) p $\in$ {letters in the word 'uniform'}

6 Describe in words each of the following sets.

  (i) A = {September, October, November}

  (ii) X = {a, b, c, d, e, f, g, h}

  (iii) H = {hearts, clubs, spades, diamonds}

  (iv) B = {spoon, fork, knife}

  (v) Y = {Monday}

7 P = {a, b, c, d, e} and Q = {5, 10, 15, 20}. State whether the following statements are true or false.

  (i) #P = 6   (vi) 15 $\notin$ Q

  (ii) 10 $\notin$ P (vii) d $\notin$ Q

  (iii) #P = #Q (viii) #P + #Q = 9

  (iv) #P − #Q = 1   (ix) a $\notin$ P

  (v) $t \in P$ (x) 5 $\in$ Q

8 The sets A, B and C are as follows:

A = {a, b, c, d}, B = {x, y, z} and C = {c, f, i, l}.

Write out the following statements, putting in the correct symbol ($\in$ or $\notin$):

  (i) e ___ A (vi) y ___ B

  (ii) c ___ C (vii) z ___ B

  (iii) x ___ B (viii) l ___ C

  (iv) d ___ C (ix) c ___ A

  (v) r ___ A (x) x ___ A

9 Given D = { } and E = { }

Find the value of:

  (i) #D (ii) #E (iii) #D − #E (iv) #D + #E

Sets

Section 1B **The Null Set and Subsets**

The Null Set

- The **null set** is the set that contains no elements or members.
- The symbol for the null set is **{ }** or ∅.
  The null set is also called the **empty set**.
- We say 'the' empty set because there is only one empty set.

Example 1

List the elements in set $D = \{$days of the week that begin with the letter P$\}$.

Solution

As there are no days of the week that begin with the letter P, we write $D = \{\ \}$.

Subsets

A **subset** can be described as a set within a set.

Set A is a subset of set B if every element of A is also in B.

For example:

Given the following sets,

$A = \{3, 6\}$, $B = \{3, 6, 9\}$ and $C = \{3, 10\}$

- We can say that A is a subset of B as all the elements in set A are also in set B.
- C is not a subset of B as not all the elements of C are in B.
- In symbols we write:

$$A \subset B \quad \text{reads } A \text{ 'is a subset of' } B.$$

$$C \not\subset B \quad \text{reads } C \text{ 'is not a subset of' } B.$$

- Every set is a subset of itself.
- The null set is a subset of every set.

Example 2

(i) Write out all the subsets of {Tom, Tim, Terry}.

(ii) How many subsets are there in total?

Solution

(i) Subsets with 0 element: { }

 Subsets with 1 element: {Tom}, {Tim}, {Terry}

 Subsets with 2 elements: {Tom, Tim}, {Tom, Terry}, {Tim, Terry}

 Subsets with 3 elements: {Tom, Tim, Terry}

(ii) There are 8 subsets in all.

Example 3

If B = {2, 4, 6, 8}

(i) Write out all the subsets of the set B.

(ii) How many subsets of B are there in total?

Solution

(i) The subsets of set B are:

Subsets with 0 element:	{ }
Subsets with 1 element:	{2}, {4}, {6}, {8}
Subsets with 2 elements:	{2, 4}, {2, 6}, {2, 8}, {4, 6}, {4, 8}, {6, 8}
Subsets with 3 elements:	{2, 4, 6}, {2, 4, 8}, {2, 6, 8}, {4, 6, 8}
Subsets with 4 elements:	{2, 4, 6, 8}

(ii) There are 16 subsets in all.

Activity 1.2

1 List all the subsets of each of the following sets:

(i) A = {2, 5}   (ii) B = {heads, tails}   (iii) C = {1, 3, 5}

2 A = {1, 5, 6, 8, 9, 11}, B = {2, 4, 5, 11, 12} and C = {1, 5, 11}.

State whether the following statements are true or false.

(i) {1, 8, 11} ⊂ A   (iv) #B ≠ #C   (vii) #A = #B   (ix) {4, 5} ⊂ B

(ii) C ⊂ B   (v) {6, 12} ⊄ A   (viii) B ⊂ A   (x) { } ⊄ C

(iii) {2, 5} ⊄ B   (vi) {1, 11} ⊄ C

3 List all the subsets of the set {a, b, c}.

4 List all the subsets of the set {w, x, y, z}.

5 The sets X and Y are:

X = {the odd numbers from 30 to 40}

Y = {the whole numbers from 30 to 40}.

(i) List the elements of the set X and set Y.

(ii) State whether the following statements are true or false:

(a) #X = 5   (b) X ⊂ Y   (c) { } ⊄ X   (d) {30, 40} ⊄ Y   (e) #Y = 10

6 (i) Copy and complete the following table.

Set	Subsets	Number of subsets
{ }		
{a}	{ }, {a}	2
{a, b}		
{a, b, c}		
{a, b, c, d}		
{a, b, c, d, e}		

(ii) What is the pattern for the number of subsets?

(iii) How many subsets does the set {a, b, c, d, e, f, g, h} have?

(iv) Give a rule in your own words for the number of subsets in any set.

7 (i) Copy the following table into your copybook. Use your table from question **6** to complete the first six rows.

Set	No. of subsets with 0 elements	No. of subsets with 1 element	No. of subsets with 2 elements	No. of subsets with 3 elements	No. of subsets with 4 elements	No. of subsets with 5 elements	No. of subsets with 6 elements	No. of subsets with 7 elements
{ }								
{a}								
{a, b}								
{a, b, c}								
{a, b, c, d}								
{a, b, c, d, e}								

(ii) Look for the pattern in the table you have completed. Use the pattern to complete the last two rows.

(iii) Look up 'Pascal's Triangle' in a reference book or on the Internet. Compare it to your pattern.

Section 1C Venn Diagrams: Union and Intersection

You will find it much easier to see things clearly in maths if you draw a picture or a diagram to help you see what is happening. This is why the English mathematician John Venn developed the Venn diagram.

John Venn (1834–1923)

Representing Sets on a Venn Diagram

- Sets are usually represented by circles or ovals.
- The **elements** or **members** of the set are labelled inside the circle or oval.
- Such a graphical representation of sets is called a **Venn diagram**.

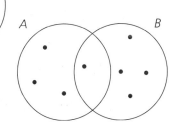

For example:

If $A = \{1, 2, 3\}$ and $B = \{3, 4, 5, 6\}$, then we can represent these sets on a Venn diagram as shown:

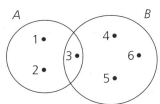

When drawing a Venn diagram:

- We show an element once only.
- If an element belongs to both sets, we position it in the middle section where the circular shapes overlap or intersect.
- The empty set is hatched (filled with parallel lines) to show that it has no elements. In this diagram, A has no elements.

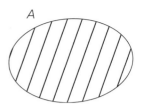

Intersection of Two Sets

The **intersection of two sets,** set A and set B, is the set of all the elements which are common to both set A **and** set B (written $A \cap B$).

$A \cap B$ is represented on a Venn diagram as shown.

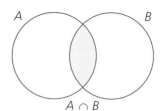

Union of Two Sets

When we put all the elements of A and B together into one set, without repeating any elements, we have 'A **union** B'.

(A union of workers is made when they all come together in one group.)

We write this as $A \cup B$.

$A \cup B$ is represented on a Venn diagram as shown.

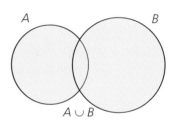

Example 1

Given the Venn diagram, list the elements of the following.

(i) P (iii) $P \cup Q$

(ii) Q (iv) $P \cap Q$

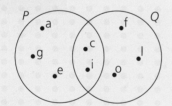

Solution

(i)

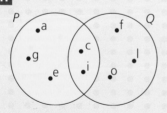

$P = \{a, c, e, g, i\}$

(ii)

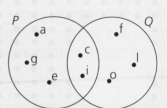

$Q = \{c, f, i, l, o\}$

(iii)

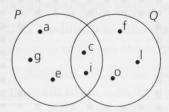

$P \cup Q = \{a, c, e, f, g, i, l, o\}$

(iv)

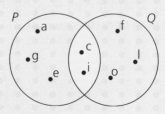

$P \cap Q = \{c, i\}$

The Commutative Property of $A \cup B$ and $A \cap B$

The order of the sets is not relevant when finding intersection or union as the answer will always be the same. So:

- $A \cup B = B \cup A$
- $A \cap B = B \cap A$ where A and B are the names of sets.

Union and intersection are called **operations** on sets.

In mathematics, we say that union and intersection are **commutative** operations. We will meet this idea again later on when we look at operations on numbers (addition, subtraction, etc.).

Example 2

List the elements of:

(i) X

(ii) Y

(iii) $X \cup Y$

(iv) $Y \cup X$

(v) $X \cap Y$

(vi) $Y \cap X$

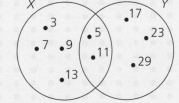

Solution

From observation we can see:

(i) $X = \{3, 5, 7, 9, 11, 13\}$

(ii) $Y = \{5, 11, 17, 23, 29\}$

(iii) $X \cup Y = \{3, 5, 7, 9, 11, 13, 17, 23, 29\}$

(iv) $Y \cup X = \{3, 5, 7, 9, 11, 13, 17, 23, 29\}$

(v) $X \cap Y = \{5, 11\}$

(vi) $Y \cap X = \{5, 11\}$

Activity 1.3

1

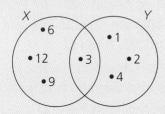

(i) List the elements of:
   (a) A (c) $A \cup B$ (e) $B \cup A$
   (b) B (d) $A \cap B$ (f) $B \cap A$

(ii) Explain why $A \cup B = B \cup A$ and $A \cap B = B \cap A$.

2 The sets X and Y are shown in the Venn diagram. The sets are:
$X = \{3, 6, 9, 12\}$ and $Y = \{1, 2, 3, 4\}$.

(i) List the elements of:
   (a) $X \cup Y$ (b) $X \cap Y$

(ii) Find the values of:
   (a) $\#X$ (c) $\#(X \cup Y)$
   (b) $\#Y$ (d) $\#(X \cap Y)$

3 The sets S and T are: $S = \{a, e, i, o, u\}$ and $T = \{a, b, c, d\}$.

(i) Copy the Venn diagram and fill in the information provided for the sets.

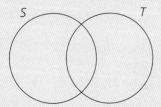

(ii) Use the Venn diagram to write down the elements of:
   (a) $S \cup T$ (b) $S \cap T$

(iii) Write the value of each of the following.

    (a) $\#(S \cup T)$ (b) $\#(S \cap T)$

4   A = {the whole numbers from 1 to 5} and B = {the odd numbers from 1 to 8}.

  (i) Copy the Venn diagram and fill in the information provided for the sets.

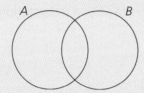

  (ii) Write down the elements of the following.

    (a) A (c) $A \cup B$ (e) $A \cap B$

    (b) B (d) $B \cup A$ (f) $B \cap A$

  (iii) Write down the value of each of the following.

    (a) $\#A$ (c) $\#(A \cup B)$

    (b) $\#B$ (d) $\#(A \cap B)$

5   Two sets X and Y are defined as follows:

X = {the students in the class who have a cat} and

Y = {the students in the class who have a dog}.

Describe, in your own words, the members of the following:

  (i) $(X \cup Y)$ (ii) $(X \cap Y)$

6   From the information provided in the Venn diagram, indicate whether each statement is true or false.

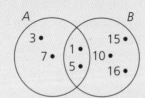

  (i) A = {1, 3, 5, 7}   (v) {15, 1} $\subset B$

  (ii) $\#(A \cup B)$ = 6   (vi) 3 $\in (A \cap B)$

  (iii) {1, 5} $\subset A$ (vii) 7 $\notin B$

  (iv) { } $\not\subset B$ (viii) B = {1, 5, 10, 15}

7   S = {the students in the school who play sport} and

M = {the students in the school who are in the school musical}.

Describe, in your own words, the members of the following.

  (i) $(S \cup M)$ (ii) $(S \cap M)$

8   Copy the Venn diagram four times and shade in each of the following.

  (i) M (iii) $M \cup N$

  (ii) N (iv) $M \cap N$

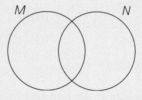

9   L = {the odd numbers between 20 and 30} and

F = {the whole numbers from 25 to 33}.

  (i) Write down the elements in set L and set F.

  (ii) Draw a Venn diagram to represent both sets.

  (iii) Write down the value of each of the following.

    (a) $\#L$ (c) $\#(L \cup F)$

    (b) $\#F$ (d) $\#(L \cap F)$

10   Set A has five elements and set B has three elements.

  (i) What is the greatest number of elements possible in $A \cap B$?

  (ii) What is the greatest number of elements possible in $A \cup B$?

11   (i) When does $P \cap Q = P$? Explain, using a diagram. Give an example of two such sets P and Q.

  (ii) When does $P \cup Q = P$? Explain, using a diagram. Give an example of two such sets P and Q.

  (iii) When does $P \cap Q = P \cup Q$? Explain, using a diagram. Give an example of two such sets P and Q.

Section 1D The Universal Set

The **universal set** is:

- the set that contains all the elements in a given question or problem
- represented by the symbol U (this is different from the union symbol $\cup$)
- shown as a square or a rectangle around the other sets in the given question.

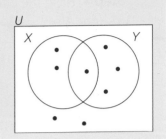

Example 1

Write down the elements in each of the following.

(i) U

(ii) A

(iii) B

(iv) $A \cup B$

(v) $A \cap B$

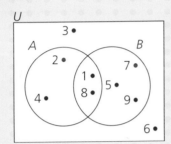

Solution

From observation, we can see that:

(i) $U = \{1, 2, 3, 4, 5, 6, 7, 8, 9\}$, all the elements in the universal set.

(ii) $A = \{1, 2, 4, 8\}$, all the elements in set A.

(iii) $B = \{1, 5, 7, 8, 9\}$, all the elements in set B.

(iv) $A \cup B = \{1, 2, 4, 5, 7, 8, 9\}$, all the elements in $A \cup B$.

(v) $A \cap B = \{1, 8\}$, all the elements in $A \cap B$.

Problem Solving with Sets

When problem solving, we use a Venn diagram to represent the cardinal number of the sets in the given question.

Example 2

In a group of 50 students, 31 have a laptop, 22 have a PC and 6 have both.

(i) Illustrate the information given on a Venn diagram.

(ii) Use the Venn diagram to find the number of students who don't have a laptop or a PC.

Solution

Identify all the information given in the question:

- $\#U = 50$ as the class of 50 students are the universal set.
- 31 students have a laptop. These students are the set 'Laptop'.
- 22 students have a PC. These students are the set 'PC'.
- 6 students from the set have both a laptop and a PC. These students are the set 'Laptop $\cap$ PC'.

(i) To fill in the Venn diagram:

Step 1. Fill in the intersection.

(Laptop ∩ PC) = 6

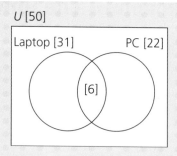

Step 2. Now fill in the remainder of the sets given.

Remainder for set Laptop

= Students with laptops – Students with both

= 31 – 6

= 25 students

Remainder for set PC

= Students with PCs – Students with both

= 22 – 6

= 16 students

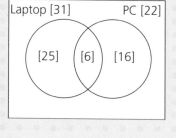

Step 3. Now fill in the remainder for the universal set *U*.

Remainder for *U* = *U* – (Laptop ∪ PC)

= 50 – (25 + 6 + 16)

= 3 students

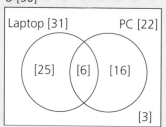

(ii) From inspection of the Venn diagram, the number of students who don't have a laptop or a PC is 3 students.

Activity 1.4

1 Write down the elements in each of the following sets based on the Venn diagram.

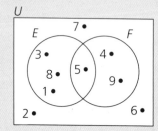

(i) *U*

(ii) *E*

(iii) *F*

(iv) *E* ∪ *F*

(v) *E* ∩ *F*

2 (i) Represent the following sets on a Venn diagram:

U = {1, 2, 3, 4, 5, 6, 7, 8, 9, 10},

P = {2, 3, 5, 7} and

Q = {2, 4, 6, 8, 10}.

(ii) Write down the elements of each of the following:

(a) *P* ∪ *Q*   (b) *P* ∩ *Q*

3 The elements of the sets U, R and S are defined below:

U = {the letters in the word 'scientific'},

R = {the letters in the word 'nice'},

S = {the letters in the word 'tense'}.

(i) Represent the given sets on a Venn diagram.

(ii) List the elements of the following:

(a) U
(d) $R \cup S$

(b) R
(e) $R \cap S$

(c) S

4 In a class of 28 students, 11 students study Home Economics, 9 study Woodwork and 2 study both.

(i) Copy the Venn diagram and fill in the information given.

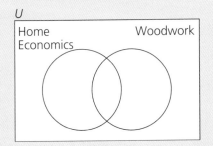

(ii) Find:

(a) The number of students who don't study either of these subjects.

(b) The number of students who only study Woodwork.

5 A drama group has 51 members. They were asked who would like to perform in a comedy show and/or work backstage. The information gathered is shown in the Venn diagram.

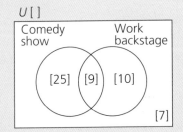

From the Venn diagram find:

(i) The number of members who only want to perform in the comedy show.

(ii) The number of members who are not involved in the comedy show.

(iii) The total number of members who will take part.

6 A football club has 47 members; they were asked if they would take part in a 5 km run and/or a 15 km cycle. 41 said they would do the cycle, 11 said they would do the run and 5 said they would do both.

(i) Copy the Venn diagram and fill in the information given.

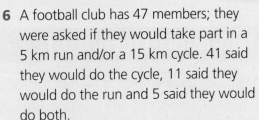

(ii) Find:

(a) The number of members doing the run only.

(b) The number of members who are not taking part.

7 A survey was carried out on first year students in a school. They were asked if they had an email account and/or a social network account.

The results are shown in the Venn diagram.

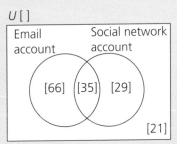

Use the Venn diagram to answer the following questions.

How many students have:

(i) an email account

(ii) a social network account

(iii) no account

(iv) both accounts

8 A class of 29 students were asked if they like pears and/or plums. 15 said they like pears, 11 said they like plums and 5 said they like both.

(i) Draw a Venn diagram to represent the information above.

(ii) How many of these students do not like pears or plums?

Revision Activity 1

1 (a) List the elements in each of the following sets.

    (i) {the set of odd numbers from 990 to 1010}

    (ii) {the set of letters in the word 'superstitious'}

    (iii) {the set of shapes with no sides}

    (iv) {the set of the last 8 letters of the alphabet}

    (v) {the set of numbers between 50 and 100 that can be divided by 5}

(b) Describe in words the elements of each of the following sets.

    (i) {2, 4, 6, 8, 10}   (iii) {Tuesday, Thursday}

    (ii) {a, e, i, o, u}   (iv) { }

2 (a) Draw a Venn diagram to represent the following sets.

    A = {a, e, i, o, u} B = {h, o, u, s, e}

(b) List the elements of the following:

    (i) $A \cup B$ (ii) $A \cap B$

3 200 people were surveyed about where they have been on holiday. 75 people said they have been to Spain, 93 people said that they have been to France and 24 people said they have been to both countries.

(a) Copy the Venn diagram and fill in the information given.

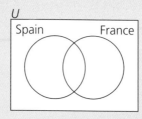

(b) How many people have been to only one country?

(c) How many people have not been to either country?

4 (a) The sets A, B and C are listed below:

    A = {9, 18, 36, 72} B = {3, 9, 27, 81, 162} C = {6, 24, 48, 96}

Based on the information given in the three sets above, state whether each of the statements below is true or false.

    (i) $6 \in B$ (vi) $\{81, 96\} \subset B$

    (ii) $8 \notin C$ (vii) $\#(A \cap B) = 1$

    (iii) $\{9\} \subset (A \cap B)$ (viii) $\{\} \subset A$

    (iv) $\#(A \cup C) = 8$ (ix) $\{\} \not\subset C$

    (v) $B \cup C$ = {3, 6, 9, 24, 27, 81, 96, 162}

(b) List all the subsets of the set A = {w, x, y}.

(c) The sets C and I are listed below:

C = {the students in your year who like Chinese food}

I = {the students in your year who like Italian food}.

Describe in your own words the members of the following:

(i) $C \cup I$ (ii) $C \cap I$

Exam-style Question

1 (a) Fill in the Venn diagram below, given that:

X = {N, I, C, O, L, A}

Y = {S, O, P, H, I, A}

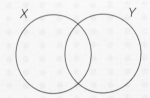

(b) Write down a **subset** of X that has 2 elements, and that is also a subset of Y.

Answer = { _____ , _____ }

(c) Write down a **subset** of X that has 2 elements, and that is **not** a subset of Y.

Answer = { _____ , _____ }

KEY WORDS AND PHRASES

- Set
- Elements/Members
- Cardinal number
- Null set

- Union
- Subset
- Venn diagram
- Intersection

- Commutative operation
- Universal set

Interactive Tool 1.1

Sets

- A **set** is a well-defined collection of objects.
- The objects which make up a set are called **elements** or **members** of the set.
- **Cardinal number (#)**
  The cardinal number of a set is the number of elements or members in the given set.
- **The Universal set (U)**
  Contains all the possible elements in a question.
- **Subset**
  A is a **subset** of B (**A ⊂ B**) if every element of A is in B.

- **Union of two sets**
  A **union** B (A ∪ B) is the set of elements
  which are in A or B or both.

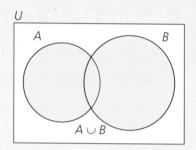

- **Intersection of two sets**
  A **intersection** B (A ∩ B) is the set of elements
  which are in A and in B.

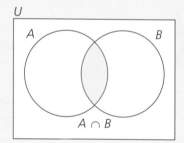

Symbol	Definition	Example
∈	is an element of	5 ∈ {3, 4, 5, 6, 7}
∉	is not an element of	2 ∉ {1, 3, 5, 7}
#	the number of elements in	#{a, b, c, d, e} = 5
{ } or Ø	the empty or null set	{ } ⊂ all sets
⊂	is a subset of	{c, a, r} ⊂ {c, a, s, p, e, r}
⊄	is not a subset of	{4, 77, 145} ⊄ {6, 54, 79, 147}
∪	union of two sets	{2, 3, 6} ∪ {1, 3, 5} = {1, 2, 3, 5, 6}
∩	intersection of two sets	{2, 3, 6} ∩ {1, 3, 5} = {3}
U	universal set	

Natural Numbers

Learning Intentions

In this chapter, you will learn about:

- Place value
- Addition, subtraction, multiplication and division of Natural numbers
- Using array models to multiply or divide large numbers
- Factors, multiples, prime numbers and prime factors
- The order of operations including the use of brackets
- Indices and the rules of indices
- Rounding off, estimating and approximating

> LO: N.1(a-e),
> U.5, U.6, U.13

You will need...

- a pencil
- a ruler
- a geometry set

Section 2A Introduction

> The Natural numbers are denoted by the set
> $\mathbb{N} = \{1, 2, 3, 4, 5, 6, 7, \dots\}$

- This is an **infinite set**. No matter what Natural number you take, you can always add a number to it or multiply it by a number to make it bigger (the three dots indicate this).

- The most common use of Natural numbers is to **count** the number of elements in a finite set. We can think of them as a means of counting natural things: one river, two horses, three mountain peaks etc.

- When we **add** two Natural numbers, we always get another Natural number.
- When we **multiply** two Natural numbers, we always get another Natural number.

Natural Numbers

A second use of Natural numbers is concerned with putting things in **order**. For example, we talk about the first, second or third day of the week; we say a team is 4th in the league table, etc.

- The symbols we use to denote numbers are called **numerals**.
- 5 is a **single-digit** number, 23 is a **two-digit** number, 147 is a **three-digit** number, etc.

Key Points

The **number line** is a way of helping us to put numbers in order.

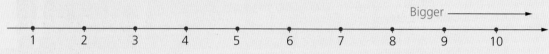

Bigger ⟶

| 1 | 2 | 3 | 4 | 5 | 6 | 7 | 8 | 9 | 10 |

- Numbers get bigger (**ascending**) as we read the number line **from left to right**, e.g. 9 is to the right of 3, so 9 is bigger than 3. We write this as '9 > 3'.
- Numbers get smaller (**descending**) as we read the number line **from right to left**, e.g. 4 is to the left of 7, so 4 is less than 7. We write this as '4 < 7'.
- The arrow at the end indicates that the line goes on forever.
- Numbers which differ by one are called **consecutive** numbers, e.g. 5, 6 and 7 are consecutive numbers.

Place Value

The Romans created Roman numerals for counting.

Modern numerals	1	5	8	10	20	30	34
Roman numerals	I	V	VIII	X	XX	XXX	XXXIV

Our method of counting is known as the **Hindu–Arabic system** which was devised about 800 AD. It took many centuries to develop because it is very ingenious.

Hindu		٥	۱	۲	۳	۴	۵	۶	۷	८	९
Arabic		٠	١	٢	٣	٤	٥	٦	٧	٨	٩
Modern		0	1	2	3	4	5	6	7	8	9

- When you see a Roman number XXX, each X means 'ten', so XX represents twenty and XXX represents thirty. But when you see the number 555 in our system, each of the 5s means something different. Each '5' in the number 555 is in a different place and so has a different value. This is referred to as '**place value**'.

We count in tens, probably because most people have ten 'digits' on their hands. This is called counting in **base ten**.

This requires ten different symbols or digits: 0, 1, 2, 3, 4, 5, 6, 7, 8, 9. These are used in different combinations to represent all possible numbers.

Digits: 0 1 2 3 4 5 6 7 8 9

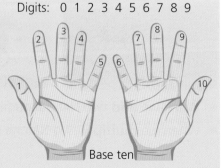

Base ten

The digits in the number 57 893 mean the following:

Ten thousands	Thousands	Hundreds	Tens	Units
5	7	8	9	3
5 × 10 000	7 × 1000	8 × 100	9 × 10	3 × 1

Addition and Subtraction of Natural Numbers

- When we add two numbers we get their **sum**, e.g. 5 is the sum of 2 and 3.
- When we subtract two numbers we get their **difference**, e.g. 2 is the difference between 9 and 7.
- Addition and subtraction are examples of **operations** on numbers. Multiplication and division are also operations on numbers.
- Subtraction is the **inverse** (opposite) operation to addition.

   For example:
   Start with 5 → add 8 → you get 13.   (5 + 8 = 13)
   Start with 13 → subtract 8 → you get back to 5.   (13 − 8 = 5)

- It follows that addition is the **inverse** (opposite) operation to subtraction.

An **inverse operation** reverses the effect of the first operation.

2

Example 1

Use a number line to calculate the following.

(i) 4 + 9   (ii) 13 − 6   (iii) 11 + 5 − 7

Solution

(i) 4 + 9 = 13

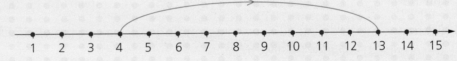

(ii) 13 − 6 = 7

(iii) 11 + 5 − 7 = 9

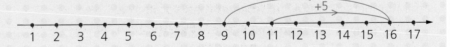

Example 2

(i) Write down the next three consecutive numbers after 6. Describe how you got them.

(ii) Suppose that x is some mystery Natural number. How could you write the next two bigger Natural numbers that come after it?

Solution

(i) 7, 8 and 9

Start with 6. Add 1 to get 6 + 1.

Then add 1 to get 6 + 1 + 1 = 6 + 2.

Now add 1 to get 6 + 2 + 1 = 6 + 3.

The numbers are (6 + 1), (6 + 2) and (6 + 3).

(ii) Start with x. Add 1 to get $x + 1$.

Add 1 to $x + 1$ to get $x + 1 + 1$ = $x + 2$.

Answer: $x + 1$ and $x + 2$

Activity 2.1

1 Without the use of a calculator, calculate each of the following.

(i) 37 + 21   (iii) 42 + 15   (v) 61 + 22   (vii) 33 + 75   (ix) 91 + 24

(ii) 93 – 31   (iv) 72 – 56   (vi) 39 – 30   (viii) 27 – 17   (x) 83 – 51

2 Using a number line, calculate each of the following.

(i) 21 + 5   (iii) 15 – 8   (v) 31 – 15   (vii) 18 – 9   (ix) 24 – 5

(ii) 36 – 12   (iv) 27 + 6   (vi) 31 + 6   (viii) 23 + 12   (x) 13 + 16

3 Find the missing value to make each statement true.

(i) 7 + 9 = 4 + __   (iii) 27 – 16 = 31 – ___   (v) 129 + 123 = 210 + __

(ii) 13 + 8 = 17 + __   (iv) 73 + 11 = __ + 36   (vi) 49 – 21 = __ – 19

4 For each of the numbers below, indicate the place value of the digit 5.

(i) 3250   (iii) 1551   (v) 5 200 321   (vii) 54 349   (ix) 250 199

(ii) 35   (iv) 950 342   (vi) 12 345   (viii) 1 543 200   (x) 205 342

5 Rearrange the following numbers in **ascending** order. Insert the symbol '<' between the numbers. < stands for 'less than'.

(i) 372   381   379   368   373   375

(ii) 4839   4893   4845   4801   4862

(iii) 27 472   27 732   27 235   27 523   27 374

6 Rearrange the following numbers in **descending** order. Insert the symbol '>' between the numbers. > stands for 'greater than'.

(i) 458 392   459 494   459 236   451 392   457 234

(ii) 560 344   563 321   567 234   560 784   562 349

(iii) 934 234   934 923   937 291   935 345   935 123

7 Evaluate each of the following without using a calculator.

(i) 3482 – 1237

(ii) 37 730 – 23 948

(iii) 103 362 + 2492

(iv) 648 291 – 12 392

(v) 3 238 372 + 1 284 928

(vi) 1 300 270 – 1 291 222

(vii) 1 284 839 – 239 986 + 138 134

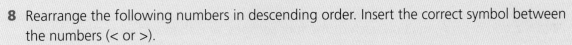

8 Rearrange the following numbers in descending order. Insert the correct symbol between the numbers (< or >).

(i) 856 784 856 235 857 349 857 350 856 440

(ii) 123 321 163 009 132 129 168 287 157 194

(iii) 382 492 391 238 397 238 381 201 391 875

9 Use some or all of the digits 3, 5, 6, 8, 9 once only to write the following.

(i) The biggest 2-digit number

(ii) The biggest 5-digit number

(iii) The smallest 3-digit number

(iv) The smallest 4-digit number

(v) The biggest number you can make.

10 (i) Write down the next three **consecutive** numbers after 15. Describe how you got them.

(ii) Suppose that n is some mystery Natural number. Write the next three consecutive Natural numbers that come after it.

Section 2B Multiplication and Division of Natural Numbers

Multiplication of Natural Numbers

We often write '2 times 3' as 2 × 3.

We can also write '2 times 3' as 2(3) or (2)(3).

For example: 4(8) = 32

(5)(10) = 50

There should be no space between the brackets in (5)(10).

When we multiply two numbers we get their **product**. For example, 6 is the product of 2 and 3.

Example 1

Calculate 48 × 31.
Show your calculations.

Solution

$$
\begin{array}{r}
48 \\
\times\ \ 31 \\
\hline
48 \\
+\ 1440 \\
\hline
1488 \\
\end{array}
$$

We can also use the **array method** for multiplication.

This method is based on splitting the numbers being multiplied into tens and units, as in the following example.

Example 2

Calculate 48 × 31 using the array method.

Solution

48 = (40 + 8) and 31 = (30 + 1)

Therefore the multiplication becomes: (40 + 8) × (30 + 1)

Draw a grid or array, multiply each of the four sections, and then add all sections to get your answer.

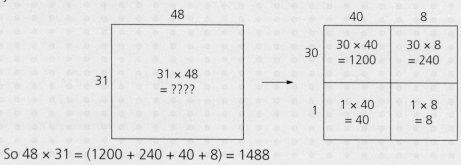

So 48 × 31 = (1200 + 240 + 40 + 8) = 1488

You can use any method you want to perform these basic calculations, but show your work clearly.

Division of Natural Numbers

Division is the **opposite of multiplication**.

- Division is where we break up a number into equal parts.

  For example, the number 20:

Multiplication ←	→ **Division**
4 groups of 5 is equal to 20	20 divided by 4 is equal to 5
5 groups of 4 is equal to 20	20 divided by 5 is equal to 4

- We say that division is the **inverse operation** of multiplication.
  Likewise, multiplication is the **inverse operation** of division.

- When we divide two numbers we get their **quotient**.

  For example, 2 is the quotient of 10 divided by 5.

Example 3

Divide 468 by 18. Show your calculations.

Solution

```
        2 6
   18) 4 6 8
      –3 6
       1 0 8
      –1 0 8
            0
```

Answer: 468 ÷ 18 = 26

Key Points

- An **even** number is a number which is a multiple of 2,
  e.g. 2, 4, 6, 8, ...
- An **odd** number is a number which is not a multiple of 2,
  e.g. 1, 3, 5, 7, ...
- Every even number has an **even units digit**, e.g. 4568 is even; 57 883 is odd.
- To **divide by 10**, take off **one** end zero, e.g. 380 ÷ 10 = 38; 5790 ÷ 10 = 579.
- To **divide by 100**, take off **two** end zeros, e.g. 6700 ÷ 100 = 67; 85 700 ÷ 100 = 857.

Some Properties of Numbers

Commutative Property

In our study of sets in the last chapter, we learned that union and intersection of sets are **commutative** operations:

$$A \cup B = B \cup A \quad \text{and} \quad A \cap B = B \cap A$$

The order of the sets is not relevant when finding the intersection or the union as the answer will always be the same.

We now look at the operations of addition, subtraction, multiplication and division of numbers.

- Addition is commutative: e.g. $2 + 3 = 3 + 2$
- Multiplication is commutative: e.g. $3 \times 4 = 4 \times 3$

This means that the order is not relevant when we **add or multiply** two numbers.

- Subtraction is **not** commutative: e.g. $8 - 4 \neq 4 - 8$
- Division is **not** commutative: e.g. $12 \div 4 \neq 4 \div 12$

Associative Property

Suppose that we want to add three numbers: $3 + 4 + 5$.

We can add $3 + 4$ first ($= 7$) and then add on 5 to get 12: $(3 + 4) + 5 = 7 + 5 = 12$.

We could also add $4 + 5$ first ($= 9$) and then add 3 to get 12: $3 + (4 + 5) = 3 + 9 = 12$.

This means that $(3 + 4) + 5 = 3 + (4 + 5)$.

We can add three numbers in any order.
- This is the **associative property** for **addition**: $(a + b) + c = a + (b + c)$.
- Multiplication is also associative: e.g. $(3 \times 4) \times 2 = 3 \times (4 \times 2) = 24$

We can multiply three numbers in any order.

This is the **associative property** for **multiplication**: $(a \times b) \times c = a \times (b \times c)$.

- Division is **not** associative: e.g. $(12 \div 6) \div 2 = 2 \div 2 = 1$
  $$12 \div (6 \div 2) = 12 \div 3 = 4$$
- Subtraction is **not** associative: e.g. $(10 - 6) - 2 = 4 - 2 = 2$
  $$10 - (6 - 2) = 10 - 4 = 6$$

Distributive Property

The distributive property means that multiplication of Natural numbers **distributes** over addition or subtraction.

For example: $\mathbf{3(7 + 9) = (3 \times 7) + (3 \times 9)} = 21 + 27 = 48$
The same answer is found by working inside the brackets first: $3(7 + 9) = 3(16) = 48$

Another example: $\mathbf{2(7 - 3) = (2 \times 7) - (2 \times 3)} = 14 - 6 = 8$
The same answer is found by working inside
the brackets first: $2(7 - 3) = 2(4) = 8$

> **The distributive law:**
> $a \times (b + c) = (a \times b) + (a \times c)$

We will use the distributive law a lot in later chapters
when we study algebra.

1 Copy and complete the following multiplication table.

×	2	4	6	8	10	12
1						
3						
5		20				
7					70	
9						
11			66			

2 Write down the answers to the following problems without using a calculator.

   (i) 7×3 (ii) $2(9)$ (iii) 5×6 (iv) $20 \div 4$ (v) $18 \div 3$ (vi) $24 \div 8$ (vii) 9×3

3 Calculate the following without using a calculator.

   (i) $23(15)$ (ii) 17×19 (iii) 13×21 (iv) $12(32)$ (v) 25×17 (vi) 27×13

4 Calculate the following without using a calculator.

   (i) $156 \div 13$ (ii) $224 \div 16$ (iii) $247 \div 19$ (iv) $372 \div 31$ (v) $368 \div 23$

5 Copy and complete the following arrays to calculate the multiplications.

   (i) 27×15 (ii) 36×13 (iii) 43×24 (iv) 64×11

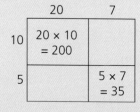

6 Use an array model to calculate the following:

   (i) 23×15 (ii) 17×19 (iii) 13×21 (iv) 12×32 (v) 25×17 (vi) 27×13

7 Show by an example that the addition of numbers is commutative.

8 Show by examples that the multiplication of numbers is commutative but division of numbers is not commutative.

9 State which of the properties of numbers is being used in these statements.

   (i) $(2 + 8) = (8 + 2)$

   (ii) $5 \times 8 = 8 \times 5$

   (iii) $(4 \times 5) \times 3 = 4 \times (5 \times 3)$

   (iv) $(7 + 3) + 4 = 7 + (3 + 4)$

   (v) $(12 - 8) - 2 \neq 12 - (8 - 2)$

   (vi) $(6)(3)(2) = (3)(6)(2)$

   (vii) $3(5) + 3(4) = 3(5 + 4)$

   (viii) $3(14 - 5) = 3(14) - 3(5)$

   (ix) $9(7 + 2) = 9(7) + 9(2)$

   (x) $10 \div 5 \neq 5 \div 10$

   (xi) $7 - 4 \neq 4 - 7$

   (xii) $(12 \div 6) \div 2 \neq 12 \div (6 \div 2)$

Section 2C Factors

The word **factor** means part. For example, parts for a car can be bought in a motor factor's shop. Like cars, numbers can be broken into parts or factors.

> A **factor** (or **divisor**) of a number is another number that divides exactly into it.

For example, the number 18 has the following pairs of factors:

18 = 1 × 18

18 = 2 × 9

18 = 3 × 6

The set of **divisors** (**factors**) of 18 = {1, 2, 3, 6, 9, 18}.

The number 12 has the following pairs of factors:

12 = 1 × 12

12 = 2 × 6

12 = 3 × 4

The set of divisors of 12 = {1, 2, 3, 4, 6, 12}.

Compare the elements of the two sets:

{1, 2, 3, **6**, 9, 18}

{1, 2, 3, 4, **6**, 12}

The **highest common factor** of 18 and 12 = 6, since 6 is the biggest number common to the two sets.

Highest Common Factor (HCF)

> The HCF of two or more numbers is the **highest** number that **divides exactly** into the numbers in question.

Example 1

Find the HCF of 8, 16 and 20.

Solution

The set of divisors of 8 = {1, 2, 4, 8}

The set of divisors of 16 = {1, 2, 4, 8, 16}

The set of divisors of 20 = {1, 2, 4, 5, 10, 20}

The highest common factor = 4.

Prime Numbers

> A **prime number** (or **prime**) is a number that has exactly two divisors, itself and 1.

For example, 13 is a prime number. The set of divisors of 13 = {1, 13}.

Prime numbers have fascinated mathematicians for millennia. It was Euclid who wrote down the first theorems about prime numbers, including that the set of prime numbers is an infinite set.

However, prime numbers had no real-world application until the onset of the digital age. In particular, the field of cryptography uses prime numbers as part of the algorithms used to encrypt data securely. This is very relevant in a world where online purchasing companies use this technology to keep our money safe!

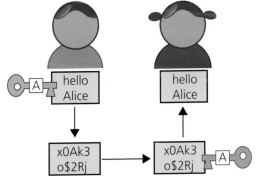

4 is not a prime number. Its divisors are {1, 2, 4}.

- The set of prime numbers is an infinite set:
  {2, 3, 5, 7, 11, …}.

  (Euclid proved that there are infinitely many primes in 300 BC.)

- **Twin primes** are a pair of prime numbers that differ by 2.

  For example, 3 and 5 are twin primes. So too are 17 and 19.

Key Points

- Remember that 1 is **not** a prime number.
- 2 is the only even prime number.

Composite Numbers

A **composite number** is a number which is not a prime number.

For example, 9, 28 and 100 are all composite numbers. They all have more than two divisors.

An interesting fact about composite numbers is that they can all be written as a product of prime numbers. This was discovered by the Ancient Greeks about 2000 years ago.

For example,

$$45 = 3 \times 3 \times 5 \qquad 68 = 2 \times 2 \times 17$$

Prime Factors

The **prime factors** of a number are the factors of that number that are prime numbers.

Example 2

Find the prime factors of 420.

Solution

To work out the prime factors of a given number:

- Divide by the **smallest prime number** which is a divisor of it.

2	420
	210

- Now divide 210 by the **smallest prime number** which is a divisor of it.

2	420
2	210
	105

- Now divide 105 by the smallest prime number which is a divisor of it.

2	420
2	210
3	105
	35

- Now, 3 won't go in exactly again, so we try the next prime number.

2	420
2	210
3	105
5	35
	7

- Now, 7 is a prime number, so if we divide by 7 we get 1.

2	420
2	210
3	105
5	35
7	7
	1

  (When we get to 1 we are finished.)

So the prime factors of 420 are:

$2 \times 2 \times 3 \times 5 \times 7$ or

$2^2 \times 3 \times 5 \times 7$

You can also get the prime factors of a number on the **Casio fx-83GT plus** calculator by keying in the number and pressing the EQUALS-shift-FACT buttons:

Multiples

■ The **multiples** of a Natural number are the numbers into which it divides exactly.

The set of multiples of 3 = {3, 6, 9, 12, 15, … }

The set of multiples of 6 = {6, 12, 18, 24, 30, … }

■ We could say that the multiples of 2 are $2 \times n$ where n is any whole number. These are the even numbers 2, 4, 6, …

■ The **lowest common multiple** (LCM) of 3 and 6 is 6 because that is the lowest number in both sets.

> The **LCM** of two or more numbers is the lowest number that these numbers will divide into exactly.

Example 3

Find the prime factors of each of the numbers 20 and 48.

Use these factors to find the LCM and HCF of 20 and 48.

Solution

Prime factors of 20:

```
2 | 20
2 | 10
5 |  5
     1
```

Prime factors of 48:

```
2 | 48
2 | 24
2 | 12
2 |  6
3 |  3
     1
```

$20 = 2 \times 2 \times 5$

$48 = 2 \times 2 \times 2 \times 2 \times 3$

To find the HCF: Pick out the common factors: $2 \times 2 = 4$.

To find the LCM:

■ Write down the common factors once: 2×2.

■ Multiply this by the non-common factors: $2 \times 2 \times 2 \times 2 \times 3 \times 5 = 240$.

Key Points

• **5** is a factor of any number with a units digit of **0** or **5**, e.g. 5 is a factor of 2355 and a factor of 450, but not a factor of 566.

• **10** is a factor of any number with a units digit of **0**, e.g. 10 is a factor of 2550 and a factor of 55 500, but not a factor of 55 556.

Activity 2.3

1 List the first five multiples of each of the following Natural numbers:

   (i) 8   (iii) 15   (v) 24

   (ii) 11   (iv) 19

2 (i) List the factors of:

     (a) 6   (c) 15   (e) 13

     (b) 10   (d) 24

   (ii) Which one of the numbers in part (i) is a prime number?

3 List the first seven prime numbers.

4 List the composite numbers between 10 and 20.

5 (i) List the set of divisors of:
   (a) 15   (b) 35
   (ii) Write down the HCF of 15 and 35.

6 (i) List the set of divisors of:
   (a) 24   (b) 36
   (ii) Write down the HCF of 24 and 36.

7 Find the HCF of these pairs of numbers:
   (i) 6 and 8   (v) 14 and 42
   (ii) 2 and 18   (vi) 24 and 56
   (iii) 10 and 30   (vii) 140 and 112
   (iv) 11 and 55   (viii) 135 and 150

8 (i) List the first five multiples of:
   (a) 4   (b) 6
   (ii) Write down the LCM of 4 and 6.

9 (i) List the first five multiples of:
   (a) 9   (b) 12
   (ii) Write down the LCM of 9 and 12.

10 Find the LCM of each of the following:
   (i) 5 and 7   (iv) 13 and 10
   (ii) 12 and 14   (v) 15 and 18
   (iii) 9 and 11   (vi) 16 and 20

11 Find the prime factors of each of the following numbers:
   (i) 45   (iii) 100   (v) 382
   (ii) 60   (iv) 236   (vi) 510

12 Write down all the divisors of each of the following Natural numbers:
   (i) 50   (iii) 122   (v) 999
   (ii) 86   (iv) 230

13 For each of the following:
   (i) 2, 3 and 4   (iv) 5, 10 and 20
   (ii) 6, 8 and 12   (v) 10, 14 and 35
   (iii) 2, 3 and 5

   (a) Find the HCF.
   (b) Find the LCM.

14 Which of the following numbers are divisible by 5?
   345, 270, 237, 4565, 2348, 12 345, 8764, 88 885

15 Which of the following numbers are divisible by 10?
   355, 270, 2370, 47 765, 2348, 12 345, 8 764 000, 888 850

16 A number is divisible by 3 if the sum of its digits is a multiple of 3.
   (i) Which of the following numbers is divisible by 3?
      206, 358, 4569, 34 798, 357 942, 515 567
   (ii) Check your answers to part (i) by using division.

17 A number is divisible by 9 if the sum of its digits is a multiple of 9.
   (i) Which of the following numbers is divisible by 9?
      2007, 3528, 4569, 34 798, 357 948, 515 567
   (ii) Check your answers to part (i) by using division.

18 Kevin can complete a lap of a running field in 8 minutes, Paul can complete the same lap in 6 minutes and Keith can complete the same lap in 4 minutes. If they all start running at the same time, on which lap will they all cross the finish line together?

19 Sinéad visits her favourite shop every 6 days exactly. Tom visits the same shop every 14 days exactly. If they met in the shop today, after how long will they both visit the shop again on the same day?

20 A green lighthouse flashes every 12 seconds. A red lighthouse flashes every 16 seconds. If they both flash at exactly 10am, when will they flash together again?

Section 2D Powers and Square Roots

In studying maths, you see a lot of symbols which are often quick ways of writing something.

- 3^5 (we say '3 to the power of 5') is a short way of writing $3 \times 3 \times 3 \times 3 \times 3$.
- The number 5 is called the **index**. (The plural of **index** is **indices**.)
- The number 3 is called the **base**.

For example:

$3^2 = 3 \times 3 = 9$

$4^3 = 4 \times 4 \times 4 = 64$

- The expression 6^2 is pronounced '**six to the power of two**' or '**six squared**'.

- The expression 6^3 is pronounced '**six to the power of three**' or '**six cubed**'.

Natural Numbers

Example 1

Evaluate: (i) $3^2 \times 2^3$ (ii) $10^3 \times 6$

Solution

(i) $3^2 \times 2^3 = 3 \times 3 \times 2 \times 2 \times 2 = 9 \times 8 = 72$

(ii) $10^3 \times 6 = 10 \times 10 \times 10 \times 6 = 1000 \times 6 = 6000$

Rules for Indices

Multiplication

Example 2

Write $3^2 \times 3^4$ as a single power of 3.

Solution

$3^2 \times 3^4 = (3 \times 3) \times (3 \times 3 \times 3 \times 3) = 3 \times 3 \times 3 \times 3 \times 3 \times 3 = 3^6$

or $3^2 \times 3^4 = 3^{2+4} = 3^6$

Key Point

This shows that you **add the indices to multiply** (only when the base is the same for each number).

Division

Example 3

Write $\dfrac{5^7}{5^5}$ as a single power of 5.

Solution

$\dfrac{5^7}{5^5} = \dfrac{5 \times 5 \times 5 \times 5 \times 5 \times 5 \times 5}{5 \times 5 \times 5 \times 5 \times 5} = 5 \times 5 = 5^2$

or

$\dfrac{5^7}{5^5} = 5^{7-5} = 5^2$

Key Point

This shows that you **subtract the indices to divide** (only when the base is the same for each number).

Powers

We can raise a power to a higher power.

Example 4

Write $(3^2)^4$ as a single power of 3.

Solution

$(3^2)^4$ is read as '3 to the power of 2 raised to the power of 4'.

$(3^2)^4 = 3^2 \times 3^2 \times 3^2 \times 3^2 = 3^8$

or

$(3^2)^4 = 3^{2 \times 4} = 3^8$

 Key Point

This shows that you **multiply the indices to raise from one power to another**.

Square Roots

When you find the square root of a **square number**, the answer is a Natural number.

For example:

- $\sqrt{9}$ (we say 'the square root of 9') = the number which multiplied by itself gives 9 = 3
- We can also write $\sqrt{9} = 9^{\frac{1}{2}}$
- $\sqrt{9} = 3$

So 9 is a square number.

So $100^{\frac{1}{2}} = 10$ and $64^{\frac{1}{2}} = 8$

A calculator has buttons for working out powers and square roots.

Look for symbols like these:

9 is a square number

A summary of the above results is given in this table:

Rule in symbols	Rule in words	Example
$a^m \times a^n = a^{m+n}$	Add indices to multiply when the bases are the same.	$3^4 \times 3^5 = 3^9$
$\dfrac{a^m}{a^n} = a^{m-n}$	Subtract indices to divide when the bases are the same.	$\dfrac{2^6}{2^4} = 2^2$
$(a^m)^n = a^{mn}$	Multiply the indices to raise from one power to another.	$(5^2)^4 = 5^8$
$a^{\frac{1}{2}}$ is the same as $\sqrt{a}$		$9^{\frac{1}{2}} = \sqrt{9} = 3$

Note

$a^0 = 1$. Any number to the power of 0 = 1, e.g. $5^0 = 1$, $7^0 = 1$, $1000^0 = 1 \dots$, etc.

1 Write each of the following in index form: The first one is done for you.

    (i) $2 \times 2 \times 2 \times 2 = 2^4$

    (ii) $5 \times 5 \times 5 \times 5$

    (iii) $(5 \times 5) \times (5 \times 5) \times (5 \times 5)$

    (iv) $2 \times 2 \times 2 \times 5 \times 5 \times 5$

    (v) $5 \times 5 \times 5 \times 5 \times 7 \times 7$

    (vi) $3 \times 3 \times 4 \times 4 \times 4$

2 Evaluate each of the following:

    (i) $4^2 - 3^1$

    (ii) $6^3 + 2^2$

    (iii) $5^3 + 4^2$

    (iv) $4^4 - 3^3$

    (v) $7^4 - 5^3$

    (vi) $9^2 + 3^3$

3 Express each of the following as a single power of 3:

    (i) $3^3 \times 3^4$

    (ii) $3^7 \times 3^3$

    (iii) $3^{10} \div 3^3$

    (iv) $3^5 \div 3^5$

    (v) $(3^4)^3$

    (vi) $(3^3)^3$

4 Evaluate each of the following:

    (i) $\dfrac{4^2 \times 4^2}{4^1}$ (iv) $(2^4)^2$

    (ii) $\dfrac{(3^8 \times 3^2)}{3^6}$ (v) $\dfrac{(3^3)^2}{3^4}$

    (iii) $5^2 \times \dfrac{5^3}{5^3}$ (vi) $\dfrac{(5^2)^3}{5^5}$

5 Express each of the following as a single power of 5:

    (i) $\dfrac{(5 \times 5^2 \times 5^3)}{5^4}$

    (ii) $\dfrac{(5^2)^5}{5^3}$

    (iii) $5^8 \times \dfrac{5^4}{5^3} \times 5^2$

6 Investigate whether the following statements are true or false:

    (i) $\dfrac{2^3}{2} = 2^4$ (iv) $\dfrac{(5^2 \times 5^4)}{5^3} = 5^3$

    (ii) $4^3 \times 4^7 = 4^{10}$ (v) $\dfrac{(6^2)^4}{(6^2 \times 6^2)} = 6^3$

    (iii) $(3^2)^5 = 3^7$

7 Fill in the missing □ in each of the following.

    (i) $5^4 \times 5^{\square} = 5^{10}$

    (ii) $(3^{\square})^4 = 3^{12}$

    (iii) $2^{\square} \times 2^7 = 2^9$

    (iv) $\dfrac{(5^5 \times 5^{\square})}{5^2} = 5^7$

    (v) $\dfrac{(6^8 \times 6^3)}{6^{\square}} = 6^9$

8 Suppose that n is some Natural number.

    (i) What would n^3 mean?

    (ii) Could you simplify $n^4 \times n^5$?

9 Write a list of all the square numbers between 1 and 200.

10 Find the value of each of these as a whole number:

    (i) $\dfrac{\sqrt{100} - \sqrt{49} + 9}{\sqrt{36}}$ (iii) $100^{\frac{1}{2}} + 16^{\frac{1}{2}} - 9^{\frac{1}{2}}$

    (ii) $\dfrac{25^{\frac{1}{2}} + 49^{\frac{1}{2}}}{4}$ (iv) $\sqrt{169} - 144^{\frac{1}{2}}$

11 A number is called a **perfect number** if the sum of all its factors (except the number itself) equals the number.

For example, 6 is a perfect number: its factors (excluding itself) are 1, 2 and 3 and $1 + 2 + 3 = 6$.

Perfect numbers are very rare. But there is another one between 1 and 40. Can you find it?

12 Show that 496 is a perfect number.

Section 2E Order of Operations

In mathematics, we can be asked to perform calculations such as 'add four 1 euro coins to six 5 euro notes'.

This calculation is relatively easy as six 5 euro notes give us €30 and then we add on the four 1 euro coins to get a total of €34.

Notice that we did the **multiplication** part **before** we did the **addition** part to get the answer.

It is important to understand that there is an **order of operations** in mathematics.

The order of operations is as follows:

1st   **B**rackets,

2nd   **I**ndices, **R**oots,

3rd   **D**ivision, **M**ultiplication,

4th   **A**ddition and **S**ubtraction.

Using the first letter of each we get **BIRDMAS**.

This is just a shorthand way of remembering the order of operations.
You may know others like BOMDAS and BIDMAS, which are equally suitable.

Another handy phrase to keep in mind is 'do what's in the brackets first'.

Example 1

Find the value of:

(i) $3 + 5(4 + 7)$

(ii) $3 + 5 \times 6 - 2$

(iii) $\sqrt{(16 + 9)} + 5 \times 4$

(iv) $2 \times (3)^2$

Solution

(i) $3 + 5(4 + 7) = 3 + 5(11) = 3 + 55 = 58$

(ii) $3 + 5 \times 6 - 2 = 3 + 30 - 2 = 33 - 2 = 31$

(iii) $\sqrt{(16 + 9)} + 5 \times 4 = \sqrt{25} + 20 = 5 + 20 = 25$

(iv) $2 \times (3)^2 = 2 \times 9 = 18$

Invisible Brackets

- To find the value of $\sqrt{9 + 16}$, we must be aware that this is really $\sqrt{(9 + 16)} = \sqrt{25} = 5$ (notice the 'invisible' brackets).

- Another example is:

  $\dfrac{12 + 6}{12 - 3}$ Don't be tempted to cancel the 12s!

  This is really $\dfrac{(12 + 6)}{(12 - 3)} = \dfrac{18}{9} = 2$

  Be careful with this type of fraction.

Example 2

Find the value of:

(i) $\sqrt{36 + 64}$

(ii) $\dfrac{10 + 5}{10 - 5}$

Solution

(i) $\sqrt{36 + 64} = \sqrt{100} = 10$

(ii) $\dfrac{10 + 5}{10 - 5} = \dfrac{15}{5} = 3$

Activity 2.5

1 Calculate each of the following without using a calculator:

(i) $5 + 3 \times 2$

(ii) $4 + 5 - 2 \times 4$

(iii) $7 + 3 \times 2 + 4$

(iv) $7 + 15 \div 3 + 4$

(v) $4(3 + 2^2)$

(vi) $32 \div 2 + 7 \times 3$

(vii) $82 - (31 + 2) \times 2$

(viii) $50 \div 2 - 5 + 10$

(ix) $(60 \div 10) \times (9 \div 3)$

(x) $(3 \times 8) \div (24 \div 4)$

2 Evaluate each of the following:

(i) $\dfrac{4^2(3 + 2)}{2 \times 5}$

(ii) $4 + (2 + 7)^2 - 15 + (2 \times 3)$

(iii) $2(4) + 3(7) - 2(5)$

(iv) $9(50 \div 5) - 4(3^2)$

(v) $7^2 + 2 \times 5 + 3^2$

(vi) $4(5 \times 3) - 2^2(20 \div 10)$

(vii) $\dfrac{2 \times 2^5 - 35}{20 + 9}$

(viii) $8^2 - 5^2 + 4^2$

(ix) $\dfrac{3 \times 5^2 \times 6}{5 \times 5}$

(x) $(42 \div 7)^2 + (144 \div 12)$

3 Use your calculator to calculate each of the following:

(i) $\dfrac{4(5 + 2^2)}{3^2}$

(ii) $\dfrac{14(4^2 - 3) - 6(5)}{2^2}$

(iii) $\dfrac{2(10 - 7)^2 + 5(4^2) + 1}{11}$

(iv) $\dfrac{8^2 - 3(7) - 4^2}{3^2}$

(v) $\dfrac{2(11 - 5)^2 - 4(2^3)}{2^2}$

4 Evaluate each of the following without using a calculator:

(i) $\sqrt{9} \times 4$

(ii) $2(\sqrt{25}) - 2^2$

(iii) $\dfrac{27 - 6}{3}$

(iv) $\dfrac{90 \div 10 + 5}{7}$

(v) $\dfrac{(\sqrt{36})(\sqrt{16})}{\sqrt{4}}$

(vi) $\dfrac{3(4 + 1)^2}{4^2 + 3^2}$

(vii) $\dfrac{7^2 + 1}{2(5)}$

(viii) $\dfrac{250 \div \sqrt{25}}{17 + 8}$

(ix) $\dfrac{11(9) - 2(11 - 8)^3}{3 \times 3}$

(x) $\dfrac{24 \div 2 + 8 - 5}{3^1}$

5 Evaluate each of the following:

(i) $2(9 - 4)^2 + 3\sqrt{16}$

(ii) $\dfrac{4 + 3 \times 7}{19 - 14}$

(iii) $\dfrac{9 \times 8 - 1}{\sqrt{4}}$

(iv) $3\sqrt{25} \times 4 + 7$

(v) $\dfrac{(3)^3 + 10 - 1}{\sqrt{36}}$

(vi) $\dfrac{\sqrt{144} + \sqrt{49}}{5^2 - \sqrt{16} - 2}$

(vii) $4(3)^2 - 2(2^3)$

(viii) $\dfrac{(2 \times 3)^2 - \sqrt{25} - 6}{(81 - 6 \times 9 + 2)}$

(ix) $\dfrac{\sqrt{400} \times 3 - 5}{\sqrt{25}}$

(x) $\dfrac{4(19 - 6)}{34 - 7 \times 3}$

Section 2F Rounding, Estimating and Approximating

You can use your calculator to do all number calculations, but it is essential that you have a good idea of roughly what the answer should be. Otherwise, a simple mistake like pressing a wrong button might mean a huge error that you might not notice. You get a rough idea of the answer by estimating.

Rounding is the best known estimation method. We can round a number to the nearest ten or the nearest hundred or nearest thousand etc.

- Suppose we want to round **33** to the nearest ten.

30   33   40

We can see that 33 is nearer to 30 than to 40. So 33 rounded to the nearest ten = 30.

- Suppose we want to round **37** to the nearest ten.

30   37   40

We can see that 37 is nearer to 40 than to 30. So 37 rounded to the nearest ten = 40.

- What about **35**, which is right in the middle between 30 and 40?

30   35   40

We use the '**round a 5 up**' method. This means that 35 is rounded up to 40.

We use the same method for rounding to the nearest hundred and thousand:

- When rounding to the nearest hundred, we '**round a 50 up**'.
- When rounding to the nearest thousand, we '**round a 500 up**'.

The following table shows examples of rounding:

Rounding to the nearest ten 'Round a 5 up'	Rounding to the nearest hundred 'Round a 50 up'	Rounding to the nearest thousand 'Round a 500 up'
44 rounds down to 40	349 rounds down to 300	2499 rounds down to 2000
45 **rounds up** to 50	350 **rounds up** to 400	2500 **rounds up** to 3000
87 rounds up to 90	872 rounds up to 900	67 802 rounds up to 68 000
565 **rounds up** to 570	1450 **rounds up** to 1500	123 500 **rounds up** to 124 000

Example 1

Estimate and then find the exact value for each of these.

(i) 2347 + 724 + 92   (ii) 127 × 29   (iii) 8208 ÷ 18

Solution

(i) 2347 + 724 + 92

2300 + 700 + 100 = 3100   ... Round each to the nearest 100.

2347 + 724 + 92 = 3163   ... Use your calculator to find the exact answer.

The estimate was quite accurate.

(ii) 127 × 29

    100 × 30 = 3000   ... Round 127 to the nearest 100, and 29 to the nearest 10.

    127 × 29 = 3683   ... Use your calculator to find the exact answer.

    The estimate was reasonably good.

(iii) 8208 ÷ 18

    8200 ÷ 20 = 410   ... Round 8208 to the nearest 100, and 18 to the nearest 10.

    8208 ÷ 18 = 456   ... Use your calculator to find the exact answer.

    The estimate was satisfactory.

Significant Figures

If the population of a town was 53 457, we could estimate this as 53 500 or even 53 000.

53 500 is writing 53 457 correct to three significant figures (3 figures followed by all zeros).

53 000 is writing 53 457 correct to two significant figures (2 figures followed by all zeros).

Example 2

Write 38 653 correct to three significant figures.

Solution

The first three figures from the left are 386.

The fourth figure is 5, so round up.

We get 38 700 (2 zeros replace the 5 and 3).

Example 3

Write 57 453 correct to two significant figures.

Solution

The first two figures from the left are 57.

The third figure is 4, so no change.

We get 57 000 (3 zeros replace the 4, 5 and 3).

Example 4

Write 60 723 correct to three significant figures.

Solution

The first three figures from the left are 607.

The fourth figure is 2, so no change.

We get 60 700 (2 zeros replace the 2 and 3).

Activity 2.6

1 Round these numbers to the nearest 10:

    (i) 53   (iii) 59   (v) 165   (vii) 89

    (ii) 55   (iv) 163   (vi) 168

2 Round these numbers to the nearest 100:

    (i) 149   (iv) 2149   (vi) 2188

    (ii) 150   (v) 2150   (vii) 2319

    (iii) 173

3 Round these numbers to the nearest 1000:

    (i) 42 431   (iv) 32 499   (vi) 32 593

    (ii) 998   (v) 32 500   (vii) 10 783

    (iii) 71 089

4 Copy and complete the following table. Give an estimated answer in the middle column. Give the exact answer in the right column.

	Problem	Estimate	Exact answer
(i)	389 + 214		
(ii)	706 − 489		
(iii)	33 × 9		
(iv)	69 ÷ 5		
(v)	211 × 11		
(vi)	858 ÷ 33		

5 Estimate the cost of 19 tins of paint at €48 per tin. Compare your estimate with the exact cost.

6 Estimate the cost of 392 text messages at 11 cent per message. Compare your estimate with the exact figure.

7 The diagram shows a rectangle which is 392 mm long by 113 mm wide.

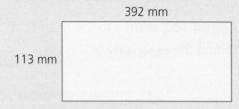

392 mm

113 mm

   (i) Estimate the total length of the four sides (the perimeter).

   (ii) Calculate the exact length and compare this with your estimate.

8 Round 37 540 to:

   (i) three significant figures

   (ii) two significant figures

   (iii) one significant figure.

9 Round 50 652 to:

   (i) three significant figures

   (ii) two significant figures

   (iii) one significant figure.

10 There were 56 542 people at a football match.

   (i) Write this number to the nearest thousand.

   (ii) Write this number to the nearest hundred.

11 The number of people at a concert was 8000, to the nearest thousand.

   (i) What was the smallest number that could have attended?

   (ii) What was the largest number that could have attended?

Revision Activity 2

1 Draw a mind-map with the theme of Natural numbers. Use the key words and phrases at the end of this chapter to help you.

2 Use the digits 2, 4, 5, 7 and 9 once only to answer the following.

   (a) Write down the biggest 2-digit number.

   (b) Write down the biggest 5-digit number.

   (c) Write down the smallest 3-digit number.

   (d) Write down the smallest 4-digit number.

   (e) Write down the largest even number.

   (f) Write down the smallest odd number.

3 (a) List the first five multiples of:

   (i) 8   (ii) 12

   (b) Write down the LCM of 8 and 12.

4 Find the LCM of each of the following.

   (a) 7 and 11   (b) 3 and 13

5 Find the prime factors of each of the following numbers.

   (a) 72   (b) 64   (c) 99

6 Write down all the divisors of each of the following Natural numbers.

   (a) 60   (b) 65   (c) 123

7 For each of the following:

   (a) Find the prime factors of each of the numbers.

   (b) Find the highest common factor (HCF).

   (c) Find the lowest common multiple (LCM).

      (i) 6, 8 and 24

      (ii) 7, 21 and 84

8 Write each of these as a single power of 5.

   (a) $5^3 \times 5^4$ (b) $(5^2)^4$ (c) $\dfrac{5^7}{5^4}$

9 Copy and complete the table.

	Number	Rounded to the nearest 10	Rounded to the nearest 100
(a)	27 016		
(b)	37 192		
(c)	7130		
(d)	9259		
(e)	10 631		
(f)	731 241		
(g)	32 738		
(h)	3999		
(i)	41 541		
(j)	55 555		

10 Copy and complete the table.

	Number	Rounded to 2 significant figures	Rounded to 3 significant figures
(a)	2734		
(b)	9876		
(c)	10 851		
(d)	199 077		
(e)	44 444		
(f)	7815		
(g)	39 999		
(h)	61 376		
(i)	659		
(j)	325		

Exam-style Question

1 The table below shows all the factors of each of the given numbers.

(a) Complete the table to show **all** the factors of 10, 11, and 12.

Number	Factors
9	1, 3, 9
10	
11	
12	

(b) Which one of the numbers 9, 10, 11, or 12 is **prime**?
   Give a reason for your answer.

   Number that is prime: 9   10   11   12
   (Tick (✓) **one** box only)   ☐   ☐   ☐   ☐

(c) Write down three **other prime** numbers between 0 and 20.

   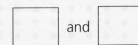

   Answer = ☐ , ☐ and ☐

(d) Find the **smallest** number that is a **multiple** of each of the three numbers
   you chose in part (c) above (i.e their Lowest Common Multiple).

   JCOL 2017

KEY WORDS AND PHRASES

- Natural numbers
- Numeral
- Digit
- Number line
- Consecutive numbers
- Ascending
- Descending
- Place value
- Hindu–Arabic system
- Base ten

- Operation
- Addition
- Subtraction
- Multiplication
- Division
- Inverse operation
- Array method
- Sum
- Difference
- Product
- Quotient

- Even number
- Odd number
- Factor
- Divisor
- Highest common factor
- Multiple
- Lowest common multiple
- Prime number (prime)
- Composite number

- Twin primes
- Prime factor
- Power
- Index
- Indices
- Square root
- Square number
- BIRDMAS
- Rounding
- Estimating
- Significant figures

Chapter Summary 2

- Natural numbers $\mathbb{N} = \{1, 2, 3, 4, 5, 6, 7, \ldots\}$
- The digits in the number 57 893 mean the following:

Ten thousands	Thousands	Hundreds	Tens	Units
5	7	8	9	3
5 × 10 000	7 × 1000	8 × 100	9 × 10	3 × 1

- A **factor** (or **divisor**) of a number is another number that divides exactly into it.
- The **Highest Common Factor** (**HCF**) of two or more numbers is the highest number that divides exactly into the numbers in question.
- A **prime number** (or **prime**) is a number that has exactly two divisors, itself and 1.
- A **composite number** is a number that is not prime.
- The **prime factors** of a number are the factors of that number that are prime numbers.
- The **Lowest Common Multiple** (**LCM**) of two or more numbers is the smallest number that these numbers will divide into exactly.

- The rules for indices:

Rule in symbols	Rule in words	Example
$a^m \times a^n = a^{m+n}$	Add indices to multiply when the bases are the same.	$3^4 \times 3^5 = 3^9$
$\dfrac{a^m}{a^n} = a^{m-n}$	Subtract indices to divide when the bases are the same.	$\dfrac{2^6}{2^4} = 2^2$
$(a^m)^n = a^{mn}$	Multiply the indices to raise from one power to another.	$(5^2)^4 = 5^8$
$a^{\frac{1}{2}}$ is the same as $\sqrt{a}$		$9^{\frac{1}{2}} = \sqrt{9} = 3$

- We use **BIRDMAS** for the order of operations.
- We use **rounding** to help us estimate quantities.
- We also round off numbers by counting **significant figures**.

There are three rules for determining how many significant figures are in a number.

- □ Non-zero digits are always significant.
- □ Any zero between two significant digits is significant.
- □ A final zero or zeros is/are significant only in the decimal portion of a number.

3 Integers

Learning Intentions

In this chapter, you will learn about:

- Using a number line to represent integers
- Adding and subtracting integers
- Multiplying and dividing integers

LO: N.1(a-b), U.5, U.6, U.13

You will need...

- a pencil
- a ruler
- a geometry set

Section 3A Introduction

We meet negative numbers in many aspects of life. For example, in December 2010 in Ireland, the temperature was –15°C in many parts of the country. When we go into a lift, the floors below ground level are marked –1, –2 etc.

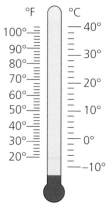

The Natural numbers are not enough for our needs, so we introduce the set of **Integers**.

The set of Integers contains zero and all whole plus (positive) numbers and minus (negative) numbers. The letter $\mathbb{Z}$ is used to denote the Integers.

We now extend the number line that we used for Natural numbers to include the negative numbers:

← smaller																			bigger →
–10	–9	–8	–7	–6	–5	–4	–3	–2	–1	0	1	2	3	4	5	6	7	8	9	10
			negative numbers										positive numbers							

- Zero separates the positive numbers from the negative numbers.
- The positive numbers are from 0 to the right.
  The **further right we go, the bigger the numbers become.**
- The negative numbers are from 0 to the left.
  The **further left we go, the smaller the numbers become.**
- $\mathbb{Z} = \{ \ldots , –4, –3, –2, –1, 0, 1, 2, 3, 4, \ldots \}$. This means that all the Natural numbers are included in the set of Integers. So $\mathbb{N} \subset \mathbb{Z}$.

Connections

We use sets to denote different types of numbers.

$\mathbb{N}$ and $\mathbb{Z}$ are examples of infinite sets.

Example

State whether the following are true or false:

(i) $4 > 2$ (ii) $-6 < 4$ (iii) $-5 > -2$

Solution

(i) $4 > 2$ This reads '4 is greater than 2'.

This is **true** because on the number line, 4 is further to the right than 2.

(ii) $-6 < 4$ This reads '−6 is less than 4'.

This is **true** because on the number line, −6 is further to the left than 4.

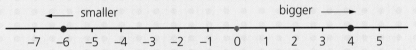

(iii) $-5 > -2$ This reads '−5 is greater than −2'.

This is **false** because on the number line, −5 is further to the left than −2.

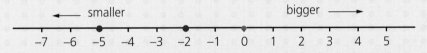

Activity 3.1

1 For each of the following number lines, find the values of A, B, C and D.

(i)
```
     A         B         C         D
  -5     -3 -2    0  1      3  4      6  7
```

(ii)
```
          B            C          D          A
  -6 -5       -3 -2 -1    1  2       4  5      7
```

(iii)
```
          B  C        D          A
  -5 -4          -1 0    2  3  4      6  7
```

2 Find the number of degrees there is between:

(i) −3°C and 15°C   (ii) 22°C and −10°C   (iii) −5°C and −15°C

Integers

3 Copy the number line below and on it label the following numbers: –6, 0, –3, 4, 2, 7 and –1.

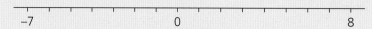

> –7   0   8

4 (i) Copy this number line into your copybook.

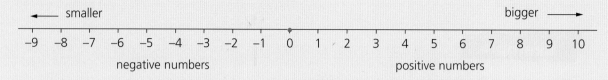

← smaller   bigger →

–9 –8 –7 –6 –5 –4 –3 –2 –1   0   1   2   3   4   5   6   7   8   9   10

negative numbers   positive numbers

(ii) Using your number line, state whether the following are true or false:

(a) –3 < 3   (c) –7 < –10   (e) 0 > 3   (g) –5 < –6   (i) –7 < –10

(b) 2 > –4   (d) –4 > –9   (f) 4 < –7   (h) –8 > –9   (j) –6 > –1

5 Choose the correct symbol, < or >, to insert between the following numbers:

(i) 7 ☐ 3   (iii) –9 ☐ –3   (v) –2 ☐ –5   (vii) –9 ☐ 0   (ix) –6 ☐ 6

(ii) –1 ☐ 0   (iv) –4 ☐ –5   (vi) 4 ☐ –3   (viii) –11 ☐ –10   (x) –1 ☐ –4

6 Rearrange the following sets of numbers so that the order is from smallest to biggest.

(i) {–1, 3, 0, –7, 2, 5}   (iv) {0, –3, 2, –1, 4, –6, 1}

(ii) {–5, 0, –8, –3, 2, 6, –4}   (v) {–5, –3, 4, –7, 9, –8, 6, –4, 1}

(iii) {9, 4, –2, 0, –5, 2, 8, –9}   (vi) {–78, –75, 89, –74, 57, –89, 76}

7 Rearrange the following sets of numbers so that the order is from biggest to smallest.

(i) {–3, 5, 1, 2, 4, 3}

(ii) {–6, 2, 1, –4, –2, 6, –3}

(iii) {14, 16, –12, 20, –15, –20, 18, –19}

(iv) {–52, –32, –45, –7, 59, –48, 61, –40, 51}

(v) {10, –13, 12, –10, 9, 22, –1}

(vi) {–1, –13, 9, –2, 14, –17, –8, 7, 13}

8 Calculate the new temperature in each of the following:

(i) 10°C hotter than 4°C   (iv) 4°C hotter than –9°C

(ii) 4°C colder than 1°C   (v) 8°C colder than –2°C

(iii) 7°C colder than –3°C   (vi) 5°C hotter than –10°C

9 Fill in the missing terms in the following sequences:

(i) 15, 9, 3, __ , __ , __   (iv) __ , –9, 0, 9, __ , __

(ii) –7, –3, 1, __ , __ , __   (v) –15, __ , –1, 6, __ , __

(iii) 10, 7, 4, __ , __ , __   (vi) 22, 14, __ , –2, __ , __

Section 3B Adding and Subtracting Integers

We can use a number line to help us add or subtract integers.

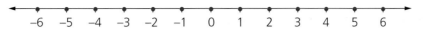

If we use a number line:

When **adding**, you **move to the right**;

when **subtracting**, you **move to the left**.

Example

Bill is a lift operator in a tall building with a deep basement.

He starts at ground level (level 0) and goes up 4 floors.

Then he goes down 6 floors.

Finally, he goes back up 8 floors.

Which floor is he now on?

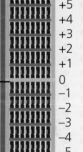

Ground floor

Solution

Start at 0.   Go up 4 floors: Now at floor 4

Go down 6 floors: $4 - 6 = -2$nd floor

Go up 8 floors: $-2 + 8 = 6$th floor

Answer: 6th floor

If you need a rule to help you:

Key Points

Rules for adding or subtracting integers:

1. If the signs are the same, add and use the common sign.
2. If the signs are different, subtract and use the sign of the bigger number.

Activity 3.2

1 Work out the following:

  (i) $4 - 3$ (iii) $-4 + 9$ (v) $-4 - 3$ (vii) $-4 - 9$ (ix) $4 - 0$

  (ii) $3 - 4$ (iv) $-9 + 4$ (vi) $4 + 3$ (viii) $9 + 4$ (x) $0 - 4$

2 Work out the following:

  (i) $20 - 35$ (iii) $-8 + 20$ (v) $-2 - 9$ (vii) $7 + 9$ (ix) $-12 + 6$

  (ii) $9 - 12$ (iv) $-4 + 5$ (vi) $-20 + 9$ (viii) $12 - 12$ (x) $-3 - 4$

Integers

3

Integers

3 Copy the following sums and fill in the missing numbers:

(i) $3 + \square = 8$ (v) $\square + 3 = -4$ (viii) $\square + 2 = -2$

(ii) $7 + \square = 1$ (vi) $\square - 8 = -3$ (ix) $-3 + \square = 8$

(iii) $-8 + \square = 0$ (vii) $10 + \square = -4$ (x) $\square + 8 = 4$

(iv) $\square - 2 = 6$

4 Write each of the following as a single number:

(i) $4 - 3 + 7$ (iii) $8 - 10 + 1$ (v) $12 - 3 - 9$ (vii) $1 + 8 - 10$

(ii) $2 - 4 - 7$ (iv) $-2 - 9 + 4$ (vi) $-5 - 4 - 3$ (viii) $-1 - 1 - 1$

5 Copy the following addition pyramids and complete each by starting at the bottom.

(i) 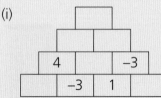   (ii) 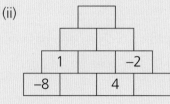   (iii)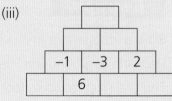

6 Write each of the following as a single number:

(i) $7 - 3 - 4 + 3$ (vi) $19 - 16 + 13 - 8$

(ii) $2 - 1 + 11 - 4$ (vii) $103 - 36 + 12 - 56$

(iii) $12 - 4 + 9 - 13$ (viii) $245 - 131 + 201 - 311$

(iv) $15 - 4 - 11 + 5$ (ix) $-75 + 98 - 56 + 26$

(v) $24 - 12 + 31 - 14$ (x) $8 - 98 + 322 - 243$

7 The table below is of different temperatures in different cities around the world on a given day. Starting with Paris at 5°C, work out the other temperatures using the information provided.

City	Warmer or colder	Temperature
Paris		5°C
Madrid	5°C warmer than Paris	
New York	7°C colder than Paris	
Dallas	8°C warmer than New York	
London	12°C colder than Madrid	
Hong Kong	13°C warmer than Paris	
Perth	10°C warmer than Hong Kong	
Stockholm	12°C colder than Madrid	
Moscow	5°C colder than New York	
Dublin	6°C colder than Paris	

8 You get into a lift on the ground floor. You go up 11 floors. Then you go down 7 floors. Then you go back up 2 floors. Which floor are you on now?

9 The temperature at 3 am was –4°C. By 9 am the temperature had risen by 7°C. What was the temperature at 9 am?

10 John had €250 in his bank account. He paid €120 into the account. Then he spent €390. What is the balance on his account now?

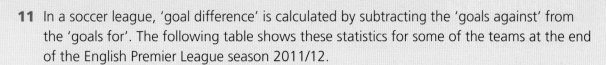

11 In a soccer league, 'goal difference' is calculated by subtracting the 'goals against' from the 'goals for'. The following table shows these statistics for some of the teams at the end of the English Premier League season 2011/12.

	Goals for	Goals against	Goal difference
Liverpool	47		+7
Fulham	48	51	
Norwich City		66	−14
Sunderland	45	46	−1
Stoke City	36	53	
Aston Villa	37		−16

Copy and complete the table.

12 (i) Calculate 7 − 4.

(ii) Calculate 4 − 7.

(iii) What do the answers to parts (i) and (ii) tell you about subtraction of numbers? (Your answer should contain the word 'commutative'.)

Section 3C Working with Signs Outside Brackets

Double Negatives

In everyday conversation, we are quite likely to use double negatives.

For example, you might say, 'It is not unlikely that we will have rain soon.'

The phrase 'not unlikely' is a double negative. It means 'likely'.

Not unlikely = likely

So the double negative gives a positive.

In mathematics, **two negatives make a positive** also.

For example: $- (-3) = +3$

$-(-10) = +10$

$5 - (-6) = 5 + 6 = 11$

This means that a **negative and a positive together make a negative**.

For example: $-(+3) = -3$

$+(-4) = -4$

$6 - (+3) = 6 - 3 = 3$

Example

Evaluate each of the following:

(i) 3 + (−2)   (ii) 7 − (−2)

Solution

(i) 3 + (−2) ⟵   + (−) = −   (ii) 7 − (−2) ⟵   − (−) = +

 3 − 2 = 1   7 + 2 = 9

Activity 3.3

Integers

1 Rewrite each of the following as single number:

(i) 9 − 8   (iii) −7 − 5   (v) 6 + 2   (vii) 1 + 4   (ix) 1 − 13

(ii) 14 + 3   (iv) 0 + 2   (vi) −8 − 8   (viii) 3 + 7   (x) −2 + 2

2 Rewrite each of the following as single number:

(i) −5 − 2 + 4   (iii) 8 + 3 − 1   (v) −4 + 2 + 1   (vii) −45 + 24 + 25   (ix) −1 + 1 + 1

(ii) 13 − 8 − 4   (iv) −3 + 8 − 1   (vi) 21 − 31 + 27   (viii) 17 − 17 − 17   (x) 0 + 4 − 3

3 State whether the following are true or false by calculating the values on the left:

(i) −6 − 2 + 4 = 12   (iv) 9 + 5 + 4 = 0   (vii) −13 − 13 + 13 = −13

(ii) −3 + 6 + 6 = −3   (v) 6 − 4 − 6 = −4   (viii) 23 + 14 − 38 = 47

(iii) −5 − 1 − 2 = −8   (vi) 8 + 2 + 4 = 2   (ix) −1 − 1 − 1 = 1

4 Simplify each of the following:

(i) − (−3)   (iii) − (+7)   (v) + (−9)   (vii) + (+4)   (ix) − (+5)

(ii) + (−4)   (iv) − (+3)   (vi) − (−8)   (viii) − (+10)   (x) + (−2)

5 Find the value of each of the following:

(i) −3 + (−2) + (+5) + (−2)   (v) 5 + (−4) + (+3) − (−4) − (+7)

(ii) 1 − (+7) − (−9) − (+3)   (vi) 74 + (+58) − (+69) − (−45) + (−66)

(iii) −4 − (−4) − (+4) + (−4)   (vii) −1 − (−1) − (−1) + (+1) + (−1) − (+1) + (−1)

(iv) 9 − (−12) + (−14) + (+8)   (viii) −56 + (−25) − (−49) − (−23) − (+54)

6 In a magic square, each row, each column and each diagonal adds up to the same number. Copy and complete each of these magic sauares:

(i)

2	7	0
	3	

(ii)

	1	
4	−3	2

(iii)

−3	−1	1
		0

Section 3D Multiplication and Division of Integers

Look at the following pattern closely.

	Pattern of answers	Is the answer + or −?
3 × 4 = 12		+
3 × 3 = 9	3 less	+
3 × 2 = 6	3 less	+
3 × 1 = 3	3 less	+
3 × 0 = 0	3 less	0
3 × (−1) = ?	?	?
3 × (−2) = ?	?	?
3 × (−3) = ?	?	?
3 × (−4) = ?	?	?

See if you can fill in the question marks before reading on.

If we continue the pattern, we get the following:

	Pattern of answers	Is the answer + or – ?
3 × 4 = 12		+
3 × 3 = 9	3 less	+
3 × 2 = 6	3 less	+
3 × 1 = 3	3 less	+
3 × 0 = 0	3 less	0
3 × (–1) = –3	3 less	–
3 × (–2) = –6	3 less	–
3 × (–3) = –9	3 less	–
3 × (–4) = –12	3 less	–

From this table we can see that:

(+ number)(+ number) = + number   e.g. (3)(4) = 12
(+ number)(– number) = – number   e.g. (3)(–4) = –12

N.B. We know from Chapter 2 that multiplication is commutative, e.g. 3 × (–4) = –4 × 3.

Now look at this pattern carefully:

	Pattern of answers	Is the answer + or – ?
–3 × 4 = –12		–
–3 × 3 = –9	3 more	–
–3 × 2 = –6	3 more	–
–3 × 1 = –3	3 more	–
–3 × 0 = 0	3 more	0
–3 × (–1) = +3	3 more	+
–3 × (–2) = +6	3 more	+
–3 × (–3) = +9	3 more	+
–3 × (–4) = +12	3 more	+

From this table we can see that:

(– number)(+ number) = – number   e.g. (–3)(4) = –12
(– number)(– number) = + number   e.g. (–3)(–4) = 12

We usually write (–2)(3) instead of –2 × 3. Notice there is no space between the brackets. The × sign is not often used.

- Remember, any number multiplied by 0 gives 0.
- Division is multiplication in reverse, so the same rules apply to division.

Key Point

When multiplying or dividing: **like signs give plus**, **unlike signs give minus**.

Example 1

Work out (7)(–4).

Solution

(7)(–4) = (+7)(–4) = –28   … unlike signs give minus when multiplying

3

Example 2

Write $(-6)(-5)$ as a single integer.

Solution

$(-6)(-5) = +30 = 30$ ... like signs give plus when multiplying

Example 3

Evaluate $\dfrac{-12}{4}$.

Solution

$\dfrac{-12}{4} = -3$ ... unlike signs give minus when dividing

Example 4

Evaluate $(-4)(2)(3)$.

Solution

$(-4)(2)(3)$ ... do these two at a time

$= (-8)(3)$ ... unlike signs give minus when multiplying

$= -24$ ... unlike signs give minus when multiplying

Example 5

Write $(-4)^3$ as a single integer.

Solution

$(-4)^3$

$= (-4)(-4)(-4)$ ... do these two at a time

$= (16)(-4)$ ... like signs give plus when multiplying

$= -64$ ... unlike signs give minus when multiplying

Example 6

Explain the difference between $(-2)^4$ and -2^4.

Solution

$(-2)^4$

$= (-2)(-2)(-2)(-2)$ ... do these two at a time

$= (4)(-2)(-2)$ ... like signs give plus when multiplying

$= (-8)(-2)$ ... unlike signs give minus when multiplying

$= +16$

-2^4 is the same as $-(2)(2)(2)(2) = -(2^4) = -(16)$

$\qquad\qquad\qquad\qquad\qquad\qquad = -16$

48

The following example involves adding/subtracting and multiplying/dividing. This needs care.

- Remember BIRDMAS for the order of operations.
- When **multiplying/dividing: like signs give plus; unlike signs give minus**.
- When **adding/subtracting on the number line: plus go right; minus go left**.

Example 7

Evaluate $\dfrac{6(2-4)}{-3-3}$.

Solution

Work out the numerator first. Then work out the denominator. Then divide.

$$\dfrac{6(2-4)}{-3-3}$$

$$= \dfrac{6(-2)}{-3-3} \quad \text{... brackets first}$$

$$= \dfrac{-12}{-6} \quad \text{... multiply top (unlike signs give minus); add bottom (down 3, then down 3 = down 6)}$$

$$= 2 \quad \text{... divide (like signs give plus)}$$

Activity 3.4

You should do all of these activities **without a calculator**.
You can check your answers using a calculator.

1 Write down the answer to each of the following:

(i) 2×3
(iii) $2 \times (-3)$
(v) $4 \times (-4)$
(vii) $(-5) \times (-3)$
(ix) $(-7) \times 3$

(ii) $(-2) \times (-3)$
(iv) $(-2) \times 3$
(vi) 12×4
(viii) $9 \times (-3)$
(x) $4 \times (-6)$

2 Write down the answer to each of the following:

(i) $12 \div 2$
(iii) $12 \div (-2)$
(v) $36 \div 9$
(vii) $16 \div (2)$

(ii) $(-12) \div (-2)$
(iv) $(-12) \div (-2)$
(vi) $(-24) \div -8$
(viii) $(-15) \div (-5)$

3 (i) Copy and complete the following multiplication table:

×	−3	−2	−1	0	1	2	3
−3							
−2		+4					
−1							
0							
1			0				
2							
3						6	

Remember, when multiplying or dividing:

- like signs give plus
- unlike signs give minus

(ii) Describe any patterns you see in the completed table.

4 Write each of the following as single integers:

(i) $-\dfrac{48}{6}$
(iii) $\dfrac{75}{-5}$
(v) $\dfrac{30}{3}$
(vii) $\dfrac{55}{11}$
(ix) $\dfrac{-150}{30}$

(ii) $\dfrac{-36}{-4}$
(iv) $\dfrac{-88}{8}$
(vi) $\dfrac{-81}{-9}$
(viii) $\dfrac{-125}{25}$
(x) $\dfrac{180}{-9}$

5 Evaluate each of these:

(i) $\dfrac{12}{-6}$

(ii) $(12)(-6)$

(iii) $12 - (-6)$

(iv) $-6 + 12$

6 Write each of the following in its simplest form:

(i) $\dfrac{5 + 7}{4}$

(ii) $\dfrac{-10 - 5}{1 - 6}$

(iii) $\dfrac{-10 + (8 - 10)}{3(6 - 4)}$

(iv) $\dfrac{5 - (3 - 7)}{1 - (3 - 5)}$

7 Simplify the following, showing your work.

(i) $\dfrac{(-7) \times (-8)}{-4}$

(ii) $\dfrac{10 \times (-11)}{-2}$

(iii) $\dfrac{(-3) \times (6)}{9}$

(iv) $\dfrac{7 \times (-6)}{14}$

(v) $\dfrac{5 \times (-4)}{-2}$

(vi) $\dfrac{(-8) \times (-5)}{-10}$

8 Write these as single integers.

(i) $(3)^3$

(ii) $(-2)^2$

(iii) $(-2)^3$

(iv) $(-2)^4$

(v) $(-2)^5$

9 Write each of the following in its simplest form.

(i) $\dfrac{-7 - 9}{2 - 4}$

(ii) $\dfrac{-12 + (4 - 7)}{3(6 - 5)}$

(iii) $\dfrac{-5 + 3(2 - 7)}{3 - 4(2)}$

10 Simplify each of the following as far as possible.

(i) $\dfrac{7 \times 4}{7}$

(ii) $\dfrac{-13 \times (-6)}{5 - 2(9)}$

(iii) $\dfrac{-4 \times (-3) \times (3)}{(-4) \times (-2)}$

(iv) $\dfrac{-5 \times (4) \times (-1)}{(-10) \times (-2)}$

(v) $\dfrac{2(-3) \times 3(-3) - 4}{(-2) \times (-5)(-1)}$

11 (i) Simplify $\dfrac{3(2 - 5)^2 - 2(3)^2}{6 - 9}$.

(ii) Simplify $\dfrac{7^2 - 3^2}{(-3)^2 - (-1)}$.

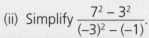

12 The temperature in a room was 6°C. It fell by 2°C every hour. What was the temperature after 5 hours?

Revision Activity 3

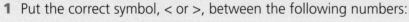

1 Put the correct symbol, < or >, between the following numbers:

(a) 8 ☐ 4

(b) –3 ☐ 1

(c) –8 ☐ –5

(d) –4 ☐ –5

(e) –2 ☐ –5

(f) 6 ☐ –1

(g) –4 ☐ 0

(h) –21 ☐ –10

(i) 3 ☐ –3

(j) –2 ☐ –6

2 Write each of the following as single numbers:

(a) 5 – 4 + 8

(b) 3 – 5 – 8

(c) 7 – 12 + 3

(d) –3 – 6 + 4

(e) 15 – 4 – 9

(f) –6 – 6 – 3

(g) 3 + 7 – 12

(h) –2 – 2 – 2

3 Rewrite each of the following as single numbers:

(a) 7 + (–3)

(b) 10 – (–5)

(c) –15 + (–10)

(d) 0 – (–10)

(e) 8 + (+4)

(f) 6 – (–5)

(g) 2 + (–3)

(h) – (–6)

(i) – (+24)

(j) + (–24)

4 Evaluate these:

(a) (–12)(–4)   (b) –12 – 4   (c) (–12) – (–2)   (d) (–12) ÷ (–4)   (e) –12 + 4   (f) $\dfrac{-12 - 4}{-4}$

5 (a) Evaluate the following:

(i) $(-1)^1$

(ii) $(-1)^2$

(iii) $(-1)^3$

(iv) $(-1)^4$

(v) $(-1)^5$

(b) Can you work out a pattern in the answers you got in part (a)? Explain your answer.

(c) Evaluate these:

(i) $(-1)^{33}$

(ii) $(-1)^{56}$

(iii) $(-1)^{100}$

(iv) $(-1)^{999}$

6 Simplify each of the following as far as possible:

(a) $\dfrac{8 \times 3}{8}$

(b) $\dfrac{-11 \times (-3)}{5 - 2(8)}$

(c) $\dfrac{-5 \times (-2) \times (4)}{(-5) \times (-2)}$

(d) $\dfrac{-7 \times (5) \times (-2)}{(-10) \times (-1)}$

(e) $\dfrac{2(-4) \times 3(-2) - 8}{(-4) \times (-5)(1)}$

7 (a) Simplify $2(5 - 6)$ using the distributive law.

(b) Simplify $2(5 - 6)$ using BIRDMAS.

Interactive Tool 3.1

Interactive Tool 3.2

KEY WORDS AND PHRASES

- **Integers**
- **Double Negatives**

Exam-style Question

1 Insert operators to make each calculation below correct.
Use the operators $\boxed{+}$, $\boxed{-}$ and $\boxed{\times}$.

Example: $3 \;\square\; 2 \;\square\; 5 = 13$

Answer: $3 \;\boxed{+}\; 2 \;\boxed{\times}\; 5 = 13$

(i) $3 \;\square\; 2 \;\square\; 5 = 6$ (ii) $3 \;\square\; 2 \;\square\; 5 = 1$

JCOL 2014

Chapter Summary 3

- $\mathbb{Z} = \{ \dots, -4, -3, -2, -1, 0, 1, 2, 3, 4, \dots \}$. $\mathbb{N} \subset \mathbb{Z}$.
- We can represent the Integers on the number line:

$\longleftarrow$ smaller   bigger $\longrightarrow$

−10 −9 −8 −7 −6 −5 −4 −3 −2 −1 0 1 2 3 4 5 6 7 8 9 10 11 12

negative numbers   positive numbers

- If we use a number line:

    When **adding** you **move to the right**.

    When **subtracting** you **move to the left**.

- **Rules for adding or subtracting Integers**:

    If the signs are the **same, add and use the common sign**.

    If the signs are **different, subtract and use the sign of the bigger number**.

- When **multiplying or dividing**:

    Like signs give **plus, unlike signs** give **minus**.

Chapter 4

Rational Numbers

Learning Intentions

In this chapter, you will learn about:

- Rational numbers (fractions)
- Proper fractions, improper fractions and mixed numbers
- Equivalent fractions
- Ordering fractions by size

- Adding and subtracting fractions
- Multiplying fractions
- Dividing fractions

LO: N.1(a-b), U.5, U.6, U.13

Section 4A Introduction to Rational Numbers

Remember:

- **Natural numbers**, $\mathbb{N}$, are the set of positive whole numbers: {1, 2, 3, … }.
  You can **add** or **multiply** any two Natural numbers and you get an answer in the set $\mathbb{N}$.

- **Integers**, $\mathbb{Z}$, are the set of positive and negative whole numbers including zero:
  { … ,–3, –2, –1, 0, 1, 2, 3, … }.
  You can **add**, **subtract** or **multiply** any two Integers and you get an answer in the set $\mathbb{Z}$.

If we **divide** 2 by 3, we don't have an answer in either of these sets. So we have to introduce another set of numbers called **rational numbers**. Rational numbers are also called **fractions**, which you studied in Primary School.

The letter $\mathbb{Q}$ is used to represent rational numbers.

A **rational number** is a number of the form $\frac{p}{q}$ where p and q are integers and $q \neq 0$ (we cannot divide by 0).

p is called the **numerator** and q is called the **denominator**.

Example 1

(i) Explain each part of the fraction $\frac{2}{3}$.

(ii) Show the fraction:

    (a) On a number line

    (b) As a part of some shape

    (c) As a portion of a number of items.

Solution

(i) $\frac{2}{3}$ means:

- two-thirds of one whole unit.

- The denominator (3) tells you that the whole is divided into 3 **equal** parts.

- The numerator (2) counts the number of parts of the whole that we want.

(ii) The fraction $\frac{2}{3}$ can be shown:

(a) On a number line as:

(b) As part of a shape. The fraction $\frac{2}{3}$ is shown as the pink highlighted parts of each shape below:

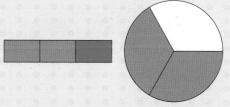

(c) As a portion of a number of cakes. The blue box contains two-thirds of the cakes.

Example 2

All the shapes below have been divided into **equal** portions. Draw the shapes in your copybook and colour in the fractions.

(i) $\frac{1}{2}$ red

(ii) $\frac{3}{5}$ pink

(iii) $\frac{1}{3}$ red, $\frac{2}{3}$ blue

(iv) $\frac{3}{12}$ red, $\frac{4}{12}$ blue, $\frac{5}{12}$ green

Solution

(i) $\frac{1}{2}$ red

(ii) $\frac{3}{5}$ pink

(ii) $\frac{1}{3}$ red, $\frac{2}{3}$ blue

(iv) $\frac{3}{12}$ red, $\frac{4}{12}$ blue, $\frac{5}{12}$ green

Rational Numbers

In the following activities, all shapes are divided into **equal** parts.

1 Match each diagram to the correct fraction.

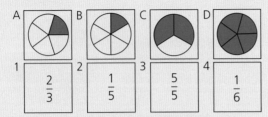

A   B   C   D

1 $\frac{2}{3}$ 2 $\frac{1}{5}$ 3 $\frac{5}{5}$ 4 $\frac{1}{6}$

2 Match each diagram to the correct fraction.

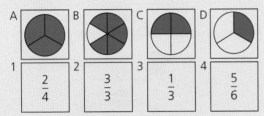

A   B   C   D

1 $\frac{2}{4}$ 2 $\frac{3}{3}$ 3 $\frac{1}{3}$ 4 $\frac{5}{6}$

3 What fraction of each fraction strip is shaded pink?

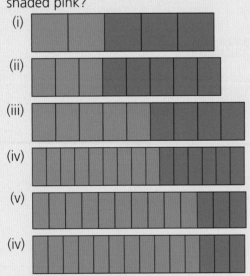

(i)

(ii)

(iii)

(iv)

(v)

(iv)

4 What fraction of each shape in question **3** is shaded blue?

5 What fraction of each shape is shaded green?

(i) 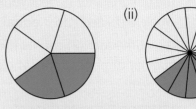 (ii)

(iii)

(iv)

(v)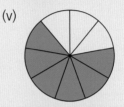

(vi)

6 (i) Explain what is meant by the fraction $\frac{4}{5}$.

(ii) Represent the fraction $\frac{4}{5}$:
   (a) On a number line
   (b) As a portion of a shape
   (c) As a portion of a number of items (pizzas, chocolate bars, etc.).

7 Draw these number lines in your copybook. On each number line, write the letter which represents each fraction.

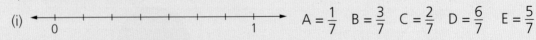

(i) 0 ——————— 1 $A = \frac{1}{7}$ $B = \frac{3}{7}$ $C = \frac{2}{7}$ $D = \frac{6}{7}$ $E = \frac{5}{7}$

(ii) 0 ——————— 1 $A = \frac{1}{8}$ $B = \frac{3}{8}$ $C = \frac{5}{8}$ $D = \frac{7}{8}$ $E = \frac{8}{8}$

(iii) 0 ——————— 1 $A = \frac{1}{5}$ $B = \frac{2}{5}$ $C = \frac{3}{5}$ $D = \frac{4}{5}$ $E = \frac{5}{5}$

(iv) 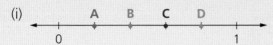 $A = \dfrac{2}{10}$ $B = \dfrac{3}{10}$ $C = \dfrac{5}{10}$ $D = \dfrac{7}{10}$ $E = \dfrac{10}{10}$

(v) 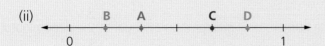 $A = \dfrac{1}{6}$ $B = \dfrac{1}{3}$ $C = \dfrac{1}{2}$ $D = \dfrac{5}{6}$ $E = \dfrac{6}{6}$

(vi) What do you notice about the answer for fraction A in parts (iii) and (iv)?

8 Write down the fraction represented by each letter on these number lines.

(i)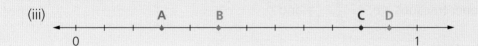

(ii)

(iii)

9 Use squared paper to draw four rectangles of the same size so that each one is directly below the one before. Represent the fractions below using one rectangle for each fraction.

(i) $\dfrac{3}{10}$ (ii) $\dfrac{1}{2}$ (iii) $\dfrac{1}{4}$ (iv) $\dfrac{3}{5}$

10 Which of the fractions in question **9** is the biggest? Explain your answer.

11 (i) Represent the fractions $\dfrac{1}{2}$ and $\dfrac{5}{10}$ on a diagram of your choice.

(ii) Are the fractions $\dfrac{1}{2}$ and $\dfrac{5}{10}$ the same? Explain your answer.

12 (i) Represent the fractions $\dfrac{1}{4}$ and $\dfrac{3}{10}$ on a diagram of your choice.

(ii) Are the fractions $\dfrac{1}{4}$ and $\dfrac{3}{10}$ equal? Explain your answer.

13 Draw a 50-square grid in your copybook, as shown.

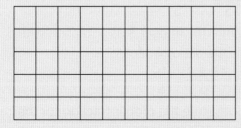

(i) Colour $\dfrac{1}{2}$ of the squares yellow.

(ii) Colour $\dfrac{1}{5}$ of the squares green.

(iii) Colour $\dfrac{1}{10}$ of the squares blue.

(iv) What fraction of the grid is coloured in?

(v) What fraction of the grid is not coloured in?

Section 4B Proper Fractions, Improper Fractions and Mixed Numbers

Type 1 – Proper Fractions

Proper fractions are fractions where the numerator is less than the denominator.

A proper fraction is always less than 1.

Examples of proper fractions are: $-\dfrac{1}{2}, \dfrac{2}{3}, -\dfrac{5}{7}$ and $\dfrac{1}{10}$.

Type 2 – Improper Fractions

Improper fractions are fractions where the numerator is greater than or equal to the denominator.

An improper fraction is always greater than or equal to 1.

Examples of improper fractions are: $\dfrac{7}{4}, \dfrac{8}{8}, \dfrac{12}{11}$ and $\dfrac{3}{1}$.

Type 3 – Mixed Numbers

Mixed numbers consist of an integer and a proper fraction.

Improper fractions can be converted into mixed numbers and vice versa.

Examples of mixed numbers are: $2\dfrac{1}{2}, 26\dfrac{1}{4}$ and $11\dfrac{7}{9}$.

Example 1

Express $3\dfrac{4}{5}$ as an improper fraction.

Solution

Method 1

$3\dfrac{4}{5}$ can be represented using fraction strips as shown:

To change the mixed number into an improper fraction, all we need to do is count how many parts are pink.

As there are 19 pink parts, then the improper fraction is $\dfrac{19}{5}$.

The mixed number $3\dfrac{4}{5}$ is equal to the improper fraction $\dfrac{19}{5}$.

Method 2

- Write out the mixed number as an integer and a proper fraction:
  $3\dfrac{4}{5} = 3 + \dfrac{4}{5}$

- Write the integer 3 as a fraction with 5 as the denominator:
  $3 = \dfrac{5 \times 3}{5} = \dfrac{15}{5}$

- Substitute the proper fraction for the integer: $3\dfrac{4}{5} = \dfrac{15}{5} + \dfrac{4}{5}$

- Add together the two numerators from the step above: $3\dfrac{4}{5} = \dfrac{15 + 4}{5}$

- Write the mixed number as an improper fraction: $3\dfrac{4}{5} = \dfrac{19}{5}$

Example 2

Express $\frac{14}{3}$ as a mixed number.

Solution

■ Write out the improper fraction: $\frac{14}{3}$

■ How many groups of 3 are there in 14?

Divide 3 into 14: $3\overline{)14}$ = 4 remainder 2

The 2 remaining parts are thirds.

So $\frac{14}{3} = 4 + \frac{2}{3} = 4\frac{2}{3}$

Activity 4.2

1. Explain the meaning of the words:

    (i) proper fraction   (ii) improper fraction   (iii) mixed number.

2. What type of fraction is $\frac{5}{3}$? If I have $\frac{5}{3}$ of a cake on the table, do I have less than or more than 1 cake? Explain your answer.

3. State whether each of the following is a proper or improper fraction.

    (i) $\frac{2}{3}$ (ii) $\frac{5}{3}$ (iii) $\frac{7}{6}$ (iv) $\frac{2}{11}$ (v) $\frac{14}{9}$ (vi) $\frac{12}{9}$ (vii) $\frac{11}{12}$

4. Write a mixed number to show how much of each row of objects is shaded.

    (i) (a)

    (b)

    (c)

    (d)

    (e)

    (f)

    (ii) Write each answer as an improper fraction.

5 (i) Express each of the following mixed numbers as an improper fraction.
Explain your answers using diagrams.

(a) $1\frac{1}{3}$ (b) $2\frac{5}{9}$ (c) $1\frac{3}{10}$ (d) $4\frac{5}{7}$ (e) $3\frac{1}{8}$ (f) $5\frac{2}{5}$ (g) $2\frac{2}{3}$

(ii) Use a calculator to confirm your answers.

6 (i) Express each of the following improper fractions as a mixed number.
Explain your answers using diagrams.

(a) $\frac{3}{2}$ (b) $\frac{9}{4}$ (c) $\frac{19}{6}$ (d) $\frac{17}{3}$ (e) $\frac{14}{5}$ (f) $\frac{19}{4}$ (g) $\frac{49}{6}$

(ii) Use a calculator to confirm your answers.

 7 A teacher shares out 50 sweets among 4 students. If each student gets the same number of whole sweets:

(i) How many sweets will each get?

(ii) What fraction of the total number of sweets is left over?

Section 4C Equivalent Fractions

Two fractions are **equivalent** if:

- both fractions represent the same portion of the whole unit
- you **multiply** or **divide** the numerator and denominator of one fraction by the same number to get the other fraction.
  - $\frac{3}{4} = \frac{27}{36}$ by **multiplying** above (numerator) and below (denominator) by 9.
  - $\frac{125}{150} = \frac{5}{6}$ by **dividing** above (numerator) and below (denominator) by 25.

At Primary School you may have been introduced to equivalent fractions in the form of a fraction wall:

1 unit or 1 'whole'														
$\frac{1}{2}$								$\frac{1}{2}$							
$\frac{1}{3}$					$\frac{1}{3}$					$\frac{1}{3}$				
$\frac{1}{4}$				$\frac{1}{4}$				$\frac{1}{4}$				$\frac{1}{4}$			
$\frac{1}{5}$			$\frac{1}{5}$			$\frac{1}{5}$			$\frac{1}{5}$			$\frac{1}{5}$		
$\frac{1}{6}$		$\frac{1}{6}$		$\frac{1}{6}$		$\frac{1}{6}$		$\frac{1}{6}$		$\frac{1}{6}$	
$\frac{1}{7}$	$\frac{1}{7}$	$\frac{1}{7}$	$\frac{1}{7}$	$\frac{1}{7}$	$\frac{1}{7}$	$\frac{1}{7}$								
$\frac{1}{8}$	$\frac{1}{8}$	$\frac{1}{8}$	$\frac{1}{8}$	$\frac{1}{8}$	$\frac{1}{8}$	$\frac{1}{8}$	$\frac{1}{8}$							
$\frac{1}{9}$	$\frac{1}{9}$	$\frac{1}{9}$	$\frac{1}{9}$	$\frac{1}{9}$	$\frac{1}{9}$	$\frac{1}{9}$	$\frac{1}{9}$	$\frac{1}{9}$						
$\frac{1}{10}$	$\frac{1}{10}$	$\frac{1}{10}$	$\frac{1}{10}$	$\frac{1}{10}$	$\frac{1}{10}$	$\frac{1}{10}$	$\frac{1}{10}$	$\frac{1}{10}$	$\frac{1}{10}$					
$\frac{1}{11}$	$\frac{1}{11}$	$\frac{1}{11}$	$\frac{1}{11}$	$\frac{1}{11}$	$\frac{1}{11}$	$\frac{1}{11}$	$\frac{1}{11}$	$\frac{1}{11}$	$\frac{1}{11}$	$\frac{1}{11}$				
$\frac{1}{12}$	$\frac{1}{12}$	$\frac{1}{12}$	$\frac{1}{12}$	$\frac{1}{12}$	$\frac{1}{12}$	$\frac{1}{12}$	$\frac{1}{12}$	$\frac{1}{12}$	$\frac{1}{12}$	$\frac{1}{12}$	$\frac{1}{12}$			
$\frac{1}{15}$	$\frac{1}{15}$	$\frac{1}{15}$	$\frac{1}{15}$	$\frac{1}{15}$	$\frac{1}{15}$	$\frac{1}{15}$	$\frac{1}{15}$	$\frac{1}{15}$	$\frac{1}{15}$	$\frac{1}{15}$	$\frac{1}{15}$	$\frac{1}{15}$	$\frac{1}{15}$	$\frac{1}{15}$
$\frac{1}{16}$	$\frac{1}{16}$	$\frac{1}{16}$	$\frac{1}{16}$	$\frac{1}{16}$	$\frac{1}{16}$	$\frac{1}{16}$	$\frac{1}{16}$	$\frac{1}{16}$	$\frac{1}{16}$	$\frac{1}{16}$	$\frac{1}{16}$	$\frac{1}{16}$	$\frac{1}{16}$	$\frac{1}{16}$	$\frac{1}{16}$

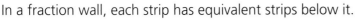
In a fraction wall, each strip has equivalent strips below it.

For example, the fraction $\frac{2}{3}$ is equivalent to all the fractions which line up with it

on the fraction wall. So $\frac{2}{3} = \frac{4}{6} = \frac{6}{9} = \frac{8}{12} = \frac{10}{15}$.

Key Points

- Equivalent fractions are obtained when you **multiply** or **divide** the numerator and denominator of one fraction by the **same** number to get the other fraction.
- This does **not** work with addition and subtraction:

  e.g. is $\frac{2}{3} = \frac{2+4}{3+4}$? Check using the fraction wall.

  e.g. is $\frac{5}{8} = \frac{5-2}{8-2}$? Check using the fraction wall.

  You should see that these are **not equal** and so be very careful about 'cancelling' when you want to simplify fractions.

Example 1

Look at the fraction strips.

State whether they represent equivalent fractions and explain your answer.

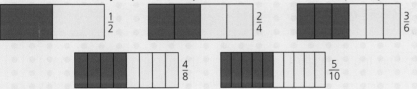

Solution

All the different fractions represent the same portion of the **same unit**.
So all the fractions are equivalent.

Example 2

Copy these and fill in the missing boxes to make equivalent fractions.

(i) $\frac{2}{7} = \frac{10}{\square}$

(ii) $\frac{4}{5} = \frac{\square}{10}$

(iii) $\frac{18}{81} = \frac{\square}{9}$

(iv) $\frac{60}{75} = \frac{4}{\square}$

Solution

(i) $\frac{2}{7} = \frac{10}{\square}$

As we have multiplied the top by 5, we need to multiply the bottom by 5.

$$\frac{2}{7} = \frac{2 \times 5}{7 \times 5} = \frac{10}{35}$$

(ii) $\frac{4}{5} = \frac{\square}{10}$

As we have multiplied the bottom by 2, we need to multiply the top by 2.

$$\frac{4}{5} = \frac{4 \times 2}{5 \times 2} = \frac{8}{10}$$

(iii) $\frac{18}{81} = \frac{\square}{9}$

As we have divided the bottom by 9, we need to divide the top by 9.

$$\frac{18}{81} = \frac{18 \div 9}{81 \div 9} = \frac{2}{9}$$

(iv) $\frac{60}{75} = \frac{4}{\square}$

As we have divided the top by 15, we need to divide the bottom by 15.

$$\frac{60}{75} = \frac{60 \div 15}{75 \div 15} = \frac{4}{5}$$

Example 3

Peter is not sure when he can 'cancel' when simplifying fractions. In each of the following statements the twos have been 'cancelled' to get the answer on the right.

Can you say which of the following statements are correct?

(i) $\dfrac{6+2}{8+2} = \dfrac{6}{8}$

(iii) $\dfrac{6 \times 2}{8 \times 2} = \dfrac{6}{8}$

(ii) $\dfrac{6-2}{8-2} = \dfrac{6}{8}$

(iv) $\dfrac{6 \div 2}{8 \div 2} = \dfrac{6}{8}$

Solution

Only parts (iii) and (iv) are correct. Remember that you must **multiply or divide** the top and bottom of the fraction by the **same** number to get a fraction of the same value.

Activity 4.3

1 Use a fraction wall to find the equivalent fractions.

(i) $\dfrac{1}{2} = \dfrac{\square}{\square} = \dfrac{\square}{\square} = \dfrac{\square}{\square} = \dfrac{\square}{\square}$

(ii) $\dfrac{2}{3} = \dfrac{\square}{\square} = \dfrac{\square}{\square}$

(iii) $\dfrac{1}{4} = \dfrac{\square}{\square}$

(iv) $\dfrac{2}{5} = \dfrac{\square}{\square}$

2 Use a fraction wall to find four fractions between (i) $\dfrac{1}{2}$ and $\dfrac{1}{3}$, (ii) $\dfrac{2}{3}$ and $\dfrac{3}{4}$.

3 Fill in the missing boxes to make an equivalent fraction in each case. Use a fraction wall if it helps you.

(i) $\dfrac{1}{2} = \dfrac{\square}{6}$

(iv) $\dfrac{6}{14} = \dfrac{3}{\square}$

(ii) $\dfrac{1}{5} = \dfrac{2}{\square}$

(v) $\dfrac{3}{5} = \dfrac{\square}{15}$

(iii) $\dfrac{2}{12} = \dfrac{1}{\square}$

(vi) $\dfrac{7}{9} = \dfrac{\square}{18}$

4 Fill in the missing boxes to make equivalent fractions.

(i) $\dfrac{2}{6} = \dfrac{\square}{36}$

(v) $\dfrac{14}{24} = \dfrac{\square}{12}$

(ii) $\dfrac{4}{11} = \dfrac{\square}{77}$

(vi) $\dfrac{1}{7} = \dfrac{8}{\square}$

(iii) $\dfrac{3}{4} = \dfrac{12}{\square}$

(vii) $\dfrac{5}{6} = \dfrac{\square}{30}$

(iv) $\dfrac{\square}{15} = \dfrac{33}{45}$

(viii) $\dfrac{8}{12} = \dfrac{\square}{48}$

5 Find equivalent fractions for each of the following.

(i) $\dfrac{4}{5} = \dfrac{\square}{15}$

(vi) $\dfrac{5}{8} = \dfrac{55}{\square}$

(ii) $\dfrac{9}{12} = \dfrac{\square}{4}$

(vii) $\dfrac{2}{9} = \dfrac{\square}{81}$

(iii) $\dfrac{36}{12} = \dfrac{\square}{2}$

(viii) $\dfrac{1}{4} = \dfrac{4}{\square}$

(iv) $\dfrac{12}{40} = \dfrac{3}{\square}$

(ix) $\dfrac{7}{8} = \dfrac{\square}{24} = \dfrac{\square}{64}$

(v) $\dfrac{18}{36} = \dfrac{\square}{6}$

6 Write down four equivalent fractions for each of the following fractions.

(i) $\frac{2}{5}$ (iii) $\frac{3}{2}$ (v) $\frac{6}{5}$ (vii) $\frac{12}{9}$

(ii) $\frac{7}{9}$ (iv) $\frac{12}{15}$ (vi) $\frac{8}{10}$ (viii) $\frac{22}{50}$

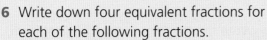

7 Here are four identical cakes cut into equal segments in four different ways.

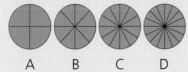

A   B   C   D

(i) How many slices of cake B are equal to 1 slice of A?

(ii) How many slices of cake D are equal to 1 slice of B?

(iii) How many slices of cake C are equal to 3 slices of A?

(iv) The cakes are distributed out fairly to 12 people at a party. What fraction of one cake will each person get?

8 Write the following fractions in their simplest form.

(i) $\frac{28}{42}$ (v) $\frac{8}{20}$ (ix) $\frac{1120}{2000}$

(ii) $\frac{15}{50}$ (vi) $\frac{246}{500}$ (x) $\frac{248}{400}$

(iii) $\frac{18}{27}$ (vii) $\frac{34}{60}$

(iv) $\frac{30}{36}$ (viii) $\frac{184}{400}$

9 (i) List five fractions equivalent to $\frac{1}{4}$ and five fractions equivalent to $\frac{1}{6}$.

(ii) Give a fraction which is between $\frac{1}{6}$ and $\frac{1}{4}$.

10 Are there any fractions between $\frac{1}{4}$ and $\frac{3}{10}$? If so, list two fractions that are between $\frac{1}{4}$ and $\frac{3}{10}$.

Section 4D Ordering Fractions

Writing equivalent fractions can help to determine which of two fractions is the bigger one.

Example 1

Ordering fractions with the same denominators

Put the following fractions in order from the smallest to the biggest:
$\frac{20}{25}, \frac{3}{25}, \frac{11}{25}, \frac{26}{25}, \frac{19}{25}$

Solution

The numerators are ordered from the smallest: 3, 11, 19, 20 and 26.
So the fractions are ordered:

$\frac{3}{25}, \frac{11}{25}, \frac{19}{25}, \frac{20}{25}, \frac{26}{25}$

Example 2

Ordering proper fractions with different denominators

Put the following fractions in order from smallest to biggest: $\frac{3}{4}, \frac{2}{3}, \frac{5}{8}, \frac{5}{6}$

Solution

■ Find the lowest common multiple (LCM) of the denominators.

The first number in common that appears in the table is 24. So the LCM is 24.

Number	Multiples
4	4, 8, 12, 16, 20, 24, 28, ...
3	3, 6, 9, 12, 15, 18, 21, 24, 27, ...
8	8, 16, 24, 32, ...
6	6, 12, 18, 24, 30, ...

- Convert all the fractions into equivalent fractions with a denominator of 24.

$$\frac{3}{4}, \frac{2}{3}, \frac{5}{8}, \frac{5}{6} \rightarrow \frac{18}{24}, \frac{16}{24}, \frac{15}{24}, \frac{20}{24}$$

- Order the equivalent fractions from the smallest to the biggest.

$$\frac{15}{24}, \frac{16}{24}, \frac{18}{24}, \frac{20}{24}$$

- Write the fractions in their original form, from the smallest to the biggest.

$$\frac{5}{8}, \frac{2}{3}, \frac{3}{4}, \frac{5}{6}$$

Example 3

Ordering fractions with the same numerator and different denominators

Put the following fractions in order from the smallest to the biggest:

$$\frac{2}{3}, \frac{2}{7}, \frac{2}{9}, \frac{2}{5}, \frac{2}{10}$$

Solution

Put the fractions in order from the smallest to biggest, by ordering the denominators from the biggest number to the smallest number.

$$\frac{2}{10}, \frac{2}{9}, \frac{2}{7}, \frac{2}{5}, \frac{2}{3}$$

Activity 4.4

1 Draw a 25-square grid in your copybook, as shown.

(i) Colour $\frac{4}{25}$ of the squares blue.

(ii) Colour $\frac{1}{5}$ of the squares green.

(iii) Colour $\frac{6}{25}$ of the squares yellow.

(iv) What fraction of the squares are coloured in now?

(v) What fraction of the squares are not coloured in now?

(vi) What colour represents the largest portion of the grid?

2 Draw two rectangles of the same size in your copybook, one below the other.

Shade in $\frac{3}{5}$ of one rectangle and $\frac{3}{4}$ of the second.

(i) Which of these fractions is closer to $\frac{1}{2}$?

(ii) Which fraction is bigger? Explain your answer by comparing them to $\frac{1}{2}$.

3 Draw two rectangles of the same size in your copybook, one below the other.

Shade in $\frac{4}{9}$ of one rectangle and $\frac{7}{12}$ of the second.

(i) Which of these fractions is closer to $\frac{1}{2}$?

(ii) Which fraction is bigger? Explain your answer by comparing them to $\frac{1}{2}$.

4 (i) Draw two rectangles of the same size in your copybook, one below the other.

Shade in $\frac{5}{6}$ of one rectangle and $\frac{2}{3}$ of the second.

(ii) Which of these two fractions is closer to 1?

(iii) Which fraction is bigger? Explain your answer.

5 In the following questions state which fraction is bigger. Explain your answer.

(i) $\frac{4}{5}$ or $\frac{7}{9}$ (iii) $\frac{2}{3}$ or $\frac{5}{9}$

(ii) $\frac{7}{12}$ or $\frac{5}{9}$ (iv) $\frac{3}{7}$ or $\frac{2}{9}$

6 Put the correct symbol between each pair of fractions: <, > or =.

(i) $\frac{5}{10}$ $\frac{4}{8}$

(ii) $\frac{4}{7}$ $\frac{5}{9}$

(iii) $\frac{5}{6}$ $\frac{1}{2}$

(iv) $\frac{7}{12}$ $\frac{5}{11}$

(v) $\frac{2}{3}$ $\frac{8}{12}$

=	'equal to'
<	'less than'
>	'greater than'

7 Put these fractions in order of size, starting with the smallest. Explain your method.

(i) $\frac{2}{9}$ (ii) $\frac{1}{9}$ (iii) $\frac{3}{9}$ (iv) $\frac{5}{9}$ (v) $\frac{9}{9}$

8 Which of the following fractions is the biggest? Explain your answer.

$\frac{1}{3}$ $\frac{1}{32}$ $\frac{1}{26}$ $\frac{1}{17}$ $\frac{1}{8}$ $\frac{1}{4}$

9 Which fraction is the smallest? Explain your answer.

$\frac{2}{3}$ $\frac{3}{5}$ $\frac{1}{2}$ $\frac{1}{4}$

10 Which fraction is the biggest? Explain your answer.

$\frac{3}{7}$ $\frac{2}{5}$ $\frac{1}{3}$ $\frac{5}{5}$

11 Order the following lists of fractions from the smallest to the biggest.

(i) $\frac{12}{15}, \frac{6}{15}, \frac{2}{15}, \frac{7}{15}, \frac{13}{15}, \frac{8}{15}$

(ii) $\frac{1}{15}, \frac{1}{17}, \frac{1}{23}, \frac{1}{5}, \frac{1}{2}, \frac{1}{9}, \frac{1}{13}$

(iii) $\frac{1}{2}, \frac{7}{10}, \frac{2}{3}, \frac{3}{5}, \frac{5}{6}$

(iv) $\frac{15}{30}, \frac{9}{30}, \frac{27}{30}, \frac{21}{30}, \frac{19}{30}, \frac{2}{30}$

(v) $\frac{3}{7}, \frac{3}{5}, \frac{1}{3}, \frac{3}{11}, \frac{1}{2}, \frac{3}{13}$

Section 4E Adding and Subtracting Fractions

When working with addition and subtraction of fractions you may find the fraction wall helpful.

Example 1

(i) Estimate the value of $\frac{8}{9} + \frac{2}{3}$.

(ii) Calculate the exact value by adding.

Solution

(i) We can use two rows from the fraction wall to imagine this sum:

| $\frac{1}{9}$ | $\frac{1}{9}$ | $\frac{1}{9}$ | $\frac{1}{9}$ | $\frac{1}{9}$ | $\frac{1}{9}$ | $\frac{1}{9}$ | $\frac{1}{9}$ | $\frac{1}{9}$ |

+

| $\frac{1}{3}$ | $\frac{1}{3}$ | $\frac{1}{3}$ |

- $\frac{8}{9} \cong 1$ where $\cong$ means 'approximately equal to'.

- $\frac{2}{3} > \frac{1}{2}$

- So, as $\frac{8}{9}$ is a little less than 1 and $\frac{2}{3}$ is a little more than $\frac{1}{2}$, we can estimate that

  $\frac{8}{9} + \frac{2}{3} \cong 1 + \frac{1}{2} = 1.5$

- We can see also that about 1 and a half strips are coloured red above.

(ii) - Find the lowest common multiple (LCM) of the denominators.

Number	Multiples
9	9, 18, 27, …
3	3, 6, 9, …

The first number in common that appears in the table is 9. So, the LCM is 9.

- Convert the fractions into equivalent fractions with a denominator of 9.

  $\frac{8}{9}, \quad \frac{2}{3} \quad \rightarrow \quad \frac{8}{9}, \quad \frac{6}{9}$

- Add the equivalent fractions, by adding the numerators together.

  $\frac{8}{9} + \frac{6}{9} = \frac{8 + 6}{9} = \frac{14}{9} = 1\frac{5}{9}$

Key Point

You can calculate this sum very quickly on a calculator, but you will need to be able to work it out yourself without a calculator when we come to algebra later.

Example 2

Claire spent $2\frac{2}{3}$ hours doing Maths homework and $1\frac{2}{9}$ hours doing Science homework.
How much time did she spend doing her homework?

Solution

- Change both times into improper fractions.

  Time spent on Maths homework = $2\frac{2}{3}$ hours = $\frac{2}{1} + \frac{2}{3} = \frac{2(3) + 2}{3} = \frac{6 + 2}{3} = \frac{8}{3}$ hours

Time spent on Science homework = $1\frac{2}{9}$ hours = $\frac{1}{1} + \frac{2}{9} = \frac{1(9)+2}{9} = \frac{9+2}{9} = \frac{11}{9}$ hours

- LCM of 3 and 9 is 9.

Write out the equivalent fractions and add the values.

$\frac{8 \times 3}{3 \times 3} + \frac{11}{9} = \frac{24}{9} + \frac{11}{9} = \frac{24+11}{9} = \frac{35}{9} = 3\frac{8}{9}$ hours

Note

In Example 2 above you may prefer to add the integer parts and fraction parts separately and then put them together.

Activity 4.5

You may find that a fraction wall will help you in these activities.

1 For each of these fraction sums:
   (i) Use strips from the fraction wall to help you to estimate the value.
   (ii) Calculate the exact value using equivalent fractions.

   (a) $\frac{1}{4} + \frac{5}{12}$ (c) $\frac{1}{7} + \frac{1}{2}$

   (b) $\frac{2}{5} + \frac{3}{7}$

2 For each of these fraction sums:
   (i) Use strips from the fraction wall to help you to estimate the value.
   (ii) Calculate the exact value using equivalent fractions.

   (a) $\frac{2}{3} + \frac{1}{4}$ (d) $\frac{8}{9} + \frac{1}{6}$

   (b) $\frac{1}{5} + \frac{1}{4}$ (e) $\frac{7}{10} + \frac{2}{5}$

   (c) $\frac{4}{7} + \frac{1}{3}$

3 Calculate each of these fraction sums:

   (i) $\frac{9}{10} - \frac{2}{5}$ (iv) $1\frac{1}{2} - \frac{5}{6}$

   (ii) $\frac{6}{7} - \frac{1}{2}$ (v) $\frac{4}{3} - \frac{1}{6}$

   (iii) $\frac{7}{4} - \frac{2}{3}$

4 Evaluate each of the following:

   (i) $\frac{3}{5} + \frac{1}{3}$ (iv) $\frac{2}{3} - \frac{1}{2}$

   (ii) $\frac{7}{9} - \frac{1}{2}$ (v) $\frac{14}{15} - \frac{2}{5}$

   (iii) $\frac{4}{7} + \frac{1}{5}$

5 Evaluate each of the following:

   (i) $\frac{3}{4} + \frac{2}{5}$ (iv) $\frac{1}{2} - \frac{2}{7}$

   (ii) $\frac{8}{9} - \frac{3}{5}$ (v) $1 - \frac{3}{8}$

   (iii) $\frac{13}{7} - \frac{2}{3}$

6 For each of the following statements, state if it is true or false. Give a reason for your answer.

   (i) $\frac{4}{7} + \frac{2}{5} = \frac{6}{12}$ (iv) $\frac{8}{12} - \frac{1}{4} = \frac{5}{12}$

   (ii) $\frac{3}{5} + \frac{1}{3} = \frac{14}{15}$ (v) $\frac{14}{15} - \frac{2}{5} = \frac{12}{10}$

   (iii) $\frac{7}{9} - \frac{1}{2} = \frac{6}{7}$

7 On Tuesday, Pat walked to school, a distance of $\frac{3}{5}$ km. After school he went to a friend's house, which was $\frac{3}{4}$ km from the school. How far did Pat walk in total on Tuesday?

8 A man walks $\frac{7}{8}$ km to a shop and then walks back. How far has the man walked?

9 Alan read $\frac{2}{5}$ of his book last night and plans to read $\frac{1}{4}$ of the book tonight. How much of the book will he have read by tomorrow?

10 A boy buys $\frac{3}{5}$ kg of jellies and $\frac{1}{4}$ kg of toffees. What is the total weight of sweets in kg?

11 Sam spent $\frac{1}{4}$ of his pocket money on art supplies and $\frac{2}{3}$ on a cinema ticket. He saved the rest of his pocket money. What fraction of his money did he save?

12 A ribbon of length $\frac{7}{9}$ m has a piece cut off of length $\frac{1}{3}$ m. How much ribbon is left?

Section 4F Multiplication of Fractions

Example 1

Multiplying a whole number by a fraction

Susan decides to have 3 of her friends over for dinner. She decides that she is going to give each person $\frac{2}{5}$ of an apple tart for dessert. How many apple tarts will she need?

Solution

There will be 4 people eating dinner, including Susan.

She will need 4 groups of $\frac{2}{5}$.

This means: $\frac{2}{5} + \frac{2}{5} + \frac{2}{5} + \frac{2}{5} = \frac{8}{5}$

It also means: $\frac{4}{1} \times \frac{2}{5} = \frac{8}{5}$

The fraction $\frac{8}{5}$ is an improper fraction and can be changed into a mixed number.

$\frac{8}{5} = 1\frac{3}{5}$, so Susan needs $1\frac{3}{5}$ apple tarts. She would need to buy 2 apple tarts.

Example 2

Multiplying a fraction by a fraction

Evaluate $\frac{1}{4} \times \frac{3}{5}$.

Solution

$\frac{1}{4} \times \frac{3}{5} = \frac{1 \times 3}{4 \times 5} = \frac{3}{20}$

Key Point

To multiply a fraction by a fraction, multiply the **top number by the top number** and the **bottom number by the bottom number**.

Example 3

Evaluate $\dfrac{2}{3} \times \dfrac{4}{5}$.

Solution

$\dfrac{2}{3} \times \dfrac{4}{5} = \dfrac{2 \times 4}{3 \times 5} = \dfrac{8}{15}$

Example 4

Evaluate $3 \times \dfrac{4}{5}$.

Solution

$3 \times \dfrac{4}{5}$

$= \dfrac{3}{1} \times \dfrac{4}{5}$

$= \dfrac{3 \times 4}{1 \times 5}$

$= \dfrac{12}{5}$

Example 5

Find $\dfrac{2}{3}$ of 36.

Solution

$\dfrac{2}{3}$ of 36

$= \dfrac{2}{3} \times \dfrac{36}{1}$

$= \dfrac{2 \times 36}{3 \times 1}$

$= \dfrac{72}{3} = 24$

Activity 4.6

1 Evaluate each of the following giving your answer as a single fraction.

(i) $4 \times \dfrac{3}{7}$ (iii) $\dfrac{2}{5} \times \dfrac{2}{3}$ (v) $\dfrac{8}{9} \times \dfrac{1}{2}$

(ii) $\dfrac{1}{3} \times \dfrac{4}{7}$ (iv) $2 \times \dfrac{5}{12}$

2 There is $\dfrac{4}{7}$ of a cake left in the fridge in the staff room. The Principal eats $\dfrac{1}{4}$ of the cake that was left. What fraction of the whole cake did the Principal eat?

3 Evaluate each of the following and express your answer as a single fraction.

(i) $2 \times \dfrac{7}{8}$ (iii) $7 \times \dfrac{2}{3}$ (v) $9 \times \dfrac{2}{5}$

(ii) $5 \times \dfrac{1}{2}$ (iv) $3 \times \dfrac{3}{4}$

4 If Niamh runs for $\dfrac{3}{4}$ of an hour, 4 days per week, how much time will she have spent running in the week?

5 Evaluate each of the following and express your answer in its simplest form.

(i) $\dfrac{2}{3} \times \dfrac{5}{6}$ (iv) $\dfrac{2}{9} \times \dfrac{3}{4}$

(ii) $\dfrac{3}{5} \times \dfrac{1}{2}$ (v) $\dfrac{3}{8} \times \dfrac{2}{3} \times \dfrac{1}{2}$

(iii) $\dfrac{1}{4} \times \dfrac{4}{5}$ (vi) $\dfrac{1}{5} \times \dfrac{7}{8} \times \dfrac{2}{3}$

6 Find:

(i) $\dfrac{3}{4}$ of $1500   (iv) $\dfrac{5}{9}$ of 270

(ii) $\dfrac{4}{5}$ of 500 kg   (v) $\dfrac{2}{3}$ of €762

(iii) $\dfrac{1}{6}$ of 150 km

7 Find $\frac{3}{5}$ of each of these amounts:

   (i) €40   (iii) 300 m   (v) 15 hours

   (ii) 200 g   (iv) 450 litres

8 A box has 120 different colour tickets in it. $\frac{1}{3}$ of them are green, $\frac{5}{8}$ of them are pink and the remaining tickets are white.

   (i) How many tickets are green?

   (ii) How many tickets are pink?

   (iii) How many tickets are white?

9 Sarah earns €8 per hour working in the local shop. How much does she get paid for working $2\frac{3}{4}$ hours?

10 Jack and Conor went to the local chip shop. Jack brought €3 and Conor brought €5. Jack spent $\frac{5}{6}$ of his money buying a portion of chips. Conor spent $\frac{7}{10}$ of his money buying a burger.

   (i) How much did the portion of chips cost Jack?

   (ii) How much did the burger cost Conor?

11 A family went on holiday. It took them 8 hours to travel from the airport to their final destination. They spent $\frac{1}{8}$ of the time waiting in the airport, $\frac{11}{16}$ of the time on the aeroplane and the remainder of the time travelling by bus to their hotel. Calculate how much time they spent:

   (i) Waiting in the airport

   (ii) On the aeroplane

   (iii) On the bus.

Section 4G Reciprocals

The **reciprocal** of a fraction is obtained by turning the fraction upside down.

For example: $\frac{2}{3}$ is the reciprocal of $\frac{3}{2}$ (and vice versa).

$\frac{1}{5}$ is the reciprocal of $\frac{5}{1}$.

The reciprocal of $3.4 = \frac{1}{3.4}$

You can get the reciprocal of any number on your calculator by using this button: x^{-1}

In the following example, we see a special relationship between a fraction and its reciprocal.

Example 1

Find the value of $\left(\frac{2}{3}\right)\left(\frac{3}{2}\right)$.

Solution

$$\left(\frac{2}{3}\right)\left(\frac{3}{2}\right) = \frac{2 \times 3}{3 \times 2} = \frac{6}{6} = 1$$

So, when we multiply a fraction by its reciprocal we get 1. (Reciprocals are also called **multiplication inverses** because of this.)

Example 2

(i) What number do you multiply $\frac{2}{7}$ by to get 1?

(ii) Divide 1 by $\frac{2}{7}$.

Solution

(i) $\left(\frac{2}{7}\right)\left(\frac{7}{2}\right) = 1$ so $\frac{7}{2}$ is the number required.

(ii) $\left(\frac{2}{7}\right)\left(\frac{7}{2}\right) = 1$

So $\dfrac{1}{\left(\frac{2}{7}\right)} = \dfrac{7}{2}$

Notice that when we divide 1 by a fraction the answer is the reciprocal of the fraction.

We will see shortly that **to divide any number by a fraction we multiply by the reciprocal of the fraction**.

Section 4H Division of Fractions

Example 1

Dividing a number by a fraction

2 cakes are divided so that each portion is $\frac{2}{5}$ of a cake. How many portions are there in the 2 cakes?

Solution

$2 \div \frac{2}{5}$ can be written as $\dfrac{2}{\left(\frac{2}{5}\right)}$.

We can get an equivalent fraction by multiplying the numerator and denominator by the same number.

If we choose the reciprocal of the denominator as this number, we get:

$$\dfrac{2}{\left(\frac{2}{5}\right)} = \dfrac{2 \times \frac{5}{2}}{\left(\frac{2}{5}\right) \times \frac{5}{2}} = \dfrac{2 \times \frac{5}{2}}{1} = 2 \times \frac{5}{2} = 5$$

So we have $2 \div \frac{2}{5} = 2 \times \frac{5}{2} = 5$

So we see that **to divide a number by $\frac{2}{5}$ we multiply by $\frac{5}{2}$**.

Example 2

Evaluate $\frac{2}{5} \div \frac{4}{15}$.

Solution

$\dfrac{2}{5} \div \dfrac{4}{15} = \dfrac{2}{5} \times \dfrac{15}{4} = \dfrac{30}{20} = \dfrac{3}{2}$

 Key Point

The general method for dividing any number by a fraction:

- Find the reciprocal of the fraction you are dividing by (i.e. turn the fraction upside down).
- Multiply the number by this reciprocal.

Rational Numbers

1 There are 4 cakes at a party. Each serving is $\frac{1}{3}$ of a cake. How many people will get a serving? Use a diagram to illustrate your answer.

2 A sack of carrots weighs 15 kg. The shopkeeper sells the carrots in $\frac{3}{4}$ kg bags. How many bags will the shopkeeper fill from the sack?

3 Evaluate each of the following:

(i) 2 divided by $\frac{2}{5}$

(ii) 4 divided by $\frac{3}{4}$

(iii) 3 divided by $\frac{3}{10}$

(iv) 6 divided by $\frac{3}{8}$

4 Divide the following fractions:

(i) $\frac{2}{3} \div \frac{3}{13}$

(ii) $\frac{17}{24} \div \frac{19}{21}$

(iii) $\frac{1}{2} \div \frac{9}{4}$

(iv) $\frac{7}{2} \div \frac{14}{3}$

(v) $\frac{3}{10} \div \frac{3}{11}$

(vi) $\frac{2}{7} \div \frac{2}{5}$

5 A factory uses $\frac{1}{4}$ of a barrel of raisins in each batch of granola bars. Yesterday, the factory used $7\frac{1}{2}$ barrels of raisins. How many batches of granola bars did the factory make yesterday?

6 Divide the following fractions:

(i) $\frac{1}{2} \div \frac{5}{2}$

(ii) $1\frac{3}{4} \div \frac{2}{7}$

(iii) $\frac{3}{4} \div \frac{1}{8}$

(iv) $\frac{7}{2} \div \frac{20}{3}$

(v) $9 \div \frac{7}{18}$

(vi) $\frac{3}{8} \div \frac{1}{12}$

7 Evaluate each of the following.

(i) $\frac{2}{3}$ divided by $\frac{1}{6}$

(ii) $\frac{8}{10}$ divided by $\frac{2}{5}$

(iii) $\frac{15}{4}$ divided by $\frac{1}{6}$

(iv) $\frac{9}{5}$ divided by $\frac{3}{10}$

(v) $\frac{5}{6}$ divided by $\frac{3}{18}$

8 (i) Find the value of $\left(\frac{3}{7}\right)\left(\frac{7}{3}\right)$ and simplify your answer.

(ii) What number do you multiply $\frac{2}{5}$ by to get 1?

(iii) Divide 1 by $\frac{2}{5}$.

(iv) What number do you multiply $\frac{7}{3}$ by to get 1?

9 (i) Find the value of $\left(\frac{4}{5}\right)\left(\frac{5}{4}\right)$ and simplify your answer.

(ii) What number do you multiply $\frac{5}{9}$ by to get 1?

(iii) Divide 1 by $\frac{5}{9}$.

10 (i) Write down the reciprocal of $\frac{3}{8}$.

(ii) Multiply $\frac{3}{8}$ by its reciprocal.

11 How many strips of timber, each $\frac{2}{3}$ m long, can be cut from a $5\frac{1}{2}$ m length of timber?

12 A man buys one bag of dog food that weighs $7\frac{1}{2}$ kilograms. He has 5 dogs that eat $\frac{2}{5}$ kg each every time they are fed. How many times can the dogs be fed from one bag of food?

13 The weight of the part of an iceberg above water is 1150 tonnes. Nine-tenths of an iceberg is below water. Find the weight of the iceberg below water.

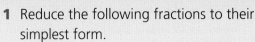

1 Reduce the following fractions to their simplest form.

(a) $\dfrac{6}{12}$

(b) $\dfrac{3}{63}$

(c) $\dfrac{8}{48}$

(d) $\dfrac{21}{357}$

(e) $\dfrac{37}{185}$

(f) $\dfrac{9}{216}$

(g) $\dfrac{12}{144}$

(h) $\dfrac{13}{104}$

(i) $\dfrac{25}{115}$

(j) $\dfrac{36}{468}$

2 Convert the following fractions into improper fractions or mixed numbers.

(a) $2\dfrac{1}{13}$

(b) $\dfrac{67}{63}$

(c) $8\dfrac{1}{9}$

(d) $\dfrac{421}{357}$

(e) $11\dfrac{3}{7}$

(f) $\dfrac{89}{20}$

(g) $12\dfrac{1}{6}$

(h) $\dfrac{12}{5}$

(i) $\dfrac{225}{112}$

(j) $7\dfrac{3}{8}$

3 Convert the following fractions into equivalent fractions.

(a) $\dfrac{12}{24} = \dfrac{\square}{2}$

(b) $\dfrac{68}{24} = \dfrac{\square}{6}$

(c) $\dfrac{1}{9} = \dfrac{13}{\square}$

(d) $\dfrac{171}{285} = \dfrac{\square}{15}$

(e) $\dfrac{88}{8} = \dfrac{11}{\square}$

(f) $\dfrac{9}{288} = \dfrac{\square}{\square}$

(g) $\dfrac{124}{31} = \dfrac{\square}{\square}$

4 Add the following fractions and write the answer in its simplest form:

(a) $\dfrac{2}{5} + \dfrac{5}{3}$

(b) $\dfrac{7}{12} + \dfrac{3}{18}$

(c) $\dfrac{4}{9} + \dfrac{5}{6}$

(d) $\dfrac{17}{18} + \dfrac{7}{9}$

(e) $\dfrac{8}{13} + \dfrac{17}{39}$

(f) $\dfrac{29}{28} + \dfrac{6}{7}$

(g) $\dfrac{18}{19} + \dfrac{3}{38}$

(h) $\dfrac{11}{12} + \dfrac{3}{8} + \dfrac{1}{2}$

(i) Show your answer for part (a) using visual representation.

5 Subtract the following fractions, and write the answer in its simplest form.

(a) $\dfrac{5}{8} - \dfrac{1}{2}$

(b) $\dfrac{9}{12} - \dfrac{1}{6}$

(c) $\dfrac{3}{7} - \dfrac{5}{14}$

(d) $\dfrac{17}{18} - \dfrac{5}{9}$

(e) $\dfrac{8}{13} - \dfrac{19}{39}$

(f) $\dfrac{27}{28} - \dfrac{3}{4}$

(g) $\dfrac{18}{23} - \dfrac{4}{46}$

(h) $\dfrac{11}{12} - \dfrac{1}{6} - \dfrac{1}{3}$

(i) Show your answer for part (a) using visual representation.

6 Multiply the following fractions.

(a) $\dfrac{5}{7} \times \dfrac{1}{2}$

(b) $\dfrac{9}{11} \times \dfrac{2}{7}$

(c) $\dfrac{5}{6} \times \dfrac{7}{10}$

(d) $\dfrac{7}{18} \times \dfrac{1}{5}$

(e) $\dfrac{7}{8} \times \dfrac{3}{4}$

(f) $\dfrac{11}{12} \times \dfrac{2}{3}$

(g) $\dfrac{18}{23} \times \dfrac{3}{5}$

(h) $\dfrac{11}{2} \times \dfrac{2}{5} \times \dfrac{1}{3}$

(i) Show your answer for part (a) using visual representation.

7 Divide the following fractions and write the answer in its simplest form.

(a) $\dfrac{1}{2} \div 8$

(b) $\dfrac{9}{11} \div 9$

(c) $\dfrac{5}{6} \div \dfrac{10}{3}$

(d) $\dfrac{7}{18} \div \dfrac{2}{9}$

(e) $\dfrac{27}{8} \div \dfrac{3}{5}$

(f) $\dfrac{11}{12} \div \dfrac{55}{3}$

(g) $\dfrac{18}{21} \div \dfrac{3}{2}$

(h) $\dfrac{121}{3} \div \dfrac{11}{5}$

(i) Show your answer for part (a) using visual representation.

8 Aisling bought 30 bars of chocolate for her class of 30 students. Only two-thirds of the class were in school that day. How many chocolate bars were left over?

9 A student has to pay €160 for music tuition fees. He has paid two-fifths of the fees. Find how much he has:

(a) paid already   (b) still to pay.

10 Emily has a beautiful garden. She has approximately 30 plants. Five-sixths of her plants have flowers. How many plants do not have flowers?

11 There is €1200 in a prize fund. The first prize is $\frac{7}{10}$ of the fund. Find the value of the first prize.

12 Aideen owns 6000 shares in a certain company. She sells two-thirds of her shares. How many shares does she own in the company now?

13 €2400 is shared between John, Mary and Anne. John gets $\frac{1}{2}$ of the money. Mary gets $\frac{1}{2}$ of the remaining money. How much does Anne get?

Exam-style Questions

1 Sheila orders two pizzas to divide evenly between herself and five friends.

(a) What fraction of pizza will each person get? Write your fraction in its simplest form.

(b) One of the friends gets a text and leaves before the pizza is delivered. What fraction will each person now get if the pizzas are divided evenly between those remaining?

(c) Find how much extra pizza each person gets.

JCOL 2012 Paper 1

2 (a) In the diagram, what fraction of row A is shaded?

(b) In the same diagram, what fraction of column R is shaded?

(c) Using the diagram or otherwise, calculate the result when your fractions in parts (a) and (b) are multiplied.

(d) Tim claims that the two fractions shown by the shading of the strips A and B are the same. Is Tim correct? Give a reason for your answer.

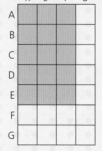

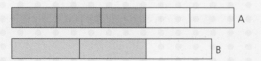

JCOL 2012 SEC Sample Paper

KEY WORDS AND PHRASES

- **Rational number**
- **Fraction**
- **Numerator**
- **Denominator**
- **LCM**
- **Portion**

- **Proper fraction**
- **Improper fraction**
- **Mixed number**
- **Equivalent fractions**
- **Reciprocal**

 Interactive Tool 4.1    Interactive Tool 4.2

Chapter Summary 4

- A **rational number (fraction)** is obtained by dividing one integer by another, in the form $\frac{p}{q}$ where p is the **numerator** and q is the non-zero integer **denominator**.

- Rational numbers are indicated by the symbol $\mathbb{Q}$.

- **Proper fractions:** represent **part** of the whole unit. For example: $\frac{5}{6}$.

- **Improper fractions:** represent **more** than the whole unit. For example: $\frac{7}{6}$.

- **Mixed numbers:** sum of a proper fraction and an integer. For example: $1\frac{1}{6}$.

- **Fractions are equivalent if:**
  - Both fractions represent the same portion of the whole unit.
  - You can multiply or divide the numerator and denominator by the same number to get the other fraction.
    - $\frac{3}{4} = \frac{27}{36}$ by multiplying above (numerator) and below (denominator) by 9.
    - $\frac{125}{150} = \frac{5}{6}$ by dividing above (numerator) and below (denominator) by 25.

- **To order fractions:**
  - If all the denominators are equal, compare the numerators e.g. $\frac{3}{7} < \frac{5}{7} < \frac{6}{7}$ ...
  - If all the numerators are equal, compare the denominators and note that the bigger the denominator the smaller the fraction e.g. $\frac{3}{4} > \frac{3}{5} > \frac{3}{7}$ ...
  - If there are different denominators and numerators, convert all the fractions to equivalent fractions **of the same denominator**, and then compare the numerator of each.

- **To multiply fractions:**
  - Write each number as a fraction $\left(\text{for example: } 4 = \frac{4}{1} \text{ and } 2\frac{2}{3} = \frac{8}{3}\right)$.
  - Multiply numerator by numerator and denominator by denominator.
  - If the answer can be simplified, then simplify it e.g. $\frac{3}{4} \times \frac{6}{7} = \frac{3 \times 6}{4 \times 7} = \frac{18}{28} = \frac{9}{14}$.
- **To divide fractions:**
  - Multiply the first (or top) fraction by the reciprocal of the second (or bottom) fraction e.g. $\frac{4}{7} \div \frac{5}{6} = \frac{4}{7} \times \frac{6}{5} = \frac{24}{35}$.

Decimals and Percentages

Learning Intentions

In this chapter, you will learn about:

- Fractions, decimals and percentages as different ways of writing the same value
- Working with decimals
- Rounding and significant figures
- Working with percentages

LO: N.2(a),
U.5, U.6, U.13

Historical background

The Babylonians devised the first decimal place value system in around 3000 BC. Their numbering system used base 60 instead of base 10. When converted to base 10, the numeral shown at the right from a Babylonian tablet is accurate to seven decimal places.

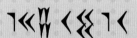

This numeral was on an old Babylonian tablet. It is an approximation for $\sqrt{2}$.

It was not until 1585 when Simon Stevin, a Flemish mathematician, published a booklet called 'De Thiende' ('The Tenth') that decimals were taught in an understandable way using base 10.

Simon Stevin 1548–1620

Fractions, **decimals** and **percentages** are just different ways of showing the same value. In this chapter we are going to look at converting fractions into decimals and percentages, and vice versa.

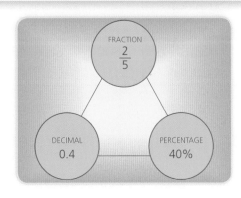

Section 5A Decimals

The diagram illustrates **place value** and its relationship to both fractions and decimals. Remember, the place value of each digit depends on its position in the number.

The **decimal point** separates the whole part of the number from the part of the number that is less than 1.

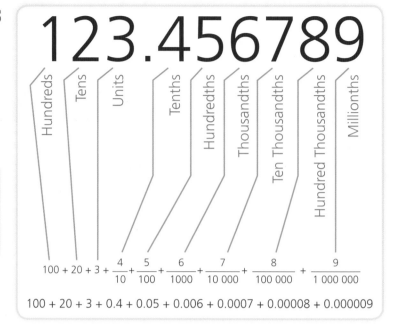

$$100 + 20 + 3 + \frac{4}{10} + \frac{5}{100} + \frac{6}{1000} + \frac{7}{10\,000} + \frac{8}{100\,000} + \frac{9}{1\,000\,000}$$

$$100 + 20 + 3 + 0.4 + 0.05 + 0.006 + 0.0007 + 0.00008 + 0.000009$$

Example 1

Using the place value diagram shown above as a guide, write the value of each digit in the number 666.66666 into the table.

Digit	6	6	6	.	6	6	6	6	6
In words									
Whole number or fraction									
Whole number or decimal									

Solution

Digit	6	6	6	.	6	6	6	6
In words	six hundreds	six tens	six units		six tenths	six hundredths	six thousandths	six ten thousandths
Whole number or fraction	600	60	6		$\frac{6}{10}$	$\frac{6}{100}$	$\frac{6}{1000}$	$\frac{6}{10\,000}$
Whole number or decimal	600	60	6		0.6	0.06	0.006	0.0006

Key Points

In general, when multiplying or dividing decimals by multiples of 10, we can follow the rules outlined in the table below.

Operation	Example	Rule
Multiply by 10	$2.0 \times 10 = 20$	Move the decimal point 1 place to the right.
Multiply by 100	$2.0 \times 100 = 200$	Move the decimal point 2 places to the right.
Multiply by 1000	$2.0 \times 1000 = 2000$	Move the decimal point 3 places to the right.
Divide by 10	$2.0 \div 10 = 0.2$	Move the decimal point 1 place to the left.
Divide by 100	$2.0 \div 100 = 0.02$	Move the decimal point 2 places to the left.
Divide by 1000	$2.0 \div 1000 = 0.002$	Move the decimal point 3 places to the left.

Example 2

State the values indicated by the letters A, B, C, D on the following number lines.

(i)

| 1.5 | A | B | C | D | 2.5 |

(ii)

| 2.8 | A | B | 2.9 | C | D | 3.0 |

Solution

(i) The number line has 10 equal segments between 1.5 and 2.5.

Each segment is equivalent to
$\dfrac{1}{10} = 0.1$

So: A = 1.5 + 2(0.1) = 1.5 + 0.2 = 1.7

  B = 1.5 + 4(0.1) = 1.5 + 0.4 = 1.9

  C = 1.5 + 7(0.1) = 1.5 + 0.7 = 2.2

  D = 1.5 + 8(0.1) = 1.5 + 0.8 = 2.3

(ii) The number line has 10 equal segments from 2.8 to 2.9, and from 2.9 to 3.0.

Therefore each segment is equivalent to
$\dfrac{1}{100} = 0.01$

So: A = 2.8 + 4(0.01) = 2.8 + 0.04 = 2.84

  B = 2.8 + 6(0.01) = 2.8 + 0.06 = 2.86

  C = 2.9 + 2(0.01) = 2.9 + 0.02 = 2.92

  D = 2.9 + 5(0.01) = 2.9 + 0.05 = 2.95

Converting Decimals to Fractions

Example 3

Write 0.625 as a fraction.

Solution

Method 1

$0.625 = 0.6 + 0.02 + 0.005$

$= \dfrac{6}{10} + \dfrac{2}{100} + \dfrac{5}{1000}$

$= \dfrac{600}{1000} + \dfrac{20}{1000} + \dfrac{5}{1000}$

$= \dfrac{625}{1000} = \dfrac{5}{8}$

Method 2

Using a calculator

Type the following into your calculator.

The fraction $\dfrac{5}{8}$ will appear on the screen.

5

Decimals and Percentages

Converting Fractions to Decimals

Example 4

Convert the fraction $\frac{3}{5}$ to a decimal.

Solution

Method 1

Find the number that you need to multiply the denominator by to get a power of 10.

Multiply numerator and denominator by 2:

$$\frac{3}{5} \times \frac{2}{2} = \frac{6}{10}$$

$\frac{6}{10} = 0.6$ (We know this from the place value diagram.)

Answer: $\frac{3}{5} = 0.6$

Method 2

Using a calculator

Type ⬛3⬛ ⬛÷⬛ ⬛5⬛ ⬛=⬛ ⬛S⇔D⬛

The decimal 0.6 will appear.

Recurring Decimals

A recurring decimal is a decimal number where the digits repeat forever.

Examples of recurring decimals are:

$$\frac{1}{6} = 0.16666666... = 0.1\dot{6}$$

$$\frac{5}{7} = 0.714285714285714285... = 0.\dot{7}1428\dot{5}$$

$$\frac{14}{33} = 0.42424242... = 0.\dot{4}\dot{2}$$

The dots above the digits indicate the repeating digits.

Activity 5.1

1 For each of the numbers below, write down the value of the digit 7, using the place value diagram as a guide.

   (i) 0.67   (iii) 57 600   (v) 9.8897   (vii) 578   (ix) 0.7

   (ii) 337   (iv) 6.878   (vi) 5.357   (viii) 75 225   (x) 56.94237

2 For each of the numbers below, write down the value of the digit 5, using the place value diagram as a guide.

   (i) 37.5281   (iv) 5.2199   (vii) 5137.21   (x) 985 321

   (ii) 21.2753   (v) 8.357   (viii) 59 722   (xi) 385.99

   (iii) 53.281   (vi) 454.24   (ix) 3746.051   (xii) 4 441 156.2

3 Write the following sums as decimals:

   (i) $4 + \dfrac{5}{10} + \dfrac{3}{100} + \dfrac{7}{1000} + \dfrac{2}{10\,000} + \dfrac{1}{100\,000} + \dfrac{8}{1\,000\,000}$

   (ii) $10 + 7 + \dfrac{1}{10} + \dfrac{0}{100} + \dfrac{1}{1000} + \dfrac{6}{10\,000} + \dfrac{0}{100\,000} + \dfrac{3}{1\,000\,000}$

   (iii) $500 + 90 + \dfrac{2}{10} + \dfrac{7}{100} + \dfrac{4}{1000} + \dfrac{5}{100\,000} + \dfrac{7}{1\,000\,000}$

4 Write each of the following decimals as a sum of two or more fractions:

  (i) 0.53   (iii) 0.67   (v) 0.903   (vii) 0.9735   (ix) 0.12937

  (ii) 0.011   (iv) 0.084   (vi) 0.808   (viii) 0.7021   (x) 0.263773

5 State the values indicated by the letters A, B, C, D and E on the following number lines.

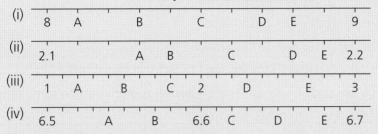

  (i)   8   A   B   C   D   E   9

  (ii)   2.1   A   B   C   D   E   2.2

  (iii)   1   A   B   C   2   D   E   3

  (iv)   6.5   A   B   6.6   C   D   E   6.7

6 Rearrange each of the following lists of decimals from largest to smallest:

  (i) 0.45, 0.273, 0.398, 0.521, 0.431

  (ii) 0.741, 0.748, 0.743, 0.740, 0.746

  (iii) 0.9823, 0.9827, 0.9821, 0.9822, 0.9826, 0.9829

  (iv) 1.005, 1.05, 1.055, 5.001, 1.5

  (v) 1.23, 2.233, 1.2332, 0.2323, 2.3223

7 Joanne receives €50 from her grandfather. Her grandfather tells her to keep €20 for herself and divide the remainder equally among her three sisters.

  (i) What fraction of the money does Joanne keep?

  (ii) Express as a decimal the proportion of the money that Joanne keeps.

  (iii) What fraction of the money does each sister get?

  (iv) Express as a decimal the proportion of the money that each sister gets.

8 (i) Convert each of the following fractions into a decimal without using a calculator:

  (a) $\dfrac{2}{5}$ (c) $\dfrac{73}{100}$ (e) $-\dfrac{17}{50}$ (g) $\dfrac{267}{1000}$ (i) $\dfrac{3267}{10\,000}$

  (b) $-\dfrac{3}{10}$ (d) $\dfrac{23}{25}$ (f) $\dfrac{48}{1000}$ (h) $\dfrac{176}{10\,000}$ (j) $-\dfrac{899\,991}{100\,000}$

  (ii) Check your answers using your calculator.

9 (i) Convert each of the following decimals into a fraction without using a calculator:

  (a) 0.25   (c) 0.35   (e) 0.62   (g) 0.65   (i) 0.82

  (b) 0.5   (d) 0.4   (f) 0.27   (h) 0.48   (j) 0.375

  (ii) Check your answers using your calculator.

10 Show the decimal 0.47 on a 100-square grid and convert it into a fraction.
Check your answer using your calculator.

11 In the following figures:

  (i) 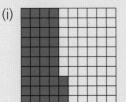   (ii)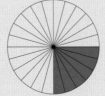

  (a) What fraction of each figure is shaded?

  (b) What decimal of each figure is shaded?

  (c) What fraction of each figure is not shaded?

  (d) What decimal of each figure is not shaded?

12 Ciara, a shop owner, is writing up a roster for Monday for her three staff members: Frank, James and Gillian. The shop stays open for 10 hours on Monday and must have two members of staff present at all times. Frank says that at most he is able to work only for the first 8 hours. James can work only for the first 4 hours and Gillian can work only for the last 3 hours.

  (i)   What fraction of the working day can Frank work?

  (ii) What fraction of the working day can Gillian work?

  (iii) What fraction of the working day can James work?

  (iv) What fraction of the working day is Ciara required to work in the shop?

  (v)   What fraction of the day are both Ciara and Frank working together at the same time?

  (vi) Express your answers for parts (i) to (v) as decimals.

13 A farmer owns 150 cows, 120 sheep and 30 hens.

  (i)   Write the number of cows as both a fraction of the total number of animals and as a decimal.

  (ii) Write the number of sheep as both a fraction of the total number of animals and as a decimal.

14 Use a calculator to express the fractions $\frac{2}{9}$ and $\frac{1}{12}$ as recurring decimals.

Section 5B Working with Decimals

Class Activity/Discussion

In everyday life, where do we use decimals?

Why is it necessary to be able to add and subtract decimals?

Why is it necessary to be able to multiply and divide decimals?

Adding and Subtracting Decimals

Example 1

Write each of the following sums as a single decimal, without the use of a calculator.

  (i) 1.34 + 0.91   (ii) 5.73 – 1.1   (iii) 7.566 – 1.2 – 1.47

Solution

(i)
```
    1.34
  + 0.91
  ------
    2.25
```

(ii) 5.73 – 1.1

Insert a zero to the end of 1.1, so both numbers have the same number of digits.
```
    5.73
  - 1.10
  ------
    4.63
```

(iii) 7.566 – 1.2 – 1.47

Insert two zeros to the end of 1.2, and one zero to the end of 1.47, so all three numbers have the same number of digits.
```
    7.566
  - 1.200
  ------
    6.366
  - 1.470
  ------
    4.896
```

Example 2

(i) Find the value of 12.2 × 0.04 without using a calculator.

(ii) Check your answer using your calculator.

Solution

(i) 12.2 × 0.04

Multiply out the numbers without the decimal points.

$$\begin{array}{r} 122 \\ \times\ \underline{\ \ 4} \\ 488 \end{array}$$

So, 122 × 4 = 448

12.2 has 1 digit after the decimal point.

0.04 has 2 digits after the decimal point.

The total number of digits counted after the decimal point is 3. The answer will have 3 digits after the decimal point.

Answer: 12.2 × 0.04 = 0.448

(ii) **Using a calculator**

Type `1 2 . 2 × 0 . 0 4 =`

The answer on the screen will be 0.448.

Example 3

(i) Find the value of $\frac{1.44}{0.12}$ without the use of a calculator.

(ii) Check your answer using your calculator.

Solution

(i) $\frac{1.44}{0.12}$

Remove the decimal point in both numbers by multiplying the numerator and denominator by a multiple of 10.
As there are 2 digits after the decimal point in the number 1.44, we need to multiply the numerator and denominator by $10^2 = 100$.

$$\frac{1.44}{0.12} \times \frac{100}{100} = \frac{144}{12} = 12$$

Answer: 12

(ii) Type `1 . 4 4 ÷ 0 . 1 2 =`

The answer on the screen will be 12.

Decimals and Percentages

Decimals and Percentages

1 Evaluate the following sums using your calculator.
  (i)   1.234 + 4.934
  (ii) 5.228 + 42.325
  (iii) 1.320447 − 1.220223
  (iv) 6.93233 + 2.16671
  (v)   213.6321 − 244.5766
  (vi) −97.8334 − 23.005

2 (i) Find the value of each of the following without the use of a calculator.
  (ii) Check your answers using a calculator.
  (a) 9.1 × 0.5   (f) 7.5 × 2.27
  (b) 1.23 × 5.7   (g) 1.65 × 3.8
  (c) 0.2 × 5.3   (h) 10.9 × 1.93
  (d) 1.38 × 8.8   (i) 3.2 × 7.68
  (e) 4.7 × 6.31   (j) 2.145 × 9.1

3 (i) Find the value of each of the following without the use of a calculator.
  (ii) Check your answers using a calculator.
  (a) $\frac{1.7}{0.2}$ (e) $\frac{23.14}{8}$
  (b) $\frac{7.68}{3}$ (f) $\frac{41.6}{0.004}$
  (c) $\frac{8.9}{0.01}$ (g) $\frac{16.9}{0.13}$
  (d) $\frac{9.312}{0.2}$ (h) $\frac{23.97}{5.1}$

4 A shop sells a brand of dog food in 5 kg and 10 kg bags. The 5 kg bag costs €3.52 and the 10 kg bag costs €6.54.
  (i) What is the cost per kilogram of dog food, if you buy the 10 kg bag?
  (ii) What is the cost per kilogram of dog food, if you buy the 5 kg bag?
  (iii) What is the cost difference per kilogram between the 5 kg and the 10 kg bag?

5 The results of a 3-lap car race are shown in the table below.

Position	Driver	Lap 1 time (seconds)	Lap 2 time (seconds)	Lap 3 time (seconds)	Total time (seconds)
1	Paul	56.05	55.75	55.15	169.95
2	Simon	56.02	56.29	55.12	167.43
3	Lucy	56.24	56.27	55.08	167.59
4	Andrew	56.31	55.81	55.49	167.61
5	Kevin	56.36	56.12	55.25	167.73

  (i) Which driver completed Lap 1 in the fastest time?
  (ii) Which driver completed Lap 2 in the fastest time?
  (iii) Which driver completed Lap 3 in the fastest time?
  (iv) What is the difference between the fastest and the slowest time in Lap 1?
  (v) What is the difference between the fastest and the slowest time in Lap 3?

6 A gardener buys 2 kg of lawn seed. He sows 0.6 kg on Saturday, 0.25 kg on Sunday and 1 kg on Monday. How much lawn seed is left?

7 Denise lives 60 km from work. She drove 7 km to the train station and travelled 37.61 km on the train until it broke down. How much further does Denise have to travel to get to work?

8 Simon goes into a shop and buys the following items:

- 7 apples at 58 cent each
- 4 oranges at 62 cent each
- 5 bananas at 95 cent each.

(i) How much in total did his fruit cost?

(ii) How much change will he get from €20?

9 The contents of a box weigh 10.85 kg. The box contains the following items:

- A kettle that weighs 1.5 kg
- 16 cups weighing 0.3 kg each
- 16 saucers weighing 0.2 kg each
- 10 spoons weighing 0.05 kg each
- A bowl that weighs 0.65 kg
- A small bag of sugar.

(i) What is the total weight of all the cups?

(ii) What is the total weight of all the saucers?

(iii) What is the total weight of all the spoons?

(iv) What is the weight of the small bag of sugar?

10 Four friends have €15 between them. They decide to spend their money on the following items:

- A 2 litre bottle of soft drink which costs €2.20
- Four 100 g bars of chocolate which cost €1.75 each.

(i) How much money do they spend in total?

(ii) How much do they have left?

(iii) If they divide the money equally, how much do they receive each?

(iv) If three of the friends drink 0.54 litres each, how much must the fourth friend drink to finish the bottle?

Section 5C Rounding and Significant Figures

Rounding is basically reducing the number of digits in a value to make it easier to work with. In real life we measure quantities such as distance, weight and temperature. In general all these quantities are rounded:

- Distance from one town to another is generally given to the nearest kilometre.
- Weights of objects are generally given to the nearest gram.
- Temperature is generally given to the nearest degree.

Rounding is also known as **approximating a value**.

Class Activity/Discussion

Can you find other examples of rounding in real life?

When rounding decimals, we do the following:

- Find the place value you want (the 'rounding digit') and look at the digit just to the right of it.
- If the number immediately to the right of the rounding digit is:
  - **5 or greater**, we **add one** to the rounding digit
  - **less than 5**, the rounding digit **remains the same** and all other digits to the right of the rounding digit are dropped.

Example 1

Write the value of 83.6475:

  (i) correct to one decimal place

  (ii) correct to two decimal places

  (iii) correct to three decimal places.

Solution

  (i) 83.6475 to one decimal place:

As the digit to the right of the rounding digit is 4 which is < 5, we keep the rounding digit the same and drop all other digits to the right.

Answer: 83.6

  (ii) 83.6475 to two decimal places:

As the digit to the right of the rounding digit is 7 which is > 5, we add one to the rounding digit and drop all other digits to the right.

Answer: 83.65

  (iii) 83.6475 to three decimal places:

As the digit to the right of the rounding digit is 5, we add one to the rounding digit and drop all other digits to the right.

Answer: 83.648

Significant Figures

In real-life situations it is often necessary to express a value with a reduced number of digits. For example, a newspaper might estimate the crowd attending a football match as 7000, when in fact the real number of people might have been 7122. When we do this, we round the value to a specified number of significant figures.

To work out if digits are significant, follow these rules:

1. **Non-zero digits are always significant.**

   For example: 22 has two significant figures.

                   22.3 has three significant figures.

2. **Zeros placed before all digits are not significant.**

   For example: 0.046 has two significant figures.

                   0.175 has three significant figures.

3. **Zeros placed between other digits are always significant.**

   For example: 1003 has four significant figures.

                   3.09 has three significant figures.

4. **Zeros at the end of *whole numbers* are not significant.**

   For example: 230 has two significant figures.

                   742 000 has three significant figures.

5. **Trailing zeros in a number containing a decimal point are significant.**

   For example: 235.0 has four significant figures.

                   799.100 has six significant figures.

Example 2

For each of the following:

(i) 23 433   (ii) 8.536   (iii) 0.03279   (iv) 204.01

    (a) Write down the number of significant figures.

    (b) Write the number correct to three significant figures.

Solution

(i) 23 433

    (a) All digits are non-zero, so the number of significant figures is 5.

    (b) The 4th significant digit is 3. As it is less than 5, the 3rd digit remains the same.

    Answer: 23 433 correct to three significant figures is 23 400.

(ii) 8.536

    (a) All digits are non-zero, so the number of significant figures is 4.

    (b) The 4th significant digit is 6. As this is more than 5, we must round up the 3rd digit.

    Answer: 8.536 correct to three significant figures is 8.54.

(iii) 0.03279

    (a) The leading zeros do not count, so the number of significant figures is 4.

    (b) The 4th significant digit is 9. As this is more than 5, we must round up the 3rd significant digit.

    Answer: 0.03279 correct to three significant figures is 0.0328.

(iv) 204.01

    (a) The zeros in between the non-zero digits are significant, so the number of significant figures is 5.

    (b) The 4th significant digit is 0. As this is less than 5, the 3rd digit remains the same.

    Answer: 204.01 correct to three significant figures is 204.

Example 3

Find the reciprocal of (i) 5.455 (ii) 56.67 correct to three significant figures.

Solution

(i) The reciprocal of $5.455 = \dfrac{1}{5.455}$

First estimate the value: $\dfrac{1}{5.455} \cong \dfrac{1}{5} = 0.2$

Use your calculator to get the value:

Type ⑤ • ④ ⑤ ⑤ x^{-1} =

This gives a value of 0.183, correct to three significant figures.

(ii) The reciprocal of $56.67 = \dfrac{1}{56.67}$

First estimate the value:

$\dfrac{1}{56.67} \cong \dfrac{1}{60} = 0.01666...$

Use your calculator to get the value: 0.0176460... = 0.0176 correct to three significant figures.

Activity 5.3

1 Round each of the following quantities to two decimal places:

   (i) 16.8477 litres   (iv) 0.5978 m   (vii) $125.679

   (ii) €21.698   (v) 28.9156°C   (viii) 19.613 ml

   (iii) 0.026 kg   (vi) 2.987 km   (ix) 77.668°F

2 Round each of the following numbers to:

   (i) the nearest whole number   (ii) one decimal place.

      (a) 27.81 cm   (d) 10.023 minutes   (g) 83.34°F   (i) 99.49

      (b) 33.24 ml   (e) 92.501 litres   (h) 564.881 km   (j) £230.01

      (c) 38.341°C   (f) €100.48

3 Find the number of significant figures in each of the following:

   (i) 8.9   (iv) 738.03 g   (vii) 0.79 km   (x) €5,903.59

   (ii) $26.78   (v) 0.003765 litres   (viii) 584 ml   (xi) 34.50

   (iii) 354.8578 m   (vi) €82.03   (ix) 2.310 km   (xii) 34.500

4 Evaluate each of the following numbers to two significant figures.

   (i) 273   (iii) 349 230   (v) 0.00471   (vii) 9810   (ix) 0.02845

   (ii) 0.0547   (iv) 2945   (vi) 21 934   (viii) 30.884   (x) 249 034

5 Use your calculator to find the reciprocal of (i) 3.456 (ii) 23.3 (iii) 0.43 correct to three significant figures.

6 The following values are conversion rates or constants.

   Round each value to:

   (i) one decimal place   (ii) three significant figures   (iii) one significant figure.

(a) 1 mile = 1.609 km	(e) 1 imperial gallon = 4.54609188 litres
(b) 1 inch = 2.540 cm	(f) $\pi \cong 3.14159265389793$
(c) 1 kilometre = 0.6214 miles	(g) The speed of sound at sea level = 340.29 m/s
(d) 1 lb = 0.453592 kg	(h) Acceleration due to gravity on Earth = 9.80665 m/s^2

7 In calculations involving the radii of planets, each radius is normally rounded to two significant figures. The table gives the radius of each planet. Copy and complete the table.

	Planet	Radius (m)	Radius correct to two significant figures (m)
(i)	Earth	6 378 000	
(ii)	Mercury	2 440 000	
(iii)	Venus	6 051 000	
(iv)	Mars	3 397 000	
(v)	Jupiter	71 492 000	
(vi)	Saturn	60 268 000	
(vii)	Uranus	25 559 000	
(viii)	Neptune	24 764 000	

8 Approximate each of the following numbers to the nearest whole number.

   (i) 3.5

   (ii) 2.8

   (iii) 1.6

Use your answers from parts (i) to (iii) to estimate the answer to the following calculation.

   (iv) $\dfrac{3.5 \times 2.8}{1.6}$

   (v) Use your calculator to find the exact value in part (iv).

9 (i) By rounding each value to the nearest whole number, estimate each of the following:

   (a) $\dfrac{6.59 - 2.59}{0.59 + 0.59}$

   (b) $\dfrac{32.44 - 15.75}{4.96 - 1.46}$

   (c) $\dfrac{59.34 - 2.90}{68.71 - 61.56}$

   (d) $\dfrac{23.85 - 12.14}{3.86 - 0.25}$

   (e) $\dfrac{9.86 - 2.25}{4.9 - 1.15}$

   (f) $\dfrac{5.2 \times 5.8}{2.7}$

   (g) $\dfrac{7.4 \times 9.5}{1.6}$

   (h) $\dfrac{3.5 \times 12.4}{2.9}$

   (ii) Now use your calculator to get an exact value for parts (i) to (viii), correct to two decimal places.

Section 5D **Percentages**

The words **per cent** mean **per hundred**. The symbol % is used to represent percentage.

For example:

- 10% means 10 out of every 100
- 39% means 39 out of every 100
- 3.4% means 3.4 out of every 100.

Percentages are useful in everyday life, for example when working out:

- Interest on bank accounts.

 For example, if a bank offers 3.1% simple interest per year, it means for every €100 that I leave in my account for a year, I get €3.10 added to my account.

Other examples of where percentages are useful in everyday life are:

- Exam results
- Mortgage interest rates
- Discounts
- Sales tax
- Tips at a restaurant.

Fractions, decimals and percentages are different ways of expressing the same value.

Example 1

Express 87.5% as a fraction and a decimal:

(i) Without a calculator

(ii) Using a calculator.

Solution

(i) 87.5% means 87.5 per 100

$$= \frac{87.5}{100} = \frac{875}{1000} = \frac{7}{8}$$

Express 87.5% as a decimal.

$$87.5\% = \frac{87.5}{100} = 0.875$$

(ii) Using a calculator.

- Express 87.5% as a fraction:
  Type the following:

  $\frac{7}{8}$ will appear on the screen.

- Express 87.5% as a decimal:
  After you have performed the above calculation on the calculator type:

  0.875 will appear on the screen.

Example 2

Express each of the following as percentages.

(i) 0.75   (ii) $\frac{5}{8}$

Always remember that **1 unit = 100%**

Solution

(i) 1 = 100%

0.75 of 1 = 0.75 of 100% = 0.75 × 100 = 75%

(ii) 1 = 100%

$\frac{5}{8}$ of 1 = $\frac{5}{8}$ of 100% = $\frac{5}{8} \times \frac{100}{1} = \frac{500}{8} = 62.5\%$

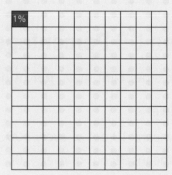

 Key Point

We can see from these examples that:
- To express a fraction or a decimal as a percentage, we simply **multiply by 100%**.

Example 3

Orla got 120 marks out of a possible 200 marks in a Maths test. Her friends Dina and Luke were helping her to work out what percentage mark she got.

What percentage did she get in the test?

Solution

Dina suggested this method:

- 200 marks = 100%

  1 mark = $\frac{100}{200}\%$

  120 marks = $\frac{100 \times 120}{200} = 60\%$

Orla worked her percentage out this way:

- 200 marks = 100%
- Put her mark over full marks as a fraction.

$$= \frac{120}{200}$$

- $\frac{120}{200}$ of 100% = $\frac{120}{200} \times 100\% = 60\%$

Luke adopted a third method using ratios:

- 120 marks per 200
  = 60 marks per 100
  = 60%

Class Activity/Discussion

Which of the methods used in Example 3 is the easiest?
If a student scored 120 marks out of 140 marks in a French test, which method would be best to work out the percentage mark?

Example 4

Express the shaded region of the following shape as a fraction, decimal and percentage.

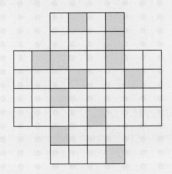

Solution

- Count the total number of squares and the shaded number of squares.
  Total number of squares = 48 = 100%
  Shaded number of squares = 12
- Express the number of shaded squares as a fraction of the total number of squares and simplify.

$$\frac{12}{48} = \frac{1}{4}$$

$\frac{1}{4}$ of 100% = $\frac{1}{4} \times 100\% = 25\%$

Therefore, the shaded area is 25% of the total area. As a decimal, this is 0.25.

Example 5

Order each of the following numbers from smallest to largest.

$\frac{4}{5}$, 65%, 0.63, $\frac{2}{3}$, 0.59, 60%

Solution

When comparing, it is easiest to write each as a decimal number first:

0.8, 0.65, 0.63, 0.666, 0.59, 0.60

Decimals in order: 0.59, 0.60, 0.63, 0.65, 0.666, 0.8

Answer: 0.59, 60%, 0.63, 65%, $\frac{2}{3}$, $\frac{4}{5}$

1 (i) Explain, in your own words, what 3% means.

(ii) A bank offers 3% interest per year if I put my savings in the bank.

   (a) How much interest would I earn on €100 after 1 year?

   (b) How much interest would I earn on €200 after 1 year?

   (c) How much interest would I earn on €300 after 1 year?

2 Express each of the following as a percentage.

(i) 0.8

(ii) $\frac{25}{100}$

(iii) 0.5

(iv) $\frac{18}{25}$

(v) 0.38

(vi) $\frac{19}{20}$

(vii) 0.675

(viii) $\frac{46}{200}$

(ix) 0.125

(x) $\frac{15}{40}$

3 State whether each of the following statements are true or false.

(i) $\frac{7}{8} = 0.875$

(ii) $\frac{3}{10} = 35\%$

(iii) $\frac{4}{5} = 0.80$

(iv) $\frac{12}{15} = 75\%$

(v) $\frac{45}{1000} = 0.045$

(vi) $\frac{3}{15} = 45\%$

(vii) $\frac{31}{50} = 0.62$

(viii) $\frac{2}{25} = 0.008$

(ix) $\frac{23}{50} = 46\%$

4 Insert the correct symbol > or < for each of the following statements.

Hint

> Convert each to a decimal number first.

(i) $\frac{3}{7}$ ☐ 55%

(ii) $\frac{8}{10}$ ☐ 61%

(iii) 25% ☐ $\frac{2}{3}$

(iv) 0.34 ☐ $\frac{5}{10}$

(v) 46% ☐ 0.48

(vi) 0.59 ☐ $\frac{3}{8}$

(vii) 99% ☐ 1

(viii) 0.11 ☐ $\frac{1}{10}$

(ix) $\frac{9}{20}$ ☐ 40%

5 Eileen has €1760 owing on her credit card. She pays 18% interest per month on what she owes.

How much will Eileen pay in interest this month if she does not pay anything off the balance on her card?

6 The shop price of a car you want is €13 500. If you have to pay VAT (Value Added Tax) at 23%, how much does the car actually cost?

7 Rearrange each of the following numbers from smallest to largest.

(i) 21%, $\frac{3}{20}$, 0.29, $\frac{4}{25}$, 25%, 0.20

(ii) 31%, 0.25, $\frac{3}{10}$, 20%, $\frac{6}{25}$, 0.28

(iii) $\frac{17}{20}$, 0.83, 86%, $\frac{41}{50}$, 0.8, $\frac{27}{100}$, $\frac{3}{4}$

8 Express the grey shaded region in each of the following shapes as a fraction, decimal and percentage of the total area.

(i)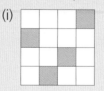

(iii)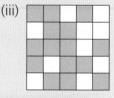

(ii)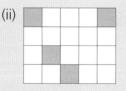

(iv)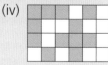

9 Express the shaded region in each of the following shapes as a fraction, decimal and percentage of the total area.

(i)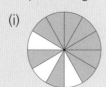

(ii)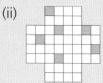

(iii)   (iv)

10 Eileen got the following results in eight subjects examined at Christmas.

Write each mark as a percentage.

(i) English = 65 out of 100

(ii) Maths = 120 out of 150

(iii) Geography = 35 out of 50

(iv) History = 112 out of 200

(v) Science = 240 out of 300

(vi) French = 96 out of 150

(vii) Irish = 44 out of 80

(viii) CSPE = 54 out of 60

11 Of the 150 people in an office, 28% of them wear glasses.
How many people wear glasses?

 12 In a school of 740 students, 80% of the students live within 3 km of the school.

(i) How many live further than 3 km from school?

Of the students who live further than 3 km from the school, 25% of them travel to school by bus.

(ii) How many students travel by bus to the school?

13 Represent each of the following as a percentage.

(i) 42 minutes as part of 1 hour

(ii) 75 cm as part of 1 metre

(iii) 350 g as part of 1 kg

(iv) 120 correct answers out of 250 questions

(v) 48 seconds as part of 2 minutes

(vi) €30 as part of €150

(vii) 18 minutes as part of 4 hours

(viii) 27 kg as part of 90 kg

(ix) 650 m as part of 2 metres

(x) 300 kg as part of 1 tonne (1 tonne = 1000 kg)

Revision Activity 5

1 Write the following fractions as decimals and percentages.

(a) $\frac{1}{2}$ (c) $\frac{1}{4}$ (e) $\frac{7}{16}$ (g) $\frac{9}{25}$ (i) $\frac{3}{75}$

(b) $\frac{1}{3}$ (d) $\frac{2}{5}$ (f) $\frac{8}{40}$ (h) $\frac{13}{50}$ (j) $\frac{73}{100}$

2 Write these decimals as both fractions (in their simplest form) and percentages.

(a) 0.1   (c) 0.25   (e) 0.75   (g) 0.56   (i) 0.375

(b) 0.3   (d) 0.6   (f) 0.22   (h) 0.81   (j) 0.615

3 Express the following percentages as fractions and decimals.

(a) 5%   (c) 50%   (e) 35%   (g) 63%   (i) 84%

(b) 10%   (d) 11%   (f) 47%   (h) 76%   (j) 99%

4 Add or subtract each of the following sums without the aid of a calculator:

(a) $1.0218 + 4.176$

(b) $18.01 - 7.301$

(c) $0.923 - 0.89$

(d) $5.91 - 3.172$

(e) $0.763 + 0.13$

(f) $8.174 + 0.71238$

(g) $11.801 - 7.77$

(h) $225.31 + 113.801$

(i) $15.0124 - 9.180219$

(j) $-23.8 + 32.029$

5 A horse eats about 60% of its own body weight in food each month. If a horse weighs 550 kilograms, how much will it eat this month?

6 The instructions on a bottle of concentrated weed killer say that the spray should be 80% water and 20% concentrate. Your sprayer takes 5 litres of liquid. How much water should you put in before topping it up with concentrate?

7 Parts for your car cost €120. If you have to pay 23% VAT, what is the total amount you must pay the garage?

8 (a) By rounding each of these numbers to the nearest whole number, estimate the value of $\dfrac{20.716}{5.2 + 2.08}$.

(b) Using a calculator, find the value of $\dfrac{20.716}{5.2 + 2.08}$ correct to three decimal places.

9 (a) Using a calculator or otherwise, express $\dfrac{1}{8}$ and $\dfrac{17}{80}$ as decimals. Hence or otherwise, put the following numbers in order, starting with the smallest: $\dfrac{1}{8}, \dfrac{17}{80}, 0.1525$.

(b) Using a calculator, evaluate $\sqrt{93.09} \times (3.75)^2 - \dfrac{1}{0.3125}$. Give your answer correct to two decimal places.

Exam-style Question

1 (a) Write $\dfrac{3}{8}$ as a decimal.

(b) Show the approximate height of water in the glass if the glass is $\dfrac{3}{8}$ full.

(c) Represent the numbers $\dfrac{3}{8}$ and 0.4 on the number line.

```
    |————————————————————|
    0                    1
```

(d) How could the number line in (c) above help you decide which is the bigger of the two numbers?

JCOL 2012 Sample Paper 1

KEY WORDS AND PHRASES

- Fraction
- Decimal
- Percentage
- Place value
- Decimal point
- Recurring decimal
- Approximate
- Rounding digit
- Estimate
- Decimal place
- Significant figures

Interactive Tool 5.1

Interactive Tool 5.2

- Fractions, decimals and percentages are ways of expressing the same value, e.g. $\frac{1}{2} = 0.5 = 50\%$

- Place value with decimals: $666.6666 = 600 + 60 + 6 + \frac{6}{10} + \frac{6}{100} + \frac{6}{1000} + \frac{6}{10\,000}$

- **Per cent** means **per hundred**.

  - 5% means 5 per 100

  - So 5% of 100 = 5, 5% of 200 = 10, 5% of 300 = 15, etc.

- To calculate 7% of €52

  - 100% = 52

  - $1\% = \frac{52}{100}$

  - $7\% = \frac{52}{100} \times 7 = €3.64$

- To express €15 as a percentage of €75

  - 15 as a fraction of $75 = \frac{15}{75}$

  - $\frac{15}{75} \times 100 = 20\%$

- To express a fraction as a decimal, divide the numerator by the denominator, e.g. $\frac{3}{5} = 0.6$

- To express a fraction as a percentage, divide the numerator by the denominator and then multiply by 100%, e.g. $\frac{3}{5} = 0.6 \times 100\% = 60\%$

- To express a decimal as a fraction: e.g. 0.65

  Step 1: Put the decimal over 1: $\frac{0.65}{1}$

  Step 2: Multiply numerator and denominator by 10 for each digit after the decimal point, to make both the numerator and denominator whole numbers.

  $$\frac{0.65}{1} = \frac{0.65 \times 100}{1 \times 100} = \frac{65}{100} = \frac{13}{20}$$

- To express a percentage as a fraction or a decimal: divide by 100, e.g. $50\% = \frac{50}{100} = \frac{1}{2} = 0.5$

When rounding decimals:

- Find the place value you want (the rounding digit) and look at the digit just to the right of it.

- If that number is:

  - **5 or greater**, then **add one** to the rounding digit

  - **less than 5**, the rounding digit **remains the same** and all other digits to the right of the rounding digit are dropped.

For significant figures:

1. **Non-zero digits are always significant.**
   For example: 22.3 has three significant figures.

2. **Zeros placed before all digits are not significant.**
   For example: 0.046 has two significant figures.

3. **Zeros placed between other digits are always significant.**
   For example: 1003 has four significant figures.

4. **Zeros at the end of *whole numbers* are not significant.**
   For example: 742 000 has three significant figures.

5. **Trailing zeros in a number containing a decimal point are significant.**
   For example: 799.100 has six significant figures.

Probability

In this chapter, you will learn about:

- The Fundamental Principle of Counting
- The language of uncertainty
- The probability scale
- Relative frequency
- Probability as long-term relative frequency
- Equally likely events

- Calculating the probability of equally likely events
- Calculating probabilities with a pack of playing cards
- Expected frequency

LO: SP.1(b), SP.2, U.5, U.6, U.13

Section 6A The Fundamental Principle of Counting

In this chapter, we will be investigating **probability (chance)** with such things as coins, dice and spinners and we'll use the **Fundamental Principle of Counting** to work out problems.

There are some terms that we need to know:

- When we toss a coin to see what the result is, we are carrying out a **trial**. Other examples of a trial are rolling a die or spinning a spinner.

- Any result from a trial is called an **outcome**. For example, if you toss a coin, there are two possible outcomes: a Head or a Tail.

- The set of all the possible outcomes is called the **sample space**, e.g. when a die is rolled the sample space is: {1, 2, 3, 4, 5, 6}.

- An **event** is a subset of the sample space, e.g. getting a six on one roll of a die.

Key Point

We can now state the Fundamental Principle of Counting:

If one event has *m* possible outcomes and a second event has *n* possible outcomes, then the total number of outcomes is *m* × *n*.

Example 1

Anna is going on holiday for the week. Each outfit she will wear consists of a pair of jeans and a top. She has packed:

> 3 pairs of jeans (black, navy and blue)
> 4 tops (white, green, yellow and red).

How many different outfits can Anna wear?

Solution

We can list all the possible outfits:

- If she chooses **black** jeans she has **four** possible outfits: (black jeans, white top), (black jeans, green top), (black jeans, yellow top), (black jeans, red top).

- If she chooses **navy** jeans she has another **four** possible outfits: (navy jeans, white top), (navy jeans, green top), (navy jeans, yellow top), (navy jeans, red top).

- If she chooses **blue** jeans she has another **four** possible outfits: (blue jeans, white top), (blue jeans, green top), (blue jeans, yellow top), (blue jeans, red top).

The Fundamental Principle of Counting states that she has 3 × 4 = 12 different outfits to wear because she has 3 pairs of jeans to combine with 4 tops.

Example 2

A building has 2 entrance doors and 3 exit doors. You may enter only by the entrance doors. You may exit only by the exit doors. How many ways are there of entering and exiting the building?

If you enter by door A, you can exit by door 1 or door 2 or door 3.

If you enter by door B, you can exit by door 1 or door 2 or door 3.

We could represent this as pairs: (A, 1), (A, 2), (A, 3), (B, 1), (B, 2), (B, 3).

The Fundamental Principle of Counting states that you have 2 × 3 = 6 ways of entering and exiting the building.

If there were 3 entrance doors and 5 exit doors, you could enter and exit in 3 × 5 = 15 ways.

Solution

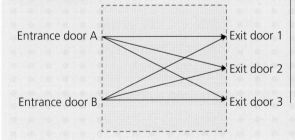

When we perform one trial after another, we get two outcomes. We use the Fundamental Principle of Counting to work out the number of possible outcomes.

Example 3

A coin is tossed and a die is rolled.

(i) How many different outcomes are possible?

(ii) List the possible outcomes.

Solution

(i) A coin toss has 2 possible outcomes: Heads or Tails.

A die roll has 6 different outcomes: 1, 2, 3, 4, 5 or 6.

The Fundamental Principle of Counting says that there are 2 × 6 = 12 possible outcomes.

(ii) We can show the possible outcomes in a **two-way table** like this, where H = Heads and T = Tails:

		Die					
		1	2	3	4	5	6
Coin	H	(H, 1)	(H, 2)	(H, 3)	(H, 4)	(H, 5)	(H, 6)
	T	(T, 1)	(T, 2)	(T, 3)	(T, 4)	(T, 5)	(T, 6)

The set of possible outcomes can be written in pairs like this:

{(H, 1), (H, 2), (H, 3), (H, 4), (H, 5), (H, 6), (T, 1), (T, 2), (T, 3), (T, 4), (T, 5), (T, 6)}.

Activity 6.1

1 A certain paint can be bought in 3 sizes and 9 colours. How many different choices of paint are available?

2 A new car comes in 5 engine sizes and 6 different colours. How many different choices are available?

3 Michael is choosing a new pair of jeans. There are 4 different styles and 6 different colours. In how many ways can Michael choose his new jeans?

4 The Fundamental Principle of Counting can be extended to three or more events.

A restaurant has a dinner menu which has:

- 3 starters

- 4 main courses

- 5 desserts.

How many different meals can be chosen?

5 A hotel has the following room options available:

- Bath or shower

- Sea view or mountain view

- 4 different size options.

How many different types of room can a guest choose from?

6 Tom is buying a new car. He can choose to buy a petrol or a diesel model. He can choose to buy an SUV, a hatchback or a saloon type car. He also has a choice of three colours: red, black, or silver.

In how many different ways can Tom choose his car?

7 A die has six sides.

  (i) If the die is rolled, list all the possible outcomes.

  (ii) How many different outcomes are possible?

8 A coin is tossed.

  (i) How many outcomes are possible?

  (ii) List all the possible outcomes.

9 A coin is tossed and a die is rolled.

  (i) How many outcomes are possible?

  (ii) List all the possible outcomes.

10 A die is rolled. Then the die is rolled again.

  (i) List all the possible outcomes using a two-way table.

  (ii) How many outcomes are possible for the two rolls?

11 A code for a combination lock consists of four single digits. The digits may be repeated. How many different codes are possible?

12 A coin is tossed. Then the coin is tossed again.

  (i) List all the possible outcomes for the two tosses in a two-way table.

  (ii) How many outcomes are possible?

Section 6B The Language of Uncertainty and Probability

In this section we will be looking at the concepts of uncertainty and probability (chance).

There are many things which are uncertain:

- Who will be next person to come to the classroom door? Will it be a student or will it be the caretaker?
- Will the next All-Ireland football championship be won by Longford?
- What are the chances of a fine day tomorrow?
- Will my numbers come up in the lotto this week?

We don't know the answer to these questions; there is **uncertainty** about them.

However, some of these are more likely to happen than others. For example, it is more likely that a student will be next to come to the classroom door than that your set of six numbers will come up in the next National Lottery draw.

> **Probability** is about uncertainty and how likely something is to happen.

Consider these two sentences which include the word 'probably':

- 'It will probably rain tomorrow.'
- 'The aeroplane will probably land safely.'

Is the word 'probably' precise enough for these two situations?
Clearly, it is much more important that the aeroplane lands safely.

It is clear that we need to put a numerical value on how likely something is to happen.

We need a probability scale.

On a probability scale:

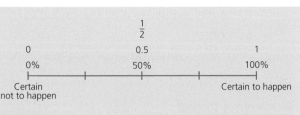

- If an event is certain to happen it has a value of 1 or 100%.

- If an event is certain not to happen it has a value of 0.

- Any other event is given a value between 0 and 1.

Example

Copy the following probability scale into your copybook.

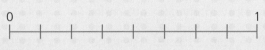

Place the following phrases, numbers and percentages at the correct position on the probability scale:

$\frac{1}{4}$ no chance   a 1 in 4 chance   even chance   certain   very likely

Solution

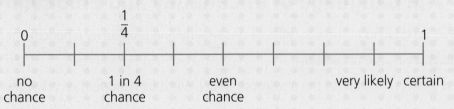

Connections

Your knowledge of fractions, decimals and percentages is very useful in this chapter.

Activity 6.2

1 (i) Write down at least five words or phrases which come to mind when you think of uncertainty. Hint: there are several phrases which contain the word **likely**.

   (ii) Write down one sentence containing each of your words or phrases.

2 'If a puppy is born, the chance of it being female is about even.'
   Write down five other events which you think have an 'even' chance of happening.

3 Copy the following probability scale into your copybook.

Place the following phrases, numbers and percentages at the correct position on the probability scale:

$\frac{3}{8}$ impossible   a 1 in 8 chance   50/50   certain   0.875

4 For each event below, estimate the probability that it will happen
   and mark this on a probability scale.

   A: It will snow in Ireland in July.

   B: Your English teacher will give you homework this weekend.

   C: Ireland will win the next soccer World Cup.

   D: You will go to bed before midnight tonight.

   E: It will rain tomorrow.

   F: My county will win the Sam Maguire Cup next year.

5 The probability scale shows the probability of five events: A, B, C, D and E.

   (i)   Which event is certain to occur?

   (ii) Which event is impossible?

   (iii) Which event is likely but not certain
         to occur?

   (iv) Which event is unlikely but could occur?

   (v)   Which event has an even chance of occurring?

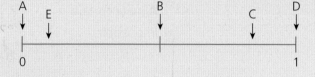

6 (i) Which of the following best describes how likely it is that each of the following events
      occurs? Write the letter corresponding to the correct answer in the box in the table.

      A. Impossible or almost impossible   D. Very likely

      B. Not very likely   E. Certain or almost certain

      C. About 50% likely

Event	How likely?
A baby will be born in Ireland tomorrow.	
If you pick one card from a standard pack of playing cards, you will pick the Queen of Spades.	
There will be 400 days in the year 2015.	
If you toss a coin, it will land on a Tail.	
It will not rain in Ireland during the month of November.	
If two ordinary dice are thrown, the sum of the numbers will be 1.	

   (ii) Draw a probability scale and show each letter in a suitable location on it.

7 For each of the following phrases write down two events which match the probability of
   it happening: very unlikely, likely, almost certain, unlikely, never.

8. The probability that each of the events A, B, C, D, E and F happens is shown on the probability scale below.

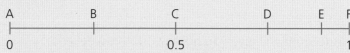

Match each event with the word or phrase in the table which best describes its probability.

Word or phrase	Event
Fifty-fifty chance	
Certain	
1 in 4 chance	
Almost certain	
Impossible	

Section 6C Relative Frequency

You will learn about statistics in the next chapter. Statistics and probability are very closely linked and we can estimate the probability of future events by what has happened in the past.

To see how probabilities can be calculated, we use models like dice and coins which we can work with more easily.

- We perform a number of trials, e.g. we roll a die a number of times.
- We record how many times an event occurs (its **frequency**), e.g. we record the number of times a six comes up.
- The **relative frequency** of an event is the number of times it occurs as a fraction or percentage of the total number of trials.

$$\text{Relative frequency} = \frac{\text{number of times an event occurs in a trial}}{\text{total number of trials}}$$

Example

A coin is tossed 50 times. It lands on Heads 26 times.

Calculate the relative frequency of getting a Head.

Solution

$$\text{Relative frequency} = \frac{\text{number of times a Head occurred}}{\text{total number of coin tosses}} = \frac{26}{50} = 0.52 \text{ (or 52\%)}$$

Give all your answers to relative frequency questions in fraction **and** decimal form.

Activity 6.3

1 A coin is tossed 100 times. A Head comes up 46 times. What is the relative frequency of getting a Head?

2 A die is tossed 60 times. A six comes up 7 times. What is the relative frequency of getting a six?

3 A school has 350 boys and 400 girls.

Find the relative frequency of a student in this school being a girl.

4 A spinner has three equal sectors: blue, red and green.

The spinner is spun 50 times and the results are tallied:

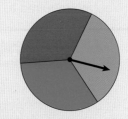

Result	Tallies	Frequency	Relative frequency
Blue	卌 卌 IIII	14	
Red	卌 卌 卌 III	18	
Green	卌 卌 卌 III	18	
Totals			

(i) Copy and complete the table.

(ii) What is the relative frequency of the spinner landing on blue?

(iii) What is the relative frequency of the spinner landing on red?

(iv) What is the relative frequency of the spinner landing on green?

(v) Explain your answer for the total of the relative frequencies.

5 A spinner has four equal sectors: blue, red, yellow and green.

The spinner is spun 100 times and the results are tallied:

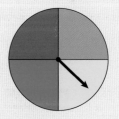

Result	Tallies	Frequency	Relative frequency
Blue	卌 卌 卌 卌 IIII	24	
Red	卌 卌 卌 卌 卌 III	28	
Yellow	卌 卌 卌 III	18	
Green	卌 卌 卌 卌 卌 卌	30	
Totals			

(i) Copy the table into your copybook.

(ii) Calculate the relative frequency of the spinner landing on each colour.

(iii) Add up the relative frequencies. Explain your answer.

6 The following colours of cars were recorded in one hour passing by a school:

Colour of car	Silver	Black	Red	Other
Frequency	35	43	28	14

(i) How many cars passed in total?

(ii) What was the relative frequency of a red car passing the school?

(iii) What was the relative frequency of a silver or black car passing the school?

7 A coin was tossed 100 times. The relative frequency of getting a Head was $\frac{14}{25}$.

(i) How many times did a Head turn up?

(ii) What was the relative frequency of getting a Tail? Give your answer as a fraction in its simplest form and also as a decimal.

8 This spinner is spun 40 times and the relative frequencies for each outcome (except for blue) are recorded in this table:

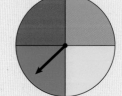

Outcome	Red	Blue	Green	Yellow
Relative frequency	0.2		0.3	0.175

(i) Calculate the relative frequency of the outcome being blue.

(ii) Calculate how many times each colour occurred as an outcome.

Section 6D Experimenting with Probability

You are required to do some experiments to see how relative frequency leads to probability.

Example

A group of students rolled a fair die 60 times and recorded their results in the table below.

Number which appears on the die (outcome of the trial)	Tallies	How many times did this happen? (Frequency)	Frequency / No. of trials (Relative frequency)	% of total (Relative frequency × 100%)
1	ⅢⅢ ⅢⅢ II	12		
2	ⅢⅢ II	7		
3	ⅢⅢ IIII	9		
4	ⅢⅢ ⅢⅢ	10		
5	ⅢⅢ ⅢⅢ II	12		
6	ⅢⅢ ⅢⅢ	10		
Totals		60		

(i) Copy and complete the table.

(ii) Use your calculator to add up the totals. What do you notice?

Solution

(i)

Number which appears on the die (outcome of the trial)	Tallies	How many times did this happen? (Frequency)	Frequency / No. of trials (Relative frequency)	% of total (Relative frequency × 100%)
1	ⅢⅢ ⅢⅢ II	12	$\frac{12}{60} = \frac{1}{5}$	20%
2	ⅢⅢ II	7	$\frac{7}{60}$	11.67%
3	ⅢⅢ IIII	9	$\frac{9}{60} = \frac{3}{20}$	15%
4	ⅢⅢ ⅢⅢ	10	$\frac{10}{60} = \frac{1}{6}$	16.67%
5	ⅢⅢ ⅢⅢ II	12	$\frac{12}{60} = \frac{1}{5}$	20%
6	ⅢⅢ ⅢⅢ	10	$\frac{10}{60} = \frac{1}{6}$	16.67%
Totals		60	$\frac{60}{60} = 1$	100.0%

(ii) The fourth column adds to 1. The fifth column adds to 100%. The reason for this is that when you roll a die, it is **certain** that the outcome must be one of the numbers 1, 2, 3, 4, 5 or 6. Therefore the total in column 4 must be 1, since **1 means certainty**. The total in column 5 is 100%. **100% also means certainty**.

Key Points

- The outcomes in the second column were the result of just 60 rolls of a regular die. This is a small number of trials. You should expect that the results for another 60 trials would not be exactly the same.
- As we will see, the more trials you do the better the results.

Activity 6.4

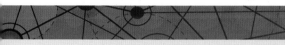

1 The table shows the results of 100 rolls of a fair die.

Number which appears on the die (outcome of the trial)	How many times did this happen? (Frequency)	Frequency / No. of trials (Relative frequency)	Relative frequency as a percentage ($\frac{Frequency}{No.\ of\ trials} \times 100\%$)
1	13		13%
2	18		
3	15		
4	20		
5	14		
6	20		
Totals			

(i) Copy and complete the table showing all the relative frequencies.

(ii) What do you notice about the totals?

2 A die was rolled 60 times by a student.

The results were as follows:

Number which appears on the die (outcome of the trial)	How many times did this happen? (Frequency)	Frequency / No. of trials (Relative frequency)	Relative frequency as a percentage ($\frac{Frequency}{No.\ of\ trials} \times 100\%$)
1	10		
2	14		
3	10		
4	10		
5	11		
6	5		
Totals			

(i) Copy and complete the table showing all the relative frequencies.

(ii) What do you notice about the totals?

3 (i) Roll a die 60 times and record the outcomes in the following table.

Number which appears on the die (outcome of the trial)	How many times did this happen? (Frequency)	Frequency / No. of trials (Relative frequency)	Relative frequency as a percentage $\left(\dfrac{\text{Frequency}}{\text{No. of trials}} \times 100\%\right)$
1			
2			
3			
4			
5			
6			
Totals			

(ii) What do you notice about the totals?

4 A die was rolled 600 times by a class of students.

The results were as follows:

Number which appears on the die (outcome of the trial)	How many times did this happen? (Frequency)	Frequency / No. of trials (Relative frequency)	Relative frequency as a percentage $\left(\dfrac{\text{Frequency}}{\text{No. of trials}} \times 100\%\right)$
1	96		
2	81		
3	93		
4	123		
5	105		
6	102		
Totals			

(i) Copy and complete the table showing all the relative frequencies.

(ii) The theoretical probability of getting any of the numbers on a die = $\dfrac{1}{6}$ $\left(\text{or } 16\dfrac{2}{3}\%\right)$.

Are the relative frequencies closer to $\dfrac{1}{6}$ than with 60 trials?

5 (i) Repeat question **4** with data from your own class.

(ii) Compare the results to those in question **4**. In what way are they similar?
How are they different?

6 A die was 'rolled' 6000 times using a computer simulation.

The results were as follows:

Number which appears on the die (outcome of the trial)	How many times did this happen? (Frequency)	Frequency / No. of trials (Relative frequency)	Relative frequency as a percentage $\left(\dfrac{\text{Frequency}}{\text{No. of trials}} \times 100\%\right)$
1	1008		
2	1006		
3	971		
4	1023		
5	972		
6	1020		
Totals			

(i) Copy and complete the table showing all the relative frequencies.

(ii) The theoretical probability of getting any of the numbers on a die = $\frac{1}{6}$.

Are the relative frequencies closer to $\frac{1}{6}$ than with 600 trials?

7 Repeat question **6** with data from your own class. You can use computer simulations to perform these trials.

Section 6E Calculating Probabilities

In the above activity we increased the number of trials from 60 to 600 to 6000.

The relative frequency for each outcome varied with the number of trials, but as the number of trials becomes very large, the relative frequency gets very close to what is called the **theoretical probability**.

■ When I roll a die, any one of the numbers 1 to 6 is **equally likely** to appear.

If I look for a 4 to appear, then an outcome of 4 is called a **favourable outcome**.

The probability of getting a 4 is one chance in six $\left(\text{i.e. } \frac{1}{6}\right)$.

We say that the probability of the outcome $4 = \frac{1}{6}$.

This can be written as P(4) = $\frac{1}{6}$.

■ In the same way, tossing a coin has two **equally likely** outcomes: a Head or a Tail.

So P(Head) = $\frac{1}{2}$.

■ When a card is picked at random from a pack of 52 cards, there are 52 **equally likely** outcomes.

So P(Ace of Hearts) = $\frac{1}{52}$.

For **equally likely outcomes**,

The probability of an event = $\dfrac{\text{number of favourable outcomes}}{\text{total number of possible equally likely outcomes}}$

Playing cards are used as a model for problem solving in probability.

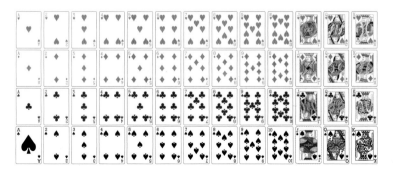

 Key Point

When we say 'pick a card at random' we mean that every card in the pack has an equal chance of being chosen.

6

Probability

Example 1

A card is picked at random from a deck of 52 cards. Find the probability that the card is:

(i) a six   (iii) a black card   (v) a Spade or a Club.

(ii) a Spade   (iv) the Queen of Hearts

Solution

(i) $P(six) = \dfrac{\text{number of sixes in the pack}}{\text{total number of cards in the pack}} = \dfrac{4}{52} = \dfrac{1}{13}$

(ii) $P(Spade) = \dfrac{\text{number of Spades in the pack}}{\text{total number of cards in the pack}} = \dfrac{13}{52} = \dfrac{1}{4}$

(iii) $P(black\ card) = \dfrac{\text{number of black cards in the pack}}{\text{total number of cards in the pack}} = \dfrac{26}{52} = \dfrac{1}{2}$

(iv) $P(Queen\ of\ Hearts) = \dfrac{\text{number of Queens of Hearts in the pack}}{\text{total number of cards in the pack}} = \dfrac{1}{52}$

(v) There are 13 Spades and 13 Clubs so we have 26 favourable outcomes.

     $P(Spade\ or\ Club) = \dfrac{26}{52} = \dfrac{1}{2}$

Example 2

A coin is tossed 300 times. How many times would you expect the outcome to be Heads?

Solution

The probability of a Head in one toss of a coin $= \dfrac{1}{2}$

In 300 tosses we expect Heads to come up $300 \times \dfrac{1}{2} = 150$ times.

This is an example of **expected frequency**.

Key Point

Expected frequency = probability × the number of trials

It is certain that an event either happens or does not happen.

- The probability of certainty = 1. Hence the **probability of an event not happening = 1 – the probability that it will happen**, e.g. if the probability that an event happens is 0.3, then the probability that the event does not happen = 0.7

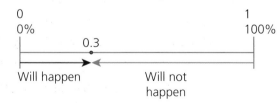

Example 3

A card is picked at random from a pack of 52 playing cards.

What is the probability that it is **not** a King?

Solution

There are 4 Kings in the pack.

Hence $P(\text{King}) = \dfrac{4}{52} = \dfrac{1}{13}$

Therefore $P(\text{the card is } \textbf{not} \text{ a King}) = 1 - \dfrac{1}{13} = \dfrac{12}{13}$

Example 4

A class has 14 boys and 10 girls.

If a student is picked at random from the class:

 (i) What is the probability that the student is a girl?

(ii) What is the probability that the student is not a girl?

Solution

 (i) $P(\text{girl}) = \dfrac{\text{number of girls in the class}}{\text{total number of students in the class}} = \dfrac{10}{24} = \dfrac{5}{12}$

(ii) We can answer this in two ways:

$P(\text{not a girl}) = P(\text{boy}) = \dfrac{14}{24} = \dfrac{7}{12}$ **or** $P(\text{not a girl}) = 1 - P(\text{girl}) = 1 - \dfrac{5}{12} = \dfrac{7}{12}$

Activity 6.5

1 There are 60 jelly beans in a bag, all either green or yellow.

Roy takes a bean from the bag without looking. There is a 50% chance that the bean is green. How many green beans are in the bag?

2 A box contains 20 counters which are either red or green in colour. A counter is taken from the box without looking. It is equally likely that it will be a red counter or a green counter.

How many red counters and how many green counters are in the box?

3 A box contains 40 counters, all either red or black. A counter is taken from the box without looking. There is a 25% chance that the counter is red.

How many counters in the box are black?

4 There are 4 small balls in a bag, all the same size. Three are blue and one is yellow.

 (i) Peter is going to take a ball from the bag without looking. He says, 'There are two colours, so it is just as likely that I will get a blue ball as a yellow ball'. Explain why Peter is wrong.

(ii) What is the probability that the ball he takes out is blue?

(iii) How many more yellow balls should he put in the bag to make it just as likely that he will take a blue ball as a yellow one?

Probability

5 A bag contains 9 balls, all either green or red, all the same size.

A ball is taken out without looking. It is more likely to be a red ball than a green one.

How many red and green balls might there be in the bag? Explain your answer.

6   (i) How many cards are there in a standard pack of playing cards (excluding jokers)?

   (ii) How many suits are there? Name them.

  (iii) How many cards are in each suit?

  (iv) How many Aces are there?

   (v) How many picture cards are there?

  (vi) How many Jacks are there?

 (vii) How many red cards are there?

(viii) Look carefully at the Jacks. What do you notice about their eyes?

7 A card is drawn at random from a pack of playing cards.

   (i) What is the probability that the card is black?

   (ii) What is the probability that the card is a Diamond?

  (iii) What is the probability that the card is a King?

  (iv) What is the probability that the card is the King of Spades?

   (v) What is the probability that the card is a picture card?

  (vi) What is the probability that the card is a two-eyed Jack?

 (vii) What is the probability that the card is a one-eyed King?

(viii) What is the probability that the card is an Ace?

  (ix) What is the probability that the card is an Ace or a King?

   (x) What is the probability that the card is not a Club?

8 These counters are put in a bag and one is drawn out at random (without looking).

   (i) What is the probability that the counter drawn is green?

   (ii) What is the probability that the counter drawn is yellow?

  (iii) What is the probability that the counter drawn is blue or yellow?

  (iv) What is the probability that the counter drawn is not yellow?

9 A number is chosen at random from the set {1, 2, 3, 4, 5, 6, 7}.

   (i) What is the probability that the number chosen is 2?

   (ii) What is the probability that the number chosen is even?

  (iii) What is the probability that the number chosen is a prime number?

  (iv) What is the probability that the number chosen is greater than 5?

10 A letter is chosen at random from the letters of the word PROBABILITY.

   (i) What is the probability that the letter chosen is a B?

   (ii) What is the probability that the letter chosen is an I?

  (iii) What is the probability that the letter chosen is a vowel?

  (iv) What is the probability that the letter chosen is not a vowel?

11 The spinner shown is spun.

Find the probability that the arrow points to:

   (i) red   (ii) blue   (iii) yellow   (iv) blue or red

12 A coin is tossed 1000 times. How many times would you expect the outcome to be Heads?

13 A die is rolled 600 times. How many times would you expect the outcome to be six?

14 Mary has a bag with three counters in it, 2 blue and 1 red.

   (i) She takes a counter from the bag without looking.
     What is the probability that she takes a red counter?

   (ii) Write down four fractions which are equivalent to $\frac{1}{2}$.

   (iii) Mary wants the probability of taking a red counter from the bag to be $\frac{1}{2}$.

     She needs to put extra counters in the bag. How many extra red and blue counters could she put in the bag? Give three possible answers. How many possible answers are there?

15 Jack has a bag with four counters in it, 3 black and 1 red.

   (i) He takes a counter from the bag without looking.
     What is the probability that he takes a red counter?

   (ii) Write down four fractions which are equivalent to $\frac{1}{3}$.

   (iii) Jack wants the probability of taking a red counter from the bag to be $\frac{1}{3}$.

     He needs to put extra counters in the bag. How many extra red and black counters could he put in the bag? Give three possible answers. How many possible answers are there?

16 A die is rolled. Then it is rolled again.

   (i) Draw a two-way table to show all the possible outcomes.

   (ii) What is the probability that two sixes appear?

Revision Activity 6

1 200 tickets were sold in a raffle and put into a box.
The colours on the tickets were as shown in this table.

Blue	Pink	White	Yellow
40	50	80	30

One ticket is drawn at random. Find the probability that the ticket is:

(a) pink   (b) white   (c) blue or white   (d) not yellow

2 A die was rolled 60 times and the outcomes were as follows:

Number on die	1	2	3	4	5	6	Totals
Frequency	8	12	7	13		5	
Relative frequency (as a fraction)							
Relative frequency (as a decimal)							

Copy the table into your copybook.

(a) How many times did a 5 occur?   (b) Complete the table.

3 A die is rolled 1200 times. How many times would you expect the outcome to be six?

4 A bag contains 3 black counters and 2 red counters.

(a) A counter is taken from the bag without looking.
What is the probability that it is a black counter?

(b) Write down four fractions which are equivalent to $\frac{3}{4}$.

(c) Emily wants the probability of taking a red counter from the bag to be $\frac{3}{4}$.
She needs to put extra counters in the bag. How many extra red and black counters could she put in the bag?

(d) How many answers could you give to part (c)?

Exam-style Question

1 (a) Lynda spins the spinner shown here. It has three sectors:
grey, black, and white.

(i) Measure the **size of the angle** in each sector of
Lynda's spinner.

Write your values into the table below.

Sector	Grey	Black	White
Size of angle (degrees)			

Lynda is going to spin her spinner **60 times**.

(ii) Use your answer to part (a)(i) to estimate how many times
you would expect it to land on **grey**.

(b) The table below shows the probability of four events, **A**, **B**, **C**, and **D**.

(i) Fill in the four missing values in the table below, to show the
probability of each event as a fraction, a percentage, and a decimal.
Write the fraction in its simplest form.

Event	Probability		
	Fraction	Percentage	Decimal
A	$\frac{1}{4}$	25%	0·25
B	$\frac{1}{2}$		0·5
C	$\frac{2}{5}$	40%	
D		2%	

(ii) Mark and label the probability of each of the events **A**, **B**, **C**, and **D** on the
scale below.

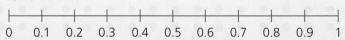

JCOL 2017

KEY WORDS AND PHRASES

- **Fundamental Principle of Counting**
- **Uncertainty**
- **Probability**
- **Trial**
- **Outcome**
- **Event**
- **Favourable outcome**
- **Sample space**

- **Probability scale**
- **Two-way table**
- **Relative frequency**
- **Pick at random**
- **Theoretical probability**
- **Equally likely events**
- **Expected frequency**

Chapter Summary 6

- **Probability** deals with uncertainty and measures the likelihood of an event.

- The **Fundamental Principle of Counting:**

  If one event has m possible outcomes and a second event has n possible outcomes, then the total number of outcomes is $m \times n$.

- The **probability scale** goes from 0 (certain not to happen) to 1 (certain to happen).

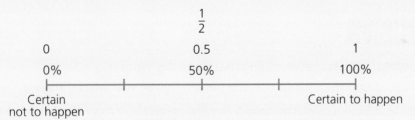

- **Relative frequency** $= \dfrac{\text{number of times an event occurs in a trial}}{\text{total number of trials}}$

- As the number of trials increases, the relative frequency leads to better estimates of the **probability** of an event.

- For **equally likely outcomes**,

  Probability of an event $= \dfrac{\text{number of favourable outcomes}}{\text{total number of possible equally likely outcomes}}$

- Probability of an event **not happening** $= 1 -$ probability that it will happen

- **Expected frequency** $=$ probability of the event $\times$ number of trials

Chapter 7 · Statistics

Learning Intentions

In this chapter, you will learn about:

- The purpose of statistics
- The use of statistics to gather information from a sample of the population with the intention of making generalisations about the whole population
- Planning and conducting an investigation involving statistics
- The different ways of collecting data
- The different types of data

- Summarising data in diagrammatic form including spreadsheets
- Measures of central tendency: mean, mode, median
- Range as a measure of spread
- Using bar charts, line plots, and stem-and-leaf plots to display data
- Selecting appropriate graphical methods to describe the sample

> LO: SP.3(a-g), U.5, U.6, U.13

Section 7A Introduction to Statistics

Class Activity

We hear the word 'statistics' every day. What does this word mean to you? Spend a minute or two discussing with the person beside you what it means to you. Jot down a selection of words which come to your mind when you think of statistics.

Statistics is a very important part of our lives in the world of the 21st century. It seems that everywhere we go and in everything we do, people are collecting pieces of information (data) about us. Information is collected on the population of the country, the attitude of people to political parties, the number of people being born each day and the number of students who will need schools ten years from now. All of this is necessary for planning for the future. Sports coaches collect statistics about each player and each match in order to help them see where improvements need to be made.

The reason why statistics is important is that **variation** is a fact of life. We are all different in many ways. We all vary in our physical characteristics, attitudes, types of goods we consume, our talents, career choices, health etc.

I am different

We need statistics to make sense of the variation inherent in our world.

Statistics is about variation.

The following activities are an introduction to working with some statistics.

Key Point

If we were to summarise in one word what statistics is all about it is **variation**.

Activity 7.1

1 The following is an extract from the medals table from the Rio 2016 Olympics.

Rank by Gold	Country	Gold	Silver	Bronze	Total
1	United States of America	46	37	38	**121**
2	Great Britain	27	23	17	**67**
3	People's Republic of China	26	18	26	**70**
4	Russian Federation	19	17	19	**55**
5	Germany	17	10	15	**42**
6	Japan	12	8	21	**41**
7	France	10	18	14	**42**
8	Republic of Korea	9	3	9	**21**
9	Italy	8	12	8	**28**
10	Australia	8	11	10	**29**
62	Ireland	0	2	0	**2**

(i) How many medals did Ireland win altogether?
In what position on the table is Ireland?

(ii) How many medals did the Russian Federation win altogether?

(iii) How many medals did Great Britain win altogether?

(iv) Compare the medals totals for Great Britain and China.
Why is Great Britain ahead of China in the table?

(v) How many more medals than Australia did Japan win?

(vi) Some people said that Australia's medal count is low compared to other countries. Do you agree? Give a reason for your answer.

2 The table below gives the estimated populations (in 2017) of the countries listed in the medals table in question **1**.

Country	Estimated population (2017)	Population to the nearest million
United States	326 621 000	
Great Britain	65 648 000	
People's Republic of China	1 389 210 000	
Russian Federation	146 877 088	
Germany	82 521 653	
Japan	126 590 000	
France	67 201 000	
South Korea	51 446 201	
Italy	60 498 707	
Australia	24 810 200	
Ireland	4 792 500	

(i) Make a table of these countries giving their populations to the nearest 1 million, e.g. Great Britain's population to the nearest million is 66 million.

(ii) How many times greater is the population of the US than the population of Australia?

(iii) Does this change what you might have thought about Australia's medal total?

(iv) Compare the populations of China and Ireland. How many times greater is China's population than Ireland's population?

(v) How did Ireland fare overall in your opinion? Take the medal total and population into account.

Section 7B **A Statistical Investigation**

By asking and answering statistical questions, we can learn more about the world around us. Statistics is used every day to help us gain insight into questions that affect our lives: Is our population growing or shrinking? What is the safest way to invest money? Will eating more fruit and vegetables really help us to be fitter and healthier?

Statistics is the science of learning from data.

Data are information about some group of individuals.

But where do we get data? One way is to conduct a **census**.

A census is a statistical investigation where the entire population is given a questionnaire to fill in. More often an investigation or **survey** is carried out on a smaller number of people or other subjects of interest. This is known as taking a **sample** from the population.

There are four stages to a statistical investigation:

1. **Pose a question** that can be answered with data
2. **Collect data** (information)
3. **Analyse the data** using graphs and numerical summaries
4. **Interpret the results** and relate them back to the original question.

We call this the **data handling cycle**.

You might remember these steps as **P-C-A-I**.

We will look at each of these steps in the following sections.

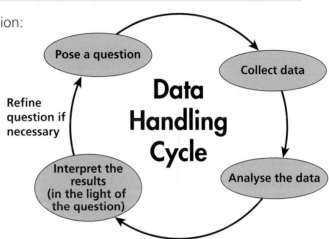

Section 7C Posing a Question and Collecting Data

The best way to understand statistics is to collect our own data. We think about a problem and get some data. We tell others about what we have discovered.
That's what statistics is really all about.

So let's get down to it. First, we find a question or questions that we would like to answer. How do we go about this?

Key Points

When posing a question, we need to pay attention to the following points:
- What are you trying to find out?
- Is your question answerable?
- What will you need to measure?
- What units of measurement will you use?
- How will you get your data?
- What sort of data will you get?
- What will you do with the data?
- What problems, if any, do you foresee?

The Story of Our Class

As a simple starting investigation, we are going to look at 'The story of our class'.
We will pose some simple questions which will help us to get to know our classmates better.

We might ask questions such as:

- What is the most popular sport in our class?
- Would the girls' preferences be different from the boys'?
- What is the typical height for students in our class?
- How far do students in our class travel to school?
- Is our class typical of students of our age in the rest of Ireland?
- Is our class typical of students of our age in other parts of the world?

A **questionnaire** is a set of questions designed to obtain data from.

The following is a simple questionnaire which we can use to get us started.

Note: when you see this icon **Q** in this chapter, we are referring to this questionnaire.

Questionnaire Q

1. Gender   Male ☐   Female ☐

2. In which month were you born?

3. How tall are you? (Answer to the nearest centimetre.)

4. What is the length of your right foot? (Answer to the nearest centimetre.)

5. Which of the following superpowers would you most like to have?

   (a) Invisibility   (d) Super-strength

   (b) Ability to fly   (e) Ability to freeze time

   (c) Telepathy (ability to read minds)

6. What sport are you most interested in?

Hurling		Rugby	
Gaelic football		Soccer	
Basketball		Swimming	
Tennis		Martial arts	
Horse riding		Camogie	
Hockey		Golf	
Athletics		None	
		Other (please specify)	

7. How many people live in your household? (Include yourself.)

8. How long does it take you to get to school?
   (Try to be as accurate as possible and give your answer in minutes.)

9. Do you watch reality TV?   A lot ☐   Sometimes ☐   Rarely ☐   Never ☐

- When the whole class fills in the survey, we are doing a **census** of the class. A census should include data from everybody in the population.

- In this case, the population is made up of people. But the word **population** is a general word in statistics for any group of objects that we want information on.

For example, for a potato farmer, his crop of potatoes is the population. If he wants to know about the quality of his crop, he may take a **sample** of that population of potatoes.

Taking a sample is a very important part of statistics. As we can't always take data from the whole population, a sample can be used to give us information about the population.

Taking a sample is like tasting soup. One spoonful of soup from a pot of soup is a sample of what all the soup tastes like, provided we stir the soup first! This spoonful is then representative of the whole pot of soup.

- Likewise, any sample in statistics needs to be a **representative sample** if it is to give us information about the population. This means that every member of the population must have an equal chance of being part of the sample.

- **Data** are values or numbers along with their context (what they are about).

Data we use which we have collected ourselves are called **primary data**.

Data we use which was collected by others are called **secondary data**.

Secondary data can be obtained from books, journals, the Internet, etc.

Class Activity

1. Complete the questionnaire **Q**
2. Are there other questions of interest that you would like to ask?

   (Remember the guidelines above for posing a question.)

The questions in the questionnaire **Q** were given on an educational website called *CensusAtSchool* which aims to develop a greater understanding of statistics among students. Students in countries such as New Zealand, Canada, Australia and the UK take part, as well as students from Ireland. You can use it to get data from students in other countries to compare with your own.

The following spreadsheet gives the results from a group of students who answered the questionnaire **Q**. A **spreadsheet** is a rectangular array of cells which have **data** in them.

(It can also be called a **data table**.)

Spreadsheet SS

No.	Gender	Birth month	Height (cm)	Foot length (cm)	Superpower	Sport	Number in household	Time to travel to school (min)	Do you watch reality TV?
1	Female	April	143	24	Freeze time	Gaelic football	4	5	Rarely
2	Male	March	165	27	Freeze time	Rugby	4	30	Never
3	Male	June	163	26	Super-strength	Rugby	4	5	Sometimes
4	Female	February	190	25	Freeze time	Soccer	6	25	Sometimes
5	Female	October	140	19	Fly	Rugby	4	5	A lot
6	Male	June	160	25	Invisibility	Gaelic football	5	20	Sometimes
7	Female	February	180	32	Fly	Dancing	4	30	Sometimes
8	Male	September	166	25	Freeze time	Hurling	6	20	Rarely
9	Male	August	160	23	Fly	Soccer	5	10	A lot
10	Female	November	175	25	Fly	Soccer	4	15	Rarely
11	Male	June	160	22	Freeze time	Rugby	3	5	Sometimes
12	Male	November	153	23	Freeze time	Soccer	4	10	A lot
13	Female	September	164	24	Telepathy	Soccer	7	10	A lot
14	Female	January	162	22	Invisibility	Camogie	4	20	Rarely
15	Male	August	172	24	Freeze time	Soccer	6	5	Rarely
16	Female	August	140	21	Freeze time	Hockey	4	15	Rarely
17	Female	December	165	26	Telepathy	Baton twirling	4	5	A lot
18	Female	June	153	25	Invisibility	Gaelic football	9	15	Sometimes
19	Female	September	175	35	Fly	Gaelic football	4	45	Sometimes
20	Male	September	154	23	Invisibility	Gaelic football	5	45	A lot
21	Male	September	169	35	Fly	Soccer	4	1	Sometimes
22	Female	December	158	24	Telepathy	Camogie	4	20	Never
23	Male	December	175	24	Fly	Golf	6	15	Sometimes
24	Male	December	180	34	Super-strength	Soccer	6	35	Sometimes
25	Male	October	172	30	Freeze time	Hurling	5	5	Sometimes
26	Male	June	163	24	Fly	Swimming	3	5	Rarely
27	Male	March	150	23	Freeze time	Rugby	6	5	Sometimes
28	Female	October	165	21	Fly	Soccer	5	20	Rarely
29	Male	July	165	24	Super-strength	Gaelic football	6	10	Never
30	Male	August	150	23	Freeze time	Soccer	4	10	Sometimes

Note: When you see this icon **SS** in this chapter, we are referring to this spreadsheet.

Note: You can retrieve your class data in this form by registering with *CensusAtSchool* and completing a questionnaire.

Look carefully at the spreadsheet **SS**. Note the following:

- **Each row shows us the data from one individual (person)** or one questionnaire.
- **Each column represents what you ask each person**.

Each column shows **variation** in some measurement for each person. Hence each column is a 'variable'. A **variable** is something whose value we can obtain (measure) for each person. Its value can change from person to person. A variable has a name which tells you what has been measured.

So, remember, in our statistics spreadsheet: rows represent people; columns represent what you ask people (variables).

	Birth month	Height (cm)	Foot length (cm)
	April	143	24
	March	165	27
	June	163	26
	February	190	25

Section 7D Types of Data

Class Discussion

Look at the answers given to each question in the spreadsheet **SS** (i.e the data).

Glance down each column.

Spend two minutes looking at these values. Can you put them into two groups?

One way is to say that one group contains words and the other group contains numbers.

The data in words are known as **categorical data**.
The data in numbers are called **numerical data**.

Categorical data can be identified by names or categories, and can be divided into two types:

1. **Categorical data – nominal:** data which cannot be organised according to any natural order, e.g. gender, colour of eyes, place of birth.
2. **Categorical data – ordinal:** data which can be ordered in some way, e.g. exam grades (A, B, C, ...), volume levels (low, medium, high), months (January, February, March, ...).

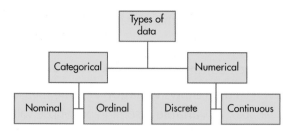

Numerical data indicate how much or how many, and can be divided into two types:

1. **Numerical data – continuous:** data which can have an infinite number of values between any two values, e.g. height.

2. **Numerical data – discrete:** data which can have finite values only, e.g. family size.

Note that sometimes data can have values that look like numerical data but are just numbers serving as labels, e.g. ISBN for a book, school roll number, PPS number, exam number. If they are numerical data then they should have **units**.

Activity 7.2

1 State whether each of the following are primary or secondary data:

   (i) Searching the internet to find out how many matches Ireland won in the last year in rugby

   (ii) Counting the number of students who arrive at school by bicycle

   (iii) Asking people outside a shop about their purchasing habits

   (iv) Looking at newspapers to find the number of cars sold each month

   (v) Surveying classmates to find out their favourite TV program

2 Match the phrase on the left with its correct definition on the right.
For example, 9F is one match.

1. Secondary data	A. Any group of objects that we want information on
2. A spreadsheet	B. Discrete data
3. A population	C. Data which we collect ourselves
4. Primary data	D. A set of questions designed for gathering information
5. A sample	E. Data which was collected by others
6. Data which can have an infinite number of values	F. Information about some group of individuals
7. Data which can have finite values only	G. A rectangular array of cells which have information in them
8. A questionnaire	H. Continuous data
9. Data	I. A subset of a population

3 Below are the four stages of a statistical investigation, but in the wrong order.
Put these four stages in the correct order:

   A. Analyse the data

   B. Collect the data

   C. Interpret the results (and refine the question if necessary)

   D. Pose a question

Statistics

4 Gerry is carrying out a survey on the students in his class.
His questions are about the apps and social media they use.
Write a question that Gerry could use that would give **numerical** data.
Your question should be about apps or social media.

5 Eithne is going to survey post-primary Geography teachers in Ireland.
Some of the questions in the survey are shown in the table below.
Put a tick (✓) in the correct box to show what type of data each question would give.

Question	Numerical Continuous	Numerical Discrete	Categorical Nominal	Categorical Ordinal
How many Geography classes do you teach each week?				
How much do you like teaching Geography? A lot ☐ A little ☐ Not at all ☐				
What subjects (other than Geography) do you teach?				

6 Look at the questionnaire **Q** and identify the type of data which you get
from each question. Copy and complete this table.

Question	Type of data
1	
2	
3	
4	
5	
6	
7	
8	
9	

7 The answers to survey questions can be classified as follows.

A. Categorical nominal data where the categories are not ordered

B. Categorical ordinal data

C. Discrete numerical data

D. Continuous numerical data

For each question below, tick (✓) what type of data the answer represents.

Question	Type of Data			
	A	B	C	D
What is your height in centimetres?				
Are you male or female?				
How much money do you earn per week?				
Tick when you were born. Before 1990 ☐ 1990 to 2000 ☐ After 2000 ☐				

Statistics

8 Write four short questions (one for each type of data) that you could include in a survey and that will give the four types of data given in question **5**.

9 Philip bought a jacket last week. Write down four questions about the jacket which will give categorical and numerical data as answers.

10 State what type of data is in each of the situations A to G:

A. The temperature of the air

B. The number of people who voted for each political party in the last general election

C. The time it takes you to run a race

D. Breeds of cat

E. The average speed of a swimmer in an Olympic 100 m race

F. The number of goals scored in a football match

G. The days of the week in which students in the class were absent.

11 Complete the questionnaire **Q** if you have not already done so.

12 Add two questions of your own. Remember to use the guidelines for posing a question.

13 Look carefully at the spreadsheet **SS** and answer the following questions.

(i) How many students does the spreadsheet give data on?

(ii) How many are male and how many are female?

(iii) What are the most common birth months?

(iv) What height is the tallest boy?

(v) What height is the tallest girl?

(vi) What is the difference between the longest and shortest foot lengths?

(vii) How many students would like to be able to fly?

(viii) Name an unusual favourite sport on the spreadsheet.

(ix) One student listed golf as his favourite sport. In what month was this student born?

How often does this student watch reality TV?

(x) Write a summary of the student in the fifth row of the spreadsheet. You should include nine pieces of information.

(xi) Write a brief summary of the student who listed swimming as a favourite sport. You should include eight more pieces of information.

Section 7E Analysing and Interpreting Data, Part 1

Averages

A set of data like you see in a spreadsheet can be difficult to make sense of. The numerical data are just one number after another. So we try to get one figure that will summarise the data. A statistical value called an **average** is used to give a simple quick summary of the data.

Averages are very useful because they represent a set of figures as a single number.
They are **measures of centre** for a set of data. There are different types of average:

1. The **mean**   2. The **mode**   3. The **median**.

The Mean

Adi has two 1-euro coins, Conor has four 1-euro coins, and Lily has six 1-euro coins.

They want to arrange it so that each has a **fair share** of the money.

They arrange their coins in a row like this:

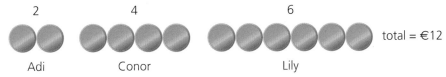

and then they rearrange them like this:

Now each has a fair share. How do we get the fair share?

The total = €12. There are 3 people. So we divide €12 by 3 and each gets €4, the fair share.

In statistics, the fair share is known as the **mean** of the data.

When people speak about an 'average' they are usually referring to the mean.

$$\text{The } \textbf{mean} \text{ of a data set} = \frac{\text{the sum of all the data values}}{\text{the number of data values}}$$

Example 1

The number of text messages sent by Grace on six days were 5, 7, 3, 6, 6, 9.

Find the mean of the data.

Solution

$$\text{The mean} = \frac{\text{the sum of all the data values}}{\text{the number of data values}} = \frac{5 + 7 + 3 + 6 + 6 + 9}{6} = \frac{36}{6} = 6 \text{ text messages}$$

The Mode

The **mode** in a data set is the item which occurs most often, i.e. it has the greatest frequency. Note: It may happen that a data set has more than one mode.

Example 2

The numbers of goals scored by a team in 12 matches were as follows:

3, 0, 5, 3, 1, 2, 3, 4, 2, 3, 2, 3

Find the mode of the data.

Solution

Drawing a **frequency table** is always a good idea:

Number of goals	0	1	2	3	4	5
Frequency	1	1	3	5	1	1

The mode = 3 goals. It has the greatest frequency (5).

Statistics

The Median

The **median** is the middle value in a complete list of all the data arranged from smallest to largest. This means that half of the data values are lower than the median and half are greater than the median.

Example 3

The number of books read by a group of students over a term was as follows:

5, 3, 2, 2, 6, 7, 9, 5, 3

Find the median number of books read.

Solution

Arrange the data in order:

2, 2, 3, 3, ⑤, 5, 6, 7, 9

The middle item = the median = 5 books

In the case of an even number of data items, the median is the mean of the middle two items, as shown in the next example.

Example 4

Another group of students had read the following number of books:

1, 3, 3, 8, 5, 4.

Find the median.

Solution

Arrange the data in order:

1, 3, ③, ④, 5, 8

There are two middle values, 3 and 4.

The median = $\dfrac{3 + 4}{2}$ = 3.5 books

The Spread of the Data

Another quick way to summarise data is to measure how **spread out** it is.

The simplest measure of **spread** is called the **range of the data**.

To find the range, find the highest (maximum) and lowest (minimum) values in the data.

Range = maximum value − minimum value

Example 5

Find the range for the data in Example 4.

Solution

The maximum = 8 books

The minimum = 1 book

The range = maximum − minimum = 8 − 1 = 7 books

When we calculate the mean, the value of every item is counted. Therefore, extreme values in the data affect the mean. The median and mode are not affected in the same way.

Look at the following example to see how.

Example 6

The following are the hourly rates of pay for six workers in a factory:

€10, €12, €12, €12, €10, €46.

(i) Calculate the range of the data.

(ii) Calculate the mean hourly pay of these workers.

(iii) Write down the median hourly pay of these workers.

(iv) Write down the mode of the data set.

(v) Which average would you say best describes the pay of a typical worker in this factory? Explain your answer.

Solution

(i) The range = maximum – minimum
$$= 46 - 10 = €36$$

(ii) The mean
$$= \frac{(10 + 12 + 12 + 12 + 10 + 46)}{6} = €17$$

(iii) Arrange data in order of size:

10, 10, 12, 12, 12, 46

$$Median = \frac{(12 + 12)}{2} = €12$$

(iv) The mode = €12.

(v) The mean of €17 seems high when we look at the data, as 5 of the 6 people earn less than it.

The value of the mean is affected by the one worker who earns €46 per hour.

It would be better to use the median or mode (€12) to summarise the data, since three of the six in the group earn this amount with one earning a bit less and only one earning a lot more.

€12 is a typical hourly rate for these workers.

Activity 7.3

1 Find the mode and the mean of each of these sets of numbers:

(i) 4, 5, 7, 4, 7, 5, 4, 4

(ii) 21, 23, 25, 23, 26, 22, 28, 23, 16

(iii) 156, 158, 159, 154, 158, 156, 158

2 Explain why there is no single mode in the following set of data:

40, 44, 45, 37, 44, 52, 45

3 Find the median and the mean of each of these sets of data. In the case of the mean, give your answer correct to one decimal place.

(i) 2, 5, 6, 7, 8, 9, 10

(ii) 165, 166, 170, 172, 175, 177, 178, 180, 184

(iii) 4.5, 5, 5.5, 6.5, 6.5, 7.4, 8.2

4 The heights in cm of 11 students in a class was recorded as follows:

142, 163, 175, 140, 166, 152, 181, 157, 175, 153, 175

(i) Rewrite the data in order of size and then find the median height.

(ii) What was the modal height (i.e. the mode)?

(iii) What was the mean height?

5 By finding half of the middle two numbers, find the median of this set of numbers:

3, 8, 5, 6, 8, 5, 7, 2

6 Find the median of each data set:

    (i) 5, 3, 6, 7, 12, 9, 10, 14

    (ii) 175, 166, 170, 172, 184,
       177, 178, 180, 184, 180

    (iii) €120, €155, €182, €127,
       €177, €123, €138, €144

7 The ages (in years) of three groups of people are given. Find the mean, median and mode of each group.

    (i) 6, 8, 11, 13, 8, 6, 4, 8, 12, 8, 4

    (ii) 4, 6, 18, 12, 24, 3, 12, 19, 10

    (iii) 22, 13, 5, 6, 8, 6, 18, 7, 4, 6

For activities 8–11, refer to the questionnaire **Q** and the data on the spreadsheet **SS**.

8 For the question, 'How long does it take you to get to school?', the spreadsheet gives the following data in minutes:

5, 30, 5, 25, 5, 20, 30, 20, 10, 15

5, 10, 10, 20, 5, 15, 5, 15, 45, 45,

1, 20, 15, 35, 5, 5, 5, 20, 10, 10

Find:

    (i) The mean travel time correct to the nearest minute

    (ii) The median travel time

    (iii) The range of travel times.

9 For the question, 'How tall are you?', the spreadsheet gives the following data in cm (Girls' data in pink):

143, 165, 163, 190, 140, 160,

180, 166, 160, 175, 160, 153,

164, 162, 172, 140, 165, 153,

175, 154, 169, 158, 175, 180,

172, 163, 150, 165, 165, 150

Use the data and a calculator to find:

    (i) The mean height of the **boys** to the nearest cm

    (ii) The median height of the boys

    (iii) The range of heights of the boys.

    (iv) Complete this sentence: 'A typical boy in this group is_____tall.'

10 Use the data from question **9** and a calculator to find:

    (i) The mean height of the **girls** to the nearest cm

    (ii) The median height of the girls

    (iii) The range of heights of the girls.

    (iv) Complete this sentence: 'A typical girl in this group is_____tall.'

11 For the question, 'How many people live in your household?', use the spreadsheet to find:

    (i) The mean number of people correct to one decimal place

    (ii) The modal family size (i.e. the mode)

    (iii) The range of 'number in household.'

12 (i) The mean of four numbers is 7.
      Write down two different lists of numbers for which the above statement is true.

    (ii) The mode of five numbers is 6.
      Write down two different lists of numbers for which the above statement is true.

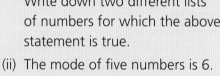

13 These are the names of ten students on the school chess team.

Seán	Emily	Lucy	Isabel	Seán
Luke	Victor	Seán	Emily	Evan

    (i) Which name is the mode?

    (ii) One person leaves the team. Another person joins the team. Now the mode is Emily.

      Name the person who leaves and the person who joins the team.

Section 7F Analysing and Interpreting Data, Part 2

Drawing Pictures of the Data

We are now going to work with the spreadsheet **SS** to **analyse** the data and convert them into real information.

We can start by drawing a table and/or a chart/graph of the data.

The type of chart/graph we use depends on the type of data that we have.

We also need to **interpret** the data. In other words, we want to know what story our table/chart is telling us about the data.

We have different types of data which can be represented in different ways.

> Charts which are suitable for categorical data and discrete numerical data are **line plots** and **bar charts**.

In the following examples and for the rest of this chapter, we are using data from the spreadsheet **SS** to illustrate how class data could be analysed and interpreted.

Line Plots

We can show categorical data graphically using **line plots** (also called **dot plots**).

A line plot is made up of dots or crosses plotted on a graph.

Example 1

Q5 of the questionnaire **Q** asked, 'Which of the following superpowers would you most like to have?'

(i) Draw a table and a line plot to show the data for this group of students.

(ii) Explain what the table and the line plot tell us about the data.

Solution

We use the spreadsheet **SS** data to produce the table below.

(i)

Superpower	Invisibility	Freeze time	Fly	Telepathy	Super-strength
Tally	IIII	NN NN I	NN IIII	III	III
Frequency	4	11	9	3	3

A line plot of the sample of data is shown below.

Invisibility	Freeze time	Fly	Telepathy	Super-strength

(ii) These are some observations (you may have more):

- We can see that the most common superpower that students in this sample would like to have is 'Freeze time'. Hence 'Freeze time' is the **mode** of the data with 10 students choosing it.
- In order of preference, the superpowers students would most like to have are 'Freeze time', 'Fly', 'Invisibility', 'Telepathy' and 'Super-strength'. The last two in the list are equally popular with both being chosen by three students.
- 20 students, that is 67%, chose either 'Freeze time' or 'Fly' as the superpowers they would most like to have.

Key Points

- Assume that each dot in a line plot represents one observation from a set of data (unless told otherwise).
- The dots are stacked in a column over a category, so the height of the column represents the frequency of observations in the category.
- Line plots are used most often to plot frequency counts within a **small** number of categories, usually with **small** sets of data.

The class in the spreadsheet **SS** is a very small **sample** of the whole **population** of students in Ireland. You can compare your own class data with this sample and see what similarities and differences exist between the two samples.

We expect that there will be **variation** between samples, but carefully chosen samples can be representative of the population.

We can also display **numerical discrete data** using a line plot.

Example 2

The data in the spreadsheet **SS** from Q7 of the questionnaire **Q**, 'How many people live in your household?' are numerical discrete data.

(i) Draw a table and a line plot to show the data for this group of students.

(ii) Explain what the table and the line plot tell us about the data.

Solution

(i) This is a frequency table for the numbers in the households:

Number in the household	3	4	5	6	7	8	9
Tally	II	|||| |||| ||||	||||	|||| II	I		I
Count/frequency	2	14	5	7	1	0	1

This is a line plot of the data for 'number of people in the household':

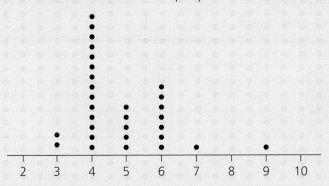

(ii) Some observations from the table and line plot:

■ We can see from the line plot that the most common number of people in the students' households is 4. Hence 4 people is the **mode** of the data.

■ The **median** of the data is also 4 people (the value of the middle dot or the average of the values of the two middle dots).

■ The **minimum** number of people in the household for this sample of data is 3 and the **maximum** number of people is 9. The **range** of the data is 9 – 3 = 6 people.

■ Nobody has 8 people in the household. There is a **gap** in the data for this value.

■ Most households have 4, 5 or 6 people, i.e. 26 out of the 30 households, which is 87% of all the households surveyed.

■ Having 9 people in a household is **unusual** for this data set.

Key Points

Look for the key words used in the examples above and try to use them when asked to analyse data:
- The **minimum**, **maximum** and **range** together tell us how **spread** out the data are.
- The **mean**, **median** and **mode** give us a measure of the centre of the data.
- **Unusual** items are important information. If the item is very unusual, it may be called an **outlier**.
- **Gaps** in the data are also worth mentioning – there might be some reason for these gaps.

Activity 7.4

1 Data are shown below for a sample of 30 students who were asked, 'How many cars belong to people in your household?'

Number of cars	0	1	2	3	4	5
Frequency	2	6	13	5	3	1

(i) What type of data is given by the question?

(ii) Represent the data using a line plot.

(iii) Write a brief summary of what the line plot tells you about the data. Your analysis should include the following terms: range, median and mode.

2 Repeat question **1** for the question 'How many bicycles belong to people in your household?', gathering data from your own class.

3 Data are shown below for a sample of students who were asked,

'How many portions of fruit do you regularly eat per day?'

Number of portions of fruit	0	1	2	3	4
Frequency	17	15	5	1	1

(i) What type of data is given by the question?

(ii) Represent the data using a line plot.

(iii) Write a brief summary of what the line plot tells you about the data. Your analysis should include the following terms: range, median and mode.

4 Repeat question **3** using data from your own class.

5 The ages (in years) of a random sample of students are given in this table:

Age	12	13	14	15	16	17
No. of students	1	4	4	6	1	4

(i) How many students were in the sample?

(ii) Write down the mode of the data.

(iii) What is the range of the data?

(iv) How many students were younger than 14 years of age?

(v) Represent the data on a line plot.

6 Refer to the data in the spreadsheet **SS** from Q2 in the questionnaire **Q**: 'In which month were you born?'

(i) Copy and complete this table using the spreadsheet.

Month	Jan	Feb	Mar	Apr	May	Jun	Jul	Aug	Sep	Oct	Nov	Dec
Tally												
Count/ Frequency	1							4				

(ii) Draw a line plot to represent the data.

(iii) Write a brief summary of what the line plot tells you about the data.

7 Draw a line plot using your own class data for Q5 from the questionnaire **Q**: 'Which of the following superpowers would you most like to have?'

Bar Charts

When the number of data items is bigger than about 50 to 60, a line plot is not suitable. We need to consider other ways to represent the data.

Bar charts can be used for categorical and discrete numerical data even if the numbers are large.

Example 1

Suppose that we ask the question:

'How does the number of males in our class compare with the number of females?'

(i) Show the data in a table and as a chart.

(ii) Explain what the table and chart tell us about the data.

Solution

(i) Gender is **categorical nominal** data and hence we can use a **bar chart** to represent our data.

We count the number of males, i.e. the **frequency** of males, and the number of females, i.e. the **frequency** of females in the 'Gender' column of the spreadsheet **SS** from Q1 in the questionnaire **Q**.

We make a **frequency table** to show the number (frequency) of males and the number of females:

Gender	Male	Female
Frequency	17	13

This is the **frequency bar chart** for this data:

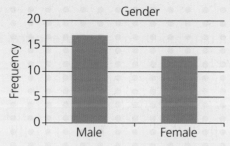

Notice:

- The categories (males and females) are marked on the horizontal axis (line).
- The frequencies are on the vertical axis.

(ii) What the table and chart tell us:

- You can see at a glance from the table and the bar chart that the males outnumber the females. There are 4 more males than females which represents approximately 13% of the whole class.
- The category 'Male' represents the **mode** of the data.

We could have used the percentages of males and females on the vertical axis:

Gender	% Male	% Female
Frequency	$\frac{17}{30} \times 100 = 57\%$	$\frac{13}{30} \times 100 = 43\%$

This gives us the **relative frequency bar chart** for the data:

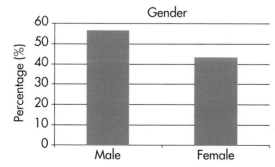

Key Points

- The categories (male and female) are marked on the horizontal axis (line).
- The **percentage** frequencies (relative frequencies) are on the vertical axis.

As you can see, the charts look the same when we have percentages on the vertical axis as when we have frequency on the vertical axis. If we were dealing with the number of males and females in all schools in Ireland, we would have very large numbers on the *y*-axis.

Writing the numbers as percentages of the total would allow us to use smaller numbers (i.e. from 0 to 100) instead of having, for example, thousands on the vertical axis.

Example 2

Refer to Q2 in the questionnaire **Q**: 'In which month were you born?'

(You have used a line plot to represent these data already.)

(i) Draw a table and a bar chart to show the birth months for this group of students.

(ii) Explain what the table and the bar chart tell us about the data.

Solution

(i) Since a question about birth months gives us **categorical nominal** data, we can analyse the data using a table and a bar chart.

From the spreadsheet, we can draw a table like this:

Month	Jan	Feb	Mar	Apr	May	Jun	Jul	Aug	Sep	Oct	Nov	Dec
Tally	I	II	II	I		ⅢⅠ	I	IIII	ⅢⅠ	III	II	IIII
Count/ Frequency	1	2	2	1	0	5	1	4	5	3	2	4

The bar chart:

(ii) Some observations:

- We see that June and September are the most common birth months. Hence we have two **modes** in these data, i.e. June and September.
- The least common birth months are January, April and July.
- At a glance, there are far more

Birth month

births from June to December than from January to May. In fact, 24 of the 30 students have birth months from June to December, which is 80% of the students.

- No one in the class has a birthday in May (a **gap** in the data).

(What additional observations can you make from these data?)

Key Points

- All the categories along with their frequencies form a **frequency distribution**.
- The word **distribution** here means all the months of the year and the frequency of each month.
- We can use a **frequency table** to show a **frequency distribution**.

You will have to draw your own bar charts. You can also use a dynamic geometry software package to do it for you.

Note some important features of a bar chart:

■ The chart has vertical and horizontal lines called **axes**.

■ Both axes should be clearly labelled.

■ The bars are drawn on the horizontal axis. They should be of equal width and if there are more than two, they should be an equal distance apart.

■ There is a **scale** on the vertical axis which shows the **frequencies**. This scale could also show percentages.

■ The scale on the vertical axis should start at 0.

■ The frequencies should be spread evenly.

■ The chart should have a title.

Activity 7.5

1 A group of students were asked whether they would prefer to be happy, rich or famous. The results are displayed in this bar chart.

(i) How many students would prefer to be famous?

(ii) How many students were surveyed?

(iii) What fraction of the students would prefer to be happy?

(iv) What percentage of students would prefer to be rich?

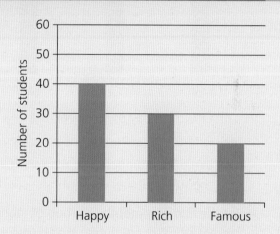

2 The bar chart below shows the number of new cars sold in one year. The chart is not complete.

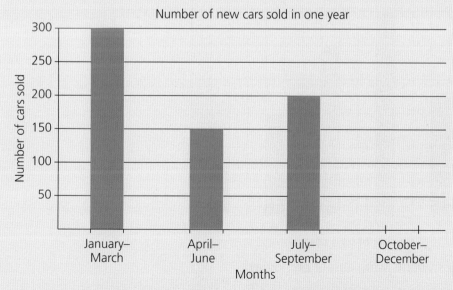

(i) How many new cars were sold in the months April-June?

(ii) In the months October-December, there were exactly **half** as many new cars sold as in April-June. How many cars were sold in October-December?

(iii) Draw the completed bar-chart in your copybook.

(iv) Calculate the **total** number of new cars sold in the year.

(v) Calculate the average (mean) number of cars sold per month in the year (answer correct to one decimal place).

3 The bar chart shows the number of hours Ava spent watching television from Monday to Friday during a mid-term break.

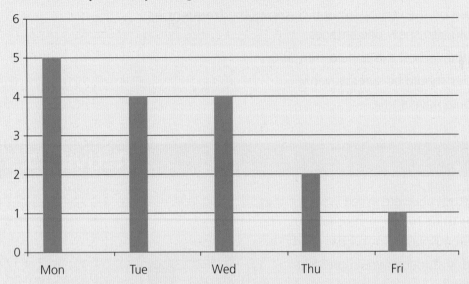

(i) On which day of the week did Ava spend most time watching television?

(ii) Find the total number of hours Ava spent watching television.

(iii) Write the number of hours Ava spent watching television on Thursday as a fraction of the total number of hours she spent watching television from Monday to Friday.

4 At the end of a month, a group of students wrote down the number of days they were absent from school during that particular month. The results are shown in the bar chart.

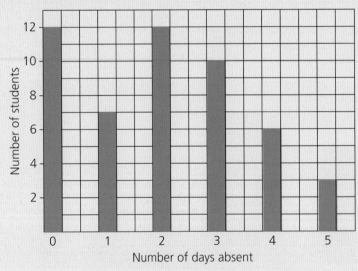

(i) How many students were absent on no day?

(ii) How many students were in the group?

(iii) Find the percentage of students who were absent for three or more days.

5 The bar chart shows the number of hours that Doug spent studying from Monday to Friday during a particular school week.

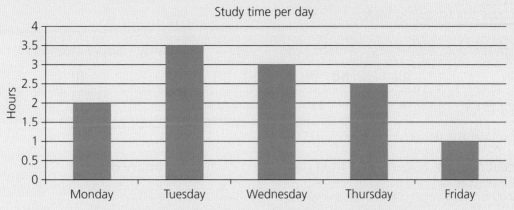

Study time per day

(i) How many hours did Doug study on the Monday of that week?

(ii) On what day of the week did Doug do the least amount of studying?

(iii) What is the mode of the data?

(iv) Find the mean number of hours per day spent studying.

(v) Express the hours of study done by Doug on Wednesday as a percentage of his total hours of study for that week.

6 A survey was taken of 40 students who owned mobile phones to find out the number of text messages that each sent on a particular day. The table shows the results of the survey.

Number of text messages	0	1	2	3	4	5
Number of students	3	5	7	5	14	6

(i) Draw a bar chart of the data.

(ii) What was the modal number of text messages sent on that day?

7 A group of 200 students was asked the following question:

'If you could have just one of the items below, which would be your first choice?'

- Television
- Computer with Internet
- Mobile phone
- Computer without Internet

- iPod/Other portable musical player
- Digital (DAB) radio
- Games console

The frequency table for the data is below.

Games console	Television	Computer with Internet	Computer without Internet	Mobile phone	iPod/Other portable musical player	Digital (DAB) radio
19	19	50	2	96	14	0

(i) Would you prefer to use a bar chart or a line plot to represent this data? Explain why you made your choice.

(ii) Display the data using a suitable graphical representation.

(iii) Write a brief summary of what your graphical representation tells you about the data.

8 Using Q5 from the questionnaire **Q**: 'Which of the following superpowers would you most like to have?' and the corresponding data from the spreadsheet **SS** (**secondary data**), we have the following table:

Superpower	Invisibility	Freeze time	Fly	Telepathy	Super-strength
Tally	IIII	NN NN I	NN IIII	III	III
Frequency	4	11	9	3	3

Represent the data using a bar chart.

9 Repeat question **8**, using data from your own class (this is **primary data**).

10 In 2016 there were 31 078 girls and 32 819 boys born in Ireland.

(i) What is the difference between the number of boys and the number of girls born in 2016?

(ii) Express the number of girls born as a percentage of the total number of babies born in 2016.

(iii) Express the number of boys born as a percentage of the total number of babies born in 2016.

(iv) What is the difference between the percentage of boys born in 2011 and the percentage of girls born in 2016?

11 Using Q6 from the questionnaire **Q**: 'What sport are you most interested in?' and the corresponding data from the spreadsheet **SS**, we have the following table:

Sport	Hurling	Gaelic football	Basketball	Tennis	Horse riding	Hockey	Athletics	Rugby	Soccer	Swimming	Martial arts	Camogie	Golf	Other	None
Tally	II	NN I				I		NN	NN NN	I		II	I	II	
Frequency	6	6	0	0	0	1	0	5	10	1	0	2	1	2	0

(i) Represent the data using a bar chart.

(ii) Write a brief summary of what the bar chart tells you about these data.

(iii) Do you think every class would have a similar summary using data from this question?

12 Repeat question **11**, this time using data from your own class.

13 Using Q9 from the questionnaire **Q**: 'Do you watch reality TV?' and the corresponding data from the spreadsheet **SS**:

(i) Copy and complete the following table from the spreadsheet:

Watch reality TV	A lot	Sometimes	Rarely	Never
Tally	ⅢⅠ Ⅰ			
Frequency	6			
Percentage %	$\frac{6}{30} \times 100 = 20$			

(ii) Draw a bar chart of the data using the 'frequency' row of the above table.

(iii) Draw a bar chart using the 'percentage' row of the above table.

(iv) Compare the two bar charts.

(v) Write a brief summary of what the bar charts tell you about the data.

14 Repeat question **13**, this time using data from your own class.

Stem-and-Leaf Plots

We can represent numerical continuous data which have been rounded using a stem-and-leaf plot.

■ A stem-and-leaf plot is a representation of data in which each data value is separated into two parts – a stem and a leaf.

For example, if the data are two-digit numbers, then the stems are the tens digits and the leaves are the units digits.

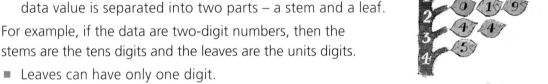

■ Leaves can have only one digit.

■ The stems are listed vertically (from smallest to largest), and the corresponding leaves for the data values are listed horizontally beside the appropriate stem.

■ The leaves are usually ordered within each stem.

■ The intervals used for each stem must be equal.

Example 1

A group of students was asked how many text messages each had sent the previous day. The results were:

15 31 6 17 15 14 4 35 41 25
8 27 33 16 40 10 15 26 29 6

(i) How many students were in the group?

(ii) Represent the data on a stem-and-leaf plot.

(iii) Use the plot to find the range of the data.

Solution

(i) There were 20 students in the group.

(ii) We can fill in the data unordered from the spreadsheet initially and then order it.

Stem-and-leaf plot unordered:

```
0 │ 6  4  6  8
1 │ 7  5  4  6  0  5  5
2 │ 5  7  6  9
3 │ 1  5  3
4 │ 1  0
        Key: 2│5 means 25 texts
```

Stem-and-leaf plot ordered:

```
0 │ 4  6  6  8
1 │ 0  4  5  5  5  6  7
2 │ 5  6  7  9
3 │ 1  3  5
4 │ 0  1
        Key: 2│5 means 25 texts
```

(iii) The minimum number is four texts and the maximum number is 41 texts.

The range of the data is (41 − 4) = 37 texts.

Example 2

Refer to Q3 in the questionnaire **Q**: 'How tall are you?'

(i) Draw a stem-and-leaf plot to show the heights for this group of students.

(ii) Use the diagram to calculate the median.

Solution

(i) The data were (in cm):

143, 165, 163, 190, 140, 160,

180, 166, 160, 175, 160, 153,

164, 162, 172, 140, 165, 153,

175, 154, 169, 158, 175, 180,

172, 163, 150, 165, 165, 150

These are three-digit data.

The stem has two digits (the hundreds and tens digits) and the leaves have only one digit, the units digit.

```
14 │ 0  0  3
15 │ 0  0  3  3  4  8
16 │ 0  0  0  2  3 (3  4) 5  5  5  5  6  9
17 │ 2  2  5  5  5
18 │ 0  0
19 │ 0
              Key: 16│3 = 163 cm
```

(ii) The median is the value that is half-way through the distribution.

There are 30 values altogether which is an even number.

So the median equals the sum of the two middle values divided by 2

$$= \frac{163 + 164}{2} = 163.5$$

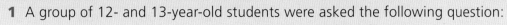

1 A group of 12- and 13-year-old students were asked the following question:

'What is your resting pulse rate in **beats per minute**?'

Below is a set of data in beats per minute from a group of first-year students in Ireland.

60	57	57	65	68	89	57
60	60	70	60	70	62	72
70	65	60	60	56	100	60
72	84	55	60	80	62	72

(i) What is the minimum resting pulse rate for these data?

(ii) What is the maximum resting pulse rate for these data?

(iii) What is the range of the data?

(iv) What is the mean of the data?

> **Note**
>
> ❯ It is important to include units with numerical data.

2 (i) Display the data in question **1** using a stem-and-leaf plot. You might find it easier to draw an unordered stem-and-leaf plot first and then an ordered stem-and-leaf plot.

(ii) Use the stem-and-leaf plot to help you find the median of the data.

(iii) What is the mode of the data?

(iv) Are there any unusual items in the data? If so, why do you think they are unusual?

(v) Why might it be difficult to display the data in a line plot?

3 A class of students measured their open arm spans in centimetres and collected the following data:

143	152	165	180	183	165	160
151	154	200	160	142	160	190
173	178	164	173	187	175	190
169	151	163	152	177	170	164

(i) (a) What is the minimum open arm span in these data?

(b) What is the maximum open arm span in these data?

(c) What is the range of the data?

(d) What is the mean arm span?

(ii) (a) Display the data using a stem-and-leaf plot.

(b) Use the stem-and-leaf plot to help you find the median of the data.

(c) Why might it be difficult to display these data set using a line plot?

4 (i) Gather data from your own class on open arm span widths and repeat question **3** using your own class data.

(ii) Compare your class's data on open arm span widths with the data given.

5 A class of students measured their heights in centimetres and collected the following data:

143	165	163	190	140	160	180	166	160	175
160	153	164	162	172	140	165	153	175	154
169	158	175	180	172	163	150	165	165	150

(i) (a) What is the minimum height in these data?

(b) What is the maximum height in these data?

(c) What is the range of the data?

(d) What is the mean height of these students?

(ii) (a) Display the data using a stem-and-leaf plot.

(b) Use the stem-and-leaf plot to help you find the median of the data.

6 Elaine's class were doing a project. They went to the computer room to get information from the Internet. Elaine recorded the time, in minutes, that each of them spent gathering information on the Internet. These are her results:

46	33	28	35	32
24	30	31	29	36
28	41	37	24	17
14	37	26	35	18

(i) Display the data in a stem-and-leaf plot.

(ii) What percentage of the students spent less than twenty minutes on the Internet?

(iii) Robert asked Elaine how long the class spent on the Internet. Elaine gave an answer that started 'Most of them spent between…'
Complete Elaine's sentence to give a good summary of the data in one sentence.

7 Tom is a salesman who travels long distances each day. These are the distances in kilometres that Tom travelled on each work day in June:

194	174	179	155	161	168	134	144	181	205	145
163	163	158	152	154	197	180	179	155	168	

(i) Draw a stem-and-leaf plot to represent this information.

(ii) Find the range of distances that Tom travelled during the month.

(iii) Find the median distance.

(iv) Use your calculator to find the mean distance that Tom travelled during June.

(v) Finish this sentence: 'On a typical work day in June, Tom travelled _____ kilometres.'

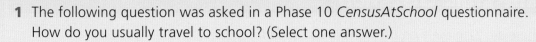
1 The following question was asked in a Phase 10 *CensusAtSchool* questionnaire.
   How do you usually travel to school? (Select one answer.)

Walk		Cycle	
Bus		Luas, Train, Dart	
Car		Other (please specify)	

The following is a sample of data for a class of 30 students for this question.

Walk	Bus	Car	Walk	Car	Car	Bus	Bus	Bus	Car
Car	Car	Walk	Car	Bus	Car	Car	Car	Walk	Car
Car	Bus	Car	Walk	Car	Walk	Car	Car	Cycle	Car

(a) Make a tally chart for the different ways of getting to school
and find the frequency for each one.

(b) Represent the data using a bar chart.

(c) Write a brief summary of what the bar chart tells you about
the different ways of getting to school for this class.

(d) Do you think every class would have a similar summary regarding
methods of travel to school?

(e) Gather data for your own class on this question and compare them
with the data given above.

2 Refer to the data in Q4 of the spreadsheet **SS** from the question, 'What is the length
of your right foot?'

(a) Copy the table below into your copybook. Using the spreadsheet, complete the table.

Foot length (cm)	19	21	22	23	24	25	26	27	30	32	34	35
Frequency	1				7							2

(b) Draw a line plot to represent the data.
Remember to show all integer foot lengths from 19 to 35.

(c) Find the mean, median and mode of the data.

(d) Find the range of the data.

(e) Complete this sentence: 'Most students have a foot length between _____ and _____.'

3 The stem-and-leaf plot shows the lengths of time
it took people to answer a quiz question.

(a) How many people answered the question?

(b) What is the range of times taken to answer
the question?

(c) What is the median time?

(d) What is the mean time to answer the question?

2	3 4
3	2 2 7 8
4	2 2 3 4 5 7
5	1 1 2 3 4 8
6	2 3
7	3

Key: 2|4 means 2.4 seconds

Exam-style Question

Statistics

1 There are 22 players on the Irish rugby squad for a game.
Their heights (in centimetres) are given below.

180, 188, 185, 180, 183, 177, 180, 183, 198, 191, 191,
185, 185, 180, 185, 196, 180, 188, 180, 183, 191, 193

(a) What is the height of the tallest player?

(b) How many players are over 184 cm in height?

(c) What percentage of the players are below 181 cm in height?
Give your answer correct to the nearest whole number.

The arm spans (in centimetres) of the same players in the same order are given below.

180, 184, 188, 178, 182, 176, 180, 185, 201, 190, 189,
185, 186, 182, 182, 196, 181, 189, 178, 184, 190, 193

(d) Find the median arm span.

(e) Complete the table below to show the height and arm span for (i) the tallest
player and (ii) the shortest player in the squad.

Player	Height	Arm span
Tallest (cm)		
Shortest (cm)		

(f) Write the ratio of height to arm span for (i) the tallest player and (ii) the shortest
player in part (e).

(g) Write each ratio in part (f) as a decimal. Give your answer correct to two
decimal places.

(h) The coach is 170 cm tall. What would you expect his arm span to be?
Give a reason for your answer.

JCOL 2012 Paper 2

KEY WORDS AND PHRASES

- Statistics
- Variation
- Data
- Primary data
- Secondary data
- Survey
- Data handling cycle
- Sample
- Representative sample
- Spreadsheet
- Data table
- Variables
- Categorical data – nominal and ordered
- Numerical data – continuous and discrete
- Bar chart
- Frequency

- Frequency table
- Tally
- Frequency distribution
- Frequency bar chart
- Relative frequency bar chart
- Averages
- Mean (fair share)
- Median
- Mode
- Spread of the data
- Maximum
- Minimum
- Range
- Unusual items of data
- Gaps in data
- Line plot (dot plot)
- Stem-and-leaf plot

Chapter Summary 7

- **Statistics** is all about **variation** (differences in people and things).
- There are four stages in a statistical investigation (**data handling cycle**):

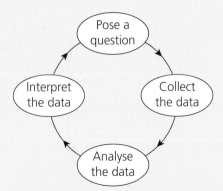

Pose a question → Collect the data → Analyse the data → Interpret the data

- A **population** is any group of things that we want to find out about.
- A **sample** is a subset of the population.

- A sample should be a **representative sample** if it is to give us information about the population.
- Data which we collect ourselves are **primary data**.
- Data which we get from books, journals and the Internet are **secondary data**.
- A **spreadsheet** is a rectangular array of cells.
- In a spreadsheet, rows represent individuals; columns are what we ask people (**variables**).
- Types of data:

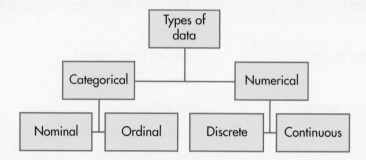

- We use **bar charts** for categorical data: frequency bar charts or relative frequency bar charts.
- There are three types of average:
  - The **mode** is the item of data which occurs most often.
  - The **mean** is the fair share: add up the values and divide by the number of values.
  - The **median** is the middle value in a complete list of all the data arranged from smallest to largest.
- The **range** of the data = maximum value – minimum value.
- A **frequency table** shows each data item and its frequency – the **frequency distribution**.
- We use a **stem-and-leaf plot** to show discrete numerical data.
- We use a **line plot** to show categorical data and discrete numerical data.

Geometry 1

In this chapter, you will learn about:

- The nature and origins of geometry
- The plane, points, lines, line segments, rays, and length of a line segment
- How axioms are used as the foundation for further learning
- Angles
- The different types of angle and how to name angles
- Estimating the size of, and then measuring angles using a protractor
- Parallel and perpendicular lines
- Vertical and horizontal lines
- Using a compass to draw circles, arcs and various shapes

LO: GT.3 (introduction), U.5, U.6, U.13

You will need...

- a pencil
- a ruler
- a geometry set

Introduction to Geometry

Geometry is one of the oldest branches of mathematics, having arisen in response to such practical problems as those found in surveying and measuring land in ancient Egypt.

The word 'geometry' comes from Greek words meaning 'Earth measurement'. It is concerned with the shape of individual objects and the way that these shapes relate to other objects.

So, we will be looking at lines, triangles, quadrilaterals and so on, some of which you have already studied in Primary School.

We will be investigating work which is over 2000 years old and is called Euclidean Geometry, after a mathematician called Euclid (c. 300 BC). One of the first things you should do is to look up 'Euclid' on the Internet or in the library and see what you find. Other famous people who contributed to this subject before Euclid were Thales, Pythagoras, Plato and Aristotle.

Geometry is still very relevant to the architects and builders of today. For example, the beautiful bridges around the world would not exist without a knowledge of geometry and its close relation, trigonometry.

An example is this wonderful bridge over the river Boyne on the M1 near Drogheda, Co. Louth.

Section 8A The Plane, Points and Lines

The geometry that you will be learning is mostly concerned with **flat** surfaces. This is called **plane geometry**. In fact, the first idea we meet in geometry is that of a plane.

A **plane** is just a flat surface, like the top of the desk or the teacher's board, except that it goes on forever in every direction. If you could imagine this, it would slice right through space and cut it in two. Try to imagine a drawing sheet going on forever in every direction; this is what a plane is.

Just imagine 'going on forever' … we call this **infinity**.

We use this symbol for infinity: ∞

The flat page you write on is the plane you will be working on. The teacher's board is the plane that your teacher will be working on.

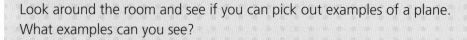

Class Activity/Discussion

Look around the room and see if you can pick out examples of a plane. What examples can you see?

A plane is made up of many little 'dots' which we call **points**. Therefore, we say that the plane is **a set of points**.

Connections

- Do you remember your study of sets?
- What do we call the objects that make up a set?
- What is an infinite set?

A point is like a dot that you would make with your pencil, only even smaller.

Strictly speaking, a point only has position; it does not have length, width or thickness.

A digital photograph is made up of millions of little dots called **pixels**. The word pixel means 'picture elements'. The points in the plane are a bit like that; there are millions and millions of them in the plane.

This is not something that you need to be concerned about, but just remember that a point has **no size**.

We denote points by capital letters such as *A*, *B*, *C*, etc.

Points in the plane:

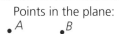

·*A*   ·*B*

·*P*

·*R*

A **plane** is an **infinite set of points.**   We will now look at some **subsets** of this set.

- This is the **line BC**. A line has no beginning or end. We name a line by any two points that it passes through. We could also call this **line CB**.

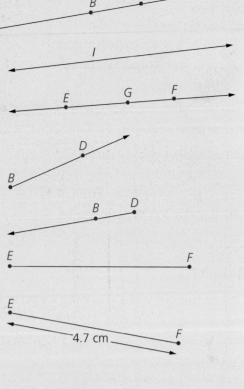

- We can also name a line by a single lower case letter (as in '**line l**')

- Points on the same line are called **collinear points**. On this line, E, G and F are collinear points.

- This is the **ray [BD**. It starts at point B and passes through D on its way to infinity. (Notice the square bracket at one end of the name.)

  The ray [BD can also be called the half-line [BD.

  This is the ray [DB. It is not the same as [BD.

- This is the **line segment [EF]**. It starts at E and finishes at F. (Notice the square brackets at each end of the name.)

  [EF] and [FE] are the same line segment.

  This line segment [EF] is 4.7 cm long. We write this as |EF| = 4.7 cm.

- The point where two lines cross is called the **point of intersection** of the two lines.

- In this diagram, S is the point of intersection of lines AB and CD.

  We can write **AB ∩ CD = {S}**

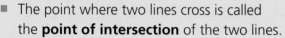

Key Point

Pay attention to the different ways we use brackets in all of the above.

Activity 8.1

(i) On a sheet of paper or a page of your copybook (this is your **plane**), mark in 10 points anywhere you like.

(ii) Give 'names' to your 10 points with capital letters (say the first 10 letters of the alphabet, A to J).

(iii) Now, use your ruler to join up points A and B, and let your pencil go beyond the two points at each end until you come to the edge of the sheet at each end.

Write 'line AB' on the line.

(iv) Could you draw a different line that also passes through A and B?
Think about it, try it yourself and discuss it in class.

(v) Draw in the lines GH and JI. Remember to extend your lines beyond the naming points.

(vi) Draw the line HD.

(vii) What point is HD ∩ GH?

(viii) Now, with your pencil and ruler draw in the ray [CD. Write 'ray [CD' on the ray.

(ix) Now draw five more rays starting at C going in different directions. Your rays do not need to pass through any of your named points, but they could, of course.

(x) Draw the line segment [EF]. Write 'line segment [EF]' on the line segment.

(xi) Use your ruler to measure the length of line segment [EF] and write your answer in your copybook. Write in '|EF| =   '.

(xii) Is |EF| = |FE|, do you think?

(xiii) Could |EF| ever be negative?

(xiv) Mark the point P anywhere on the line segment [EF].

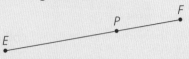

(xv) Measure |EP|, |PF| and |EF|. Write these measurements in your copybook. Write your answers in mm and in cm.

(xvi) Would you expect that |EP| + |PF| = |EF|? Using your measurements, check that this is so.

Axioms

One of the questions you were asked in Activity 8.1 was: 'Is it possible to construct two different lines through the points A and B?'

From your work, you will agree that there is exactly one line through any two points.

> In mathematics, a statement like this, which is obviously true, is called an **axiom**. We accept axioms without proving that what they say is true.

Axioms are very important because we use them to make further statements and so build upon our knowledge to learn more. Just as solid foundations are needed in building a wall, we need axioms as the foundations on which we build our further knowledge in maths.

In fact, we have two axioms from Activity 8.1:

Don't worry about the names or numbers of the axioms – just see them as statements that are true without any proof.

In questions (xii), (xiii) and (xvi) of Activity 8.1, we met more statements that we take as obviously true and these are part of another axiom:

AXIOM 1 (2 points axiom)

There is exactly one line through any two given points.

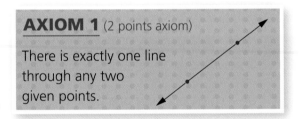

AXIOM 2 (ruler axiom)*

The distance between points has the following properties:

1. The distance |AB| is never negative.

2. |AB| = |BA|

3. If C lies on AB between A and B then |AB| = |AC| + |CB|.

4. There is only one point on the ray [AB which is a given distance from A.

* paraphrased

Copy this diagram and answer the questions below:

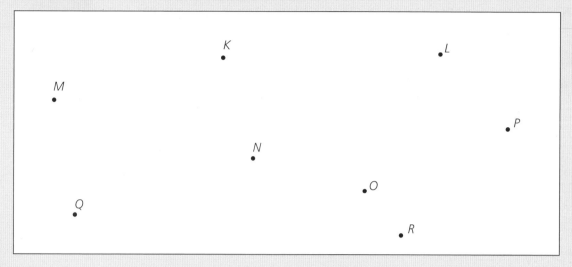

1 Join M to Q. This is line segment [MQ]. Measure the length of [MQ]. Write your answer in cm and in mm. How do we name the length of [MQ]?

2 Join P to R. This is line segment [PR]. Measure the length of [PR]. Write your answer in cm and in mm. How do we name the length of [PR]?

3 Mark the point T anywhere on [PR].

4 Measure |PT|, |TR| and |PR|. Write these measurements in mm.

5 Is |PT| + |TR| = |PR|?

6 Draw the line MN. Can you measure its length?

7 Draw the rays [PL, [PK and [PN.

8 Draw in the point W, where W = NL ∩ KO.

9 Mark the point X where X ∈ MN, but X ∉ [MN].

10 How big is a point?

11 How many points are on a line?

12 Answer true/false to the following statements:

   (i) Line MN passes through O.

   (ii) Line QP contains M.

   (iii) M, N and O are collinear points.

   (iv) P, K and M are collinear.

   (v) More than one line can be drawn through K and L.

   (vi) NL intersects LP at L.

   (vii) [KN is the same as [NK.

   (viii) Line PQ is the same as line QP.

   (ix) [PN ⊂ PN.

Section 8B Angles

This section is all about angles. You meet angles everywhere you go – all sorts and sizes of angles in buildings and rooms and even in natural things, like rocks and tree branches.

Let us start by talking about how an angle is made. When we have two rays in the same place in the plane ('on top of each other'), and we **rotate** (or turn) one about some common point, while the other stays where it is, we get an angle.

Geometry 1

This is just the way a door makes an angle with the wall as you open it.

 Key Point

In maths, we use Greek letters from time to time. We sometimes use them for naming angles. The most commonly used letters are:

Greek letter	α	β	γ	θ	π
Name	alpha	beta	gamma	theta	pi

Facts about Angles

- Every angle has a unique point, called its **vertex** (plural 'vertices').
- For every angle there is a part of the plane called the **inside** of the angle.
- The two rays [BA and [BC which make up the angle are called the **arms** of the angle.
- We can name an angle using three capital letters with the vertex in the middle of the name. We can also use a single small Greek letter like α, β or θ.
- It is not the length of the arms of the angle that determines the size of the angle but the amount of rotation which has been done. These three angles are all the same size:

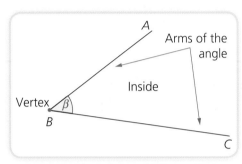

We call this $\angle\beta$ or $\angle ABC$ or $\angle CBA$.

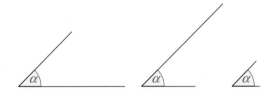

Types of Angle

We measure angles by the amount of rotation done as one arm moves and the other stays put. This is often (but not always) measured in degrees. The number of degrees in an angle is always a number between 0° and 360° (notice the symbol for degrees).

The reason for having 360° in a circle dates back to the ancient Babylonians of 2000 BC and their way of measuring the time in a day. They loved the number 60 and multiples of 60 since it has so many divisors. That is very possibly why we also have 60 seconds in a minute and 60 minutes in an hour.

Connections

- Can you list all the divisors of 360? You should have 24.
- How many pairs are there?

The following are the main types of angle. Notice that a right angle has a special symbol.

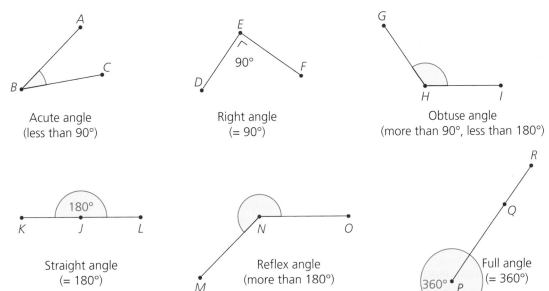

Acute angle
(less than 90°)

Right angle
(= 90°)

Obtuse angle
(more than 90°, less than 180°)

Straight angle
(= 180°)

Reflex angle
(more than 180°)

Full angle
(= 360°)

We sometimes use the term **ordinary angle** to mean an angle which is less than 180°. So, acute angles and obtuse angles could also be called ordinary angles.

When naming an angle, we refer to the ordinary (non-reflex) angle unless the word 'reflex' is before or after the name.

Class Activity/Discussion

1. Name each of the angles above using three letters in two different ways.
2. Look around the classroom and identify where angles are formed. Which types of angles are they? Which is the most common angle and which is the least common angle?

Measuring Angles

You can measure an angle using a protractor. You should try to **estimate** the size of an angle before measuring it, as you should do with all calculations. Errors in measurement can be corrected more quickly if you have a good idea of the correct answer first.

How to Use a Protractor to Measure an Angle

Example: Measure the angle EAB.

1. Place the centre point of the protractor at the vertex A so that the baseline of the protractor is along one arm of the angle.

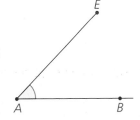
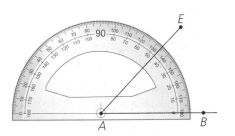

2. In this case, we use the inner scale on the protractor because *AB* passes through the zero of the inner scale. Write down the reading on the inner scale: |∠*EAB*| = 46°

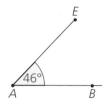

3. We use the outer scale to measure an angle from the other side:

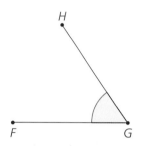
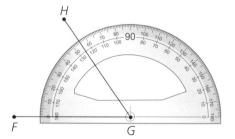

Write down the reading on the outer scale: |*HGF*| = 55°

Equal angles are angles which have the same number of degrees – they are the same size.

Activity 8.3

1 Copy the table below and for each angle:

(a) Name it in two different ways using three letters.

(b) Say what type of angle it is.

(c) Estimate its size and write down your estimate.

(d) Measure it and write down your measurement. Compare your estimate to the actual size.

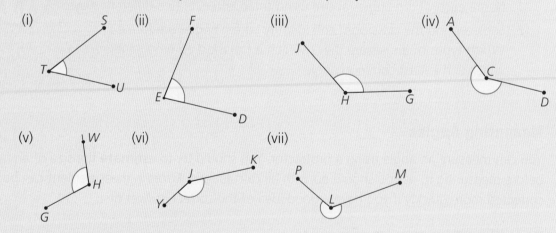

	Name of angle	Type of angle	Estimate of angle size	Actual angle size
(i)				
(ii)				
(iii)				
(iv)				
(v)				
(vi)				
(vii)				

2 (i) Find the size of each of the three angles in triangle *NOP*.

 (ii) Find the sum of the three angles.

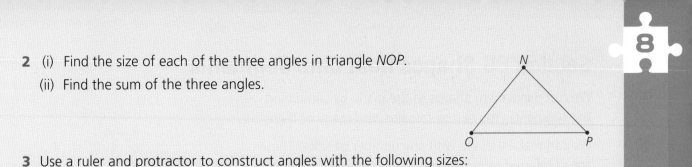

3 Use a ruler and protractor to construct angles with the following sizes:

 (i) 30°   (ii) 75°   (iii) 130°   (iv) 200°

4 Construct angles of the following sizes:

 (i) 54°   (ii) 67°   (iii) 142°   (iv) 253°   (v) 320°

5 There are two set-squares in a geometry set.

 (i) Draw around them to make two triangles.

 (ii) Measure all the angles in these triangles and mark the measurements on your triangles.

6 Name the kind of angle formed by the hands of a clock:

 (i) at 9.00 pm   (ii) at 6.00 am   (iii) at 3.00 am.

7 Find how many degrees the minute hand of a clock will rotate in:

 (i) 30 minutes   (ii) 20 minutes   (iii) 40 minutes   (iv) 45 minutes.

8 A man was facing North. He turned to face East.
Through how many degrees did he turn? Is there more than one answer?

9 Mary was facing East. She turned around until she was facing West.
Through how many degrees did she turn?

10 How many degrees are there between North and North-West?

11 Adi stood at the corner of a rectangular field facing North.
She turned and faced East. She then walked all around
the edge of the field until she came back to her starting point.
She then stopped and faced North. Through how many
degrees did she turn altogether in her walk?

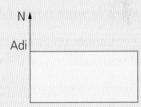

12 Count and record the number of angles that you see in each of the shapes below.
What do you notice?

13 What is a **wide-angle** lens in a camera? What does it do? What type of picture does it take?

Geometry 1

Section 8C **Shapes from Line Segments**

We can make many shapes in the plane by combining line segments. You will be familiar with many of these.

We can make a shape with any number of sides. These are all referred to as **polygons** ('poly' means 'many').

If all the sides and angles in a polygon are equal we say that it is a **regular polygon**. For example, a regular hexagon has six sides all the same length and six angles all the same size.

We will have a lot more to do with these in later sections.

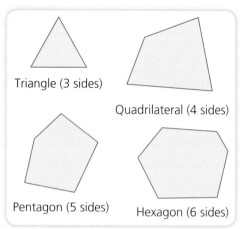

Triangle (3 sides)

Quadrilateral (4 sides)

Pentagon (5 sides)

Hexagon (6 sides)

Section 8D **Parallel and Perpendicular Lines**

There is a special name for two lines which are at an angle of 90° to each other. They are called **perpendicular** lines.

In the diagram on the right, *AB* is perpendicular to *CD*. Notice the ⌐ symbol between the lines to indicate this.

We can write **AB ⊥ CD** as shorthand.

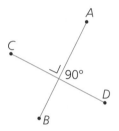

Two lines which are always the same distance apart are called **parallel** lines.

You can imagine two straight lengths of railway lines.

Line *l* is parallel to line *m*.

We can write this as **l ∥ m**.

Remember you must have <u>at least two</u> lines to compare if you want to use the words 'perpendicular' or 'parallel'.

Two more related words which you may be familiar with are 'horizontal' and 'vertical'.

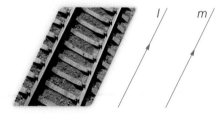

Horizontal means 'parallel to the ground or the horizon'.

Vertical means 'going straight up' so that the bottom is directly below the top.

Note: You can use the words 'horizontal' and 'vertical' when speaking of <u>one or more</u> lines.

Vertical line

Horizontal line

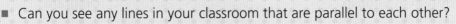

Class Activity/Discussion

- Can you see any lines in your classroom that are parallel to each other?
- Can you see any lines that are perpendicular to each other?
- Can you see any vertical lines?
- Can you see any horizontal lines?
- Can you see any parallel lines which are not vertical or horizontal?
- Can you see any perpendicular lines which are not vertical or horizontal?
- What is the relationship between horizontal and vertical lines?

Activity 8.4

1 Find and list five surfaces in your classroom which are horizontal and five which are vertical.

2 Find and list lines or surfaces which are parallel.

3 Find and list lines or surfaces which are perpendicular to each other.

4 Can you find perpendicular lines in the classroom where the lines are not vertical or horizontal?

5 What type of lines are used in the pages of your copybook?

6 Why is it important to have walls that are vertical?

7 Is it important to have floors that are horizontal? Why?

8 Do you know what a builder uses to ensure that walls are built vertically?

9 What building in Italy is famous for *not* being vertical?

10 Write down sentences (one for each word) using the words: parallel, perpendicular, vertical, horizontal.

11 Look at the following table. Three different descriptions of the same line or angle can be found in the three columns, but the information has been jumbled up.

Find the matching items in each column, e.g. (A1, B10, C8) is one of the answers.

	Column A	Column B	Column C
	Description in English	**Mathematical words/phrases**	**Diagram**
1	Line going directly upwards	Horizontal line	
2	Angle greater than 90° but less than 180°	Acute angle	
3	Line parallel to the ground	Right angle	
4	Angle of 180°	Obtuse angle	

(Continued)

	Column A	Column B	Column C
	Description in English	**Mathematical words/phrases**	**Diagram**
5	Angle greater than 180°	Straight angle	
6	Angle of 90°	Reflex angle	
7	Angle less than 180°	Ordinary angle (more than one diagram)	
8	Lines which never meet	Perpendicular lines	
9	Lines at an angle of 90° to each other	Parallel lines	
10	Angle of less than 90°	Vertical line	

Section 8E Use of the Compass and Ruler

The compass is one of the most important tools in your geometry set. You will use it for many constructions, so this section has some activities to help you gain confidence in using it. Use a sharp HB pencil in your compass and strive for accuracy and precision in your work.

When you draw a circle, you spread apart the compass point and the pencil by a certain distance. This distance is called the **radius** of the circle. The **centre** of the circle is the point where you put your compass point.

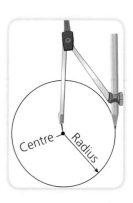

Activity 8.5

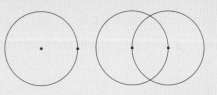

1 Construct the following shapes using your compass. Be precise with every step. First draw a circle with a radius of 5 cm. Keep your compass open at this radius.

Mark a point on the circle. Put the compass point on it and draw a second circle of the same size.

Continue drawing more circles with the same radius.
Draw the polygon shown here into your construction.

How many sides does it have? It should have six sides,
which means it is a hexagon.

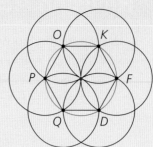

Measure each side length of this hexagon. What do you get?
Is it a regular hexagon?

Measure each of the six angles in the hexagon with your
protractor. What do you get? What is the sum of these six angles?

Can you see where you might form another larger hexagon
in your construction? Draw it in. Is it a regular hexagon?

2 Start again with another larger circle. Make it any size you
like. Keep your compass to hand with the same radius.
Mark in one point on the circle. Then use your compass
with the same radius to mark in five more points all the
same distance apart on the circle.

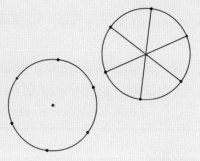

Isn't it surprising that you get exactly six points on the circle
this way? Now construct the wheel shape on the right above.

Connections

■ Now you have a nice **fraction wheel**. Shade in $\frac{1}{2}$ of the circle,
$\frac{1}{3}$ of the circle and $\frac{1}{6}$ of the circle in different colours or patterns.

■ Is all of your circle shaded in at this point? Explain why.

3 Construct the following shapes using
a circle of radius 5 cm each time.

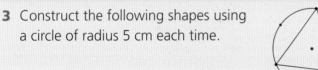

4 Construct the following shapes which
have a 3-D effect.

5 Construct the following shapes.

(i)

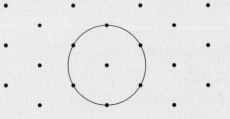

(ii)

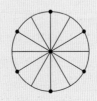

Geometry 1

1 Draw a mind map with the theme 'the plane'. You can use the KEY WORDS AND PHRASES section of this chapter to help you.

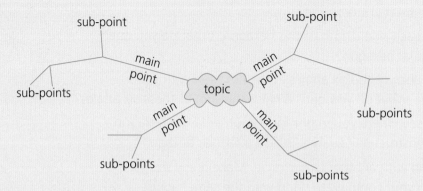

2 (a) Draw a triangle in your copybook.

(b) Use a protractor to measure the three interior angles of the triangle. Add the three angles and write down your answer.

3 (a) Use a protractor to measure the angles $\angle ABC$ and $\angle DEF$.

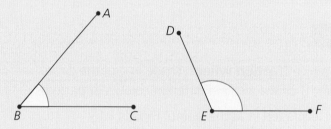

(b) The four angles $\angle M$, $\angle N$, $\angle O$ and $\angle P$ are shown in the diagrams below.

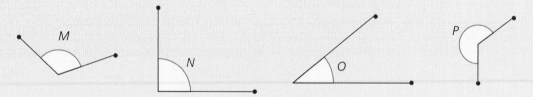

Starting with the smallest, put the four angles in order.

4 Look at these five shapes, then copy and complete the sentences below:

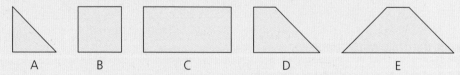

(a) Shape _____ is the only shape with three sides.

(b) Shape _____ is the only one with no right angles.

(c) Shape _____ is the only shape which cannot be folded onto itself.

(d) Shape _____ is the only shape with four _____ .

(e) Shape _____ could be formed by joining together two copies of shape _____ .

5 One complete turn is 360°. Copy and complete the following table:

Fraction of a turn	1	$\frac{1}{2}$	$\frac{1}{4}$	$\frac{1}{3}$	$\frac{1}{6}$	$\frac{1}{12}$
Angle in degrees	360°					

6 The diagram below shows two line segments.

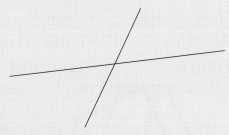

(a) Copy the diagram and write the letter *A* in an acute angle.

(b) On your diagram, write the letter *O* in an obtuse angle.

Exam-style Question

1 The diagram shows two plastic strips, pinned at their mid-points, and a protractor.

(a) From the diagram, estimate the size of angle *A*.

(b) Use your estimate to calculate the size of angle *B*.

(c) Copy and complete |∠*B*| + |∠*C*| = _____ .

(d) State the relationship between angle *A* and angle *C*. Give a reason for your answer.

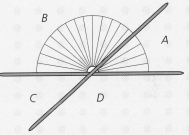

JCFL 2011

Interactive Tool 8.1

KEY WORDS AND PHRASES

- Plane
- Infinity
- Infinite set of points
- Point *A*
- Line *MN*
- Line segment [*PQ*]

- Ray [*XY*
- Collinear points
- |*RS*| = length of [*RS*]
- Triangle
- Quadrilateral
- Pentagon
- Polygon

- Regular polygon
- Angle
- Vertex (vertices)
- Arms of an angle
- Degrees
- |∠*ABC*| in degrees
- Equal angles

- Acute angle
- Right angle
- Obtuse angle
- Straight angle
- Reflex angle
- Axiom

Chapter Summary 8

- **An axiom** is a mathematical statement which we accept to be true without proof.
- **Axiom 1:** There is exactly one line through any two points.
- **Axiom 2:** The distance between points has the following properties:
  1. |*AB*| is never negative
  2. |*AB*| = |*BA*|
  3. |*AC*| + |*CB*| = |*AB*|

  4. There is only one point on the ray [*AB* that is a given distance from *A*.
- An angle is made when one ray is rotated about another ray through a common point.
- Angles can be measured in degrees. The size of any angle ∠*PQR* is written as |∠*PQR*|. |∠*PQR*| is between 0° and 360°.

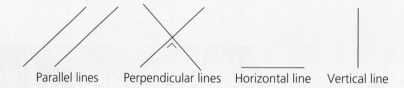

Parallel lines   Perpendicular lines   Horizontal line   Vertical line

Introduction to Co-ordinate Geometry

Chapter 9

Learning Intentions

In this chapter, you will learn about:

- The origins of co-ordinate geometry
- How points are named using co-ordinates
- Plotting points in the co-ordinate plane
- What the slope of a line means

LO: GT.5 (introduction), U.5, U.6, U.13

You will need...

- a pencil
- a ruler
- a geometry set

Section 9A Introduction to Co-ordinate Geometry

In this chapter, we are looking again at geometry.

Historical background

We are jumping in time to the early 1600s when two mathematicians named René Descartes and Pierre de Fermat independently thought of a new way to represent points in the plane by using pairs of numbers.

Descartes used to stay in bed late in the morning, and a story is told that he saw a fly on the ceiling and wondered how he might describe its exact position. The result is called co-ordinate geometry and we will see why shortly.

We use **co-ordinate geometry** everywhere these days. Some examples are the way the world is mapped with lines of longitude and latitude and that people use GPS (global positioning system) to find their destinations.

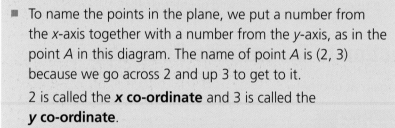

When you go to the cinema and you get a ticket for seat D7, you go up or down to row D and then go across to seat 7 in that row. That is what co-ordinate geometry is really about – finding your position.

So what did Descartes think of? His method is as follows.

■ Just pick a point – any point in the plane – and start from it. This point is called the **origin**. Then draw a horizontal number line through it.

origin

$$-4 \quad -3 \quad -2 \quad -1 \quad 0 \quad +1 \quad +2 \quad +3 \quad +4$$

■ Next we draw a vertical number line through the origin and mark it with numbers at the same space apart as on the horizontal line. On this line we agree to have + numbers to the 'north' of the origin and – numbers to the 'south' of the origin.

The horizontal line is usually called the **x-axis** and the vertical line is called the **y-axis**.

The plane is divided into four sections by the axes. These sections are known as **quadrants**.

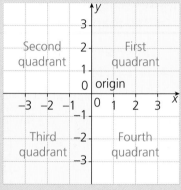

■ To name the points in the plane, we put a number from the x-axis together with a number from the y-axis, as in the point A in this diagram. The name of point A is (2, 3) because we go across 2 and up 3 to get to it.

2 is called the **x co-ordinate** and 3 is called the **y co-ordinate**.

■ (2, 3) is called a **couple** or **ordered pair**. The order is very important. We agree to have the x-value in the pair first and the y-value second (just as they appear in the alphabet).

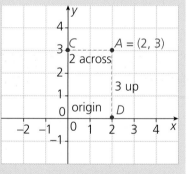

Examples

The point (3, 2) is not the same point as (2, 3).

(2, 3) is 2 units to the right and 3 units up.

(3, 2) is 3 units to the right and 2 units up.

(4, −1) is 4 units to the right and 1 unit down.

(−2, 3) is 2 units to the left and 3 units up.

(−2, −1) is 2 units to the left and 1 unit down.

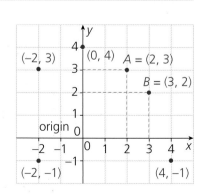

(0, 4) is 0 units to the left or right, 4 units up. (This is tricky, watch out for 0 in co-ordinates.)

Example

Locate the following points in the co-ordinate plane: $A(1, 3)$, $B(5, 2)$, $C(-1, 3)$, $D(-2, -3)$, $E(4, -2)$, $F(3, 0)$, $G(0, -3)$, $H(-3, 0)$ and $J(0, 2)$.

Solution

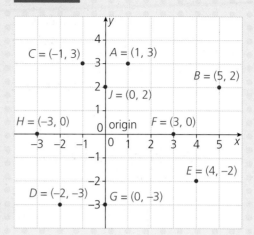

A dynamic geometry software package can help you to explore geometry and co-ordinate geometry. You can drag and pull different points and shapes and learn about their properties.

Connections

When working with co-ordinate geometry, remember that all the things you learn in Euclidean geometry are still relevant. Co-ordinate geometry is a mixture of geometry and algebra, which you will meet a little later on.

Activity 9.1

1 Copy the diagram below onto graph paper. Write down the co-ordinates of the points A to K on your graph.

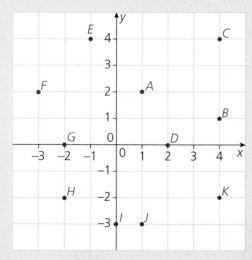

2 Use graph paper to construct a co-ordinate plane. Plot the following points on it:

$A(1, 5)$, $B(4, 2)$, $C(-2, 5)$, $D(-3, -3)$, $E(5, -2)$, $F(1, 0)$, $G(0, -4)$, $H(-2, 0)$ and $J(0, 5)$.

3 Plot the following points on graph paper: $P(-2, 4)$, $Q(3, 4)$, $R(3, -1)$ and $S(-2, -1)$.

Join the points in the order P, Q, R, S. What shape is this?

4 Descartes was famous as a philosopher as well as being a mathematician. He had a famous expression in Latin which when translated means 'I think, therefore I am', which he saw as the proof of his own existence. To get the original statement, you must 'break the code' below. To break the code, replace the points with the correct letters from the graph. What is the Latin expression?

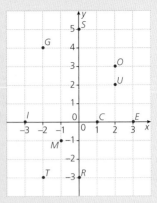

Code: (1, 0) (2, 3) (–2, 4) (–3, 0) (–2, –3) (2, 3)

(3, 0) (0, –3) (–2, 4) (2, 3)

(0, 5) (2, 2) (–1, –1)

5 Copy and complete the table below to give the co-ordinates of three points of your choosing in each of the quadrants.

	First quadrant	Second quadrant	Third quadrant	Fourth quadrant
3 points in each quadrant				

6 Give the co-ordinates of 10 points on the x-axis. What do all of these points have in common?

7 Give the co-ordinates of 10 points on the y-axis. What do all of these points have in common?

8 Use the co-ordinate plane to discover the following phrases/sentences.

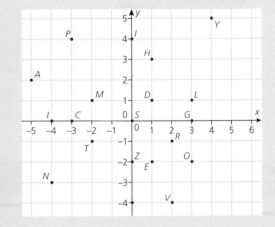

(i) (1, 3) (–5, 2) (–3, 4) (–3, 4) (4, 5) (1, –2) (–4, –3) (1, 1) (–4, 0) (–4, –3) (3, 0)

(ii) (–4, 0) (3, 1) (3, –2) (2, –4) (1, –2) (–2, 1) (–5, 2) (–2, –1) (1, 3) (0, 0)

(iii) (0, 0) (1, –2) (–4, 0) (0, –2) (1, –2) (–2, –1) (1, 3) (1, –2) (1, 1) (–5, 2) (4, 5)

(iv) (–3, 0) (–5, 2) (2, –1) (–3, 4) (1, –2) (1, 1) (–4, 0) (1, –2) (–2, 1)

9 (i) Copy the co-ordinate plane into your copybook. Mark in the co-ordinates of points A, B, C, D and E.

(ii) Copy and complete the table below by writing down the co-ordinates of each point described.

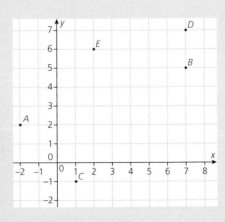

Description	Co-ordinates
The point of intersection of lines through AE and EB	
The vertex of the angle ACB	
Two points on the same line as points A and B	
The point F, which is half-way between D and B	

10 An archaeologist has discovered various items at a site.
The site is laid out in a grid and the position of each item
is shown on the grid. The items found are a brooch (B),
a plate (P), a ring (R), a statue (S) and a tile (T).

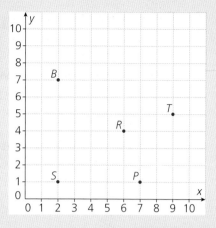

(a) Write down the co-ordinates of the position of
each item.

(b) Each square of the grid represents 1 m².
Find the total area of the grid.

(c) Which of the items is nearest to the tile (T)?

(d) Find the distance between the brooch (B) and
the statue (S).

11 The diagram below shows a map of Ireland on a co-ordinate grid. Each unit on the grid
measures 1 cm. The point B represents Bantry and the point H represents Howth.

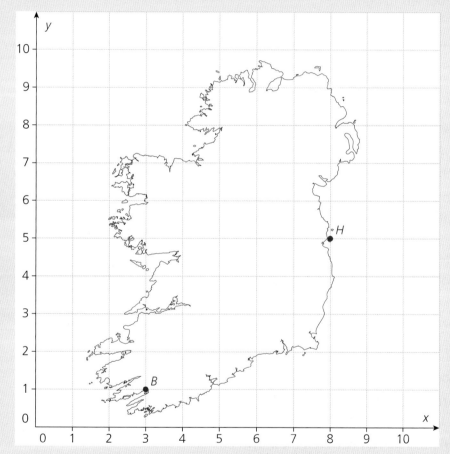

(a) Write down the coordinates of the points B and H.

(b) The distance from Dublin to Galway **on the diagram** is 4 cm. The **actual** distance
from Dublin to Galway is 180 km. Work out how many kilometres each centimetre on
the grid represents.

(c) Use your ruler to measure in centimetres the straight-line distance between
Wicklow (8, 4) and Westport (3, 6). What is this distance in reality?

Section 9B **The Slope of a Line**

You are familiar with the word 'slope'. There are lots of slopes on hills. If you do some hill-walking you will know that the slope of the ground can make it hard to make progress.

Look at these pictures of slopes:

- Going **uphill** from **left to right** (Always read from *left to right.*)

| no slope | gentle uphill slope | steeper slope | very steep slope | mega-steep! |

- Going downhill from left to right:

| no slope | gentle downhill slope | steeper slope | very steep slope | hang on! |

Describing these slopes like this is all very well, but we need to be much more precise:

- Ramps for wheelchairs have to be very carefully made with the correct **slope**.

- Engineers need to know that pipes are laid at exactly the right **slope** to carry water and waste away from a building.

- The Roman aqueducts were very important in carrying water to the cities and towns. Aqueducts moved water using gravity alone, along a slight downward gradient ('gradient' is another word for slope).

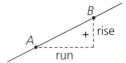

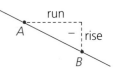

How do we measure the slope of a line?

- We take **any two points** on the line.
- We measure the **rise** between these two points, reading from left to right.
- We measure the horizontal **run** between these two points.
- We define slope as $\frac{\text{rise}}{\text{run}}$.
- If the line is downhill from left to right, we take the rise as negative.

Connections

The work we did on fractions, decimals and percentages will be very useful in understanding slopes.

In the first diagram, the line:

- **rises** by 1 square
- for a **run** of 2 squares between points *P* and *Q*.

We put $\frac{\text{rise}}{\text{run}}$ and so this line has slope = $\frac{1}{2}$.

This is a **positive slope**.

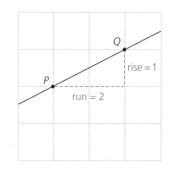

In the second diagram:

- the **rise** = –2
- for a **run** of 3 squares between points *T* and *U*.

We put $\frac{\text{rise}}{\text{run}}$ and so this line has slope = $-\frac{2}{3}$.

This is a **negative slope**.

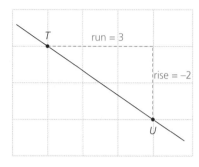

Example 1

These are the uphill slopes we described in words before.
Use the squares to find their slopes exactly.

(i)  (ii)  (iii) (iv) (v)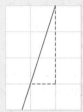

Solution

(i) rise = 0; run = 3. Slope = $\frac{\text{rise}}{\text{run}} = \frac{0}{3} = 0$ (iv) rise = 2; run = 2. Slope = $\frac{\text{rise}}{\text{run}} = \frac{2}{2} = 1$

(ii) rise = 1; run = 3. Slope = $\frac{\text{rise}}{\text{run}} = \frac{1}{3}$ (v) rise = 3; run = 1. Slope = $\frac{\text{rise}}{\text{run}} = \frac{3}{1} = 3$

(iii) rise = 1; run = 2. Slope = $\frac{\text{rise}}{\text{run}} = \frac{1}{2}$

Example 2

These are the downhill slopes we described in words before.
Use the squares to find their slopes exactly.

(i) (ii) 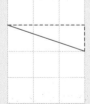 (iii) (iv) 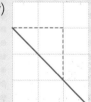 (v)

Solution

(i) rise = 0; run = 3. Slope = $\frac{\text{rise}}{\text{run}} = \frac{0}{3} = 0$

(ii) rise = −1; run = 3. Slope = $\frac{\text{rise}}{\text{run}} = -\frac{1}{3}$

(iii) rise = −1; run = 2. Slope = $\frac{\text{rise}}{\text{run}} = -\frac{1}{2}$

(iv) rise = −2; run = 2.
Slope = $\frac{\text{rise}}{\text{run}} = -\frac{2}{2} = -1$

(v) rise = −3; run = 1.
Slope = $\frac{\text{rise}}{\text{run}} = -\frac{3}{1} = -3$

Remember you can use any two points on the line to measure the slope.

 Key Point

Slopes are usually given as a fraction but you may see slopes as percentages or ratios.
So, for example, a slope of 20% would be the same as a slope of $\frac{20}{100}$ or $\frac{1}{5}$ or 1 : 5.

 Key Point

We cannot measure the slope of a vertical line.
This is because the run = 0 for a vertical line. When we put $\frac{\text{rise}}{\text{run}}$ we would have to divide by zero, which we cannot do.
So we say that the **slope of a vertical line is undefined**.

run = 0

Activity 9.2

1 Find the slopes of the following line segments:

(i)   (ii) 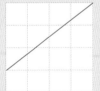 (iii) 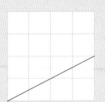 (iv)

2 Find the slopes of the following line segments:

(i)  (ii) 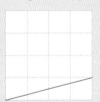 (iii)  (iv)

3 Find the slopes of the following line segments:

(i)   (ii)   (iii) 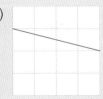 (iv)

4 Find the slopes of the lines *AB* and *CD*.

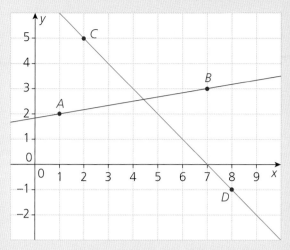

5 Find the slopes of the lines *EF* and *GH*.

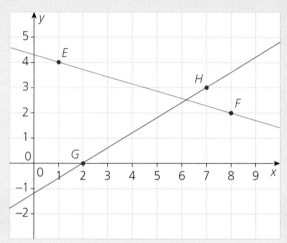

6 Find the slopes of the lines *PQ* and *RS*.

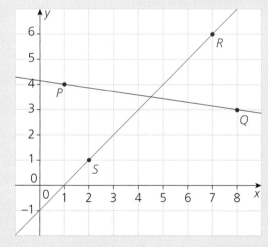

7 Use squared paper to draw lines with the following slopes.

(i) $\frac{1}{2}$ (ii) $\frac{3}{5}$ (iii) $-\frac{2}{3}$ (iv) 0

8 (i) Find the slopes of the lines *l*, *m* and *n*.

(ii) What do you notice about the slopes of *l* and *m*?

(iii) What is the relationship between lines *l* and *m*?

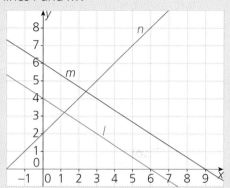

9 Use squared paper to draw lines with the following slopes.

(i) $-\frac{1}{6}$ (iii) undefined slope

(ii) $\frac{1}{4}$ (iv) 25%

10 This road sign indicates a slope of 10%.

(i) Express this slope as a fraction.

(ii) Use squared paper to show a line with slope 10%.

(iii) How would you describe the slope of this road: not very steep; quite steep; very steep?

11 This road sign gives the slope of a road.

(i) Express this slope as a fraction.

(ii) Use squared paper to show a line with a downward slope of 25%.

(iii) Why do you think the lower sign says 'Low gear now'?

12 (Work in pairs on this activity.)

(i) Use your mathematics equipment to measure the slope of the ramp at the entrance to your school. Express your answer as (a) a fraction; (b) a percentage.

(ii) Give a reason why the slope of the ramp is important.

13 The slope of a roof is often referred to as the 'pitch' of the roof.

Find the pitch of the roof of this house as a fraction.

14 Four lines *m*, *n*, *p* and *s* in the co-ordinate plane are shown in the diagram.

The slopes of the lines are in the table below.

Copy and complete the table, matching the lines to their slopes.

Slope	Line
2	
$\frac{1}{5}$	
0	
$-\frac{1}{4}$	

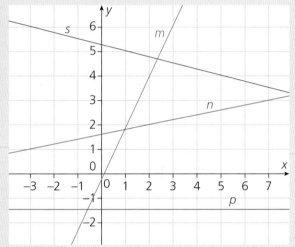

Revision Activity 9

1 Write down the co-ordinates of the points *A* to *N* in the following co-ordinate plane:

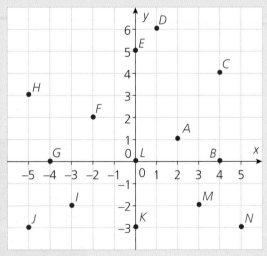

2 Plot each of the following points on a co-ordinate plane:

$A(-1, 3)$, $B(-3, 0)$, $C(-2, -2)$, $D(0, 3)$, $E(1, 4)$, $F(3, 2)$, $G(2, 3)$, $H(3, 0)$, $J(2, -2)$, $K(1, -4)$, $L(0, -4)$.

3 Find the slopes of these line segments:

(a)
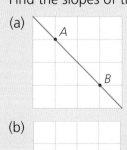

(b)
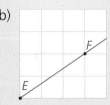

(c)
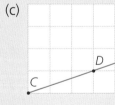

(d)
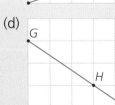

4 The diagram shows six points on the co-ordinate plane.

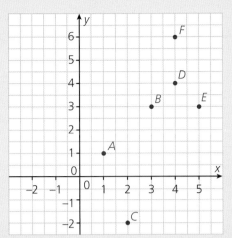

Write down the co-ordinates of each point described in the table below:

Description	Co-ordinates
The point E	
The point of intersection of DA and DE	
The vertex of the angle CAB	
A point on the same line as A and D	

Exam-style Question

1 A computer game shows the location of four flowers A(1, 7), B(1, 2), C(6, 2) and D(5, 6) on the grid. The object of the game is to collect all the nectar from the flowers in the shortest time.

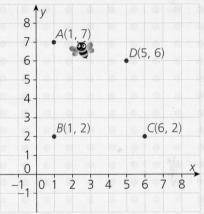

(i) A bee found a hidden flower half way between flower B and flower D. Find the co-ordinates of this hidden flower.

(ii) Another flower E can be located by completing the square ABCE. Write down the co-ordinates of the point E.

(iii) Bee 1 and Bee 2 are on flower A. Bee 1 flies directly from flower A to B and then on to C. Bee 2 flies from flower A directly to D and then on to C. Write down which bee has travelled the shortest total distance. Give a reason for your answer.

2014 Sample JCOL

KEY WORDS AND PHRASES

- Plane
- Co-ordinates
- x-axis
- y-axis
- Couple
- Ordered pair
- Quadrant

Interactive Tool 9.1

Chapter Summary 9

- In co-ordinate geometry, we name points in the plane by making couples from the *x*-axis and the *y*-axis.

- The plane is divided into four quadrants.

- The slope of a line = $\frac{\text{rise}}{\text{run}}$.

- The order in a couple matters. We agree to have the *x*-value in the pair first and the *y*-value second. Thus, for example, (2, 3) and (3, 2) are different points.

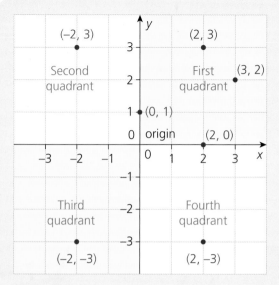

Transformation Geometry

Learning Intentions

In this chapter, you will learn about:

- Recognising images of points and objects under:
  - Central symmetry
  - Axial symmetry
  - Translations
  - Rotations
- Locating axes of symmetry and centres of symmetry in simple shapes

LO: GT.6, U.5, U.6, U.13

In this chapter, we will be introducing the mathematics that describes the mapping or 'movement' of points and objects from one position in the plane to another position. This is known as **transformation geometry**.

The word transform means 'change'. In geometry, when a 'transformation' occurs, the position of an object in the plane is changed from one place to another within the same plane.

We meet geometric transformations in everyday life. In fact, every time you look into a mirror you are seeing an **image** of yourself.

There are four transformations which we will be studying:

- Axial symmetry
- Central symmetry
- Translations
- Rotations

Section 10A Axial Symmetry

An object has 'symmetry' when it is made up of exactly similar parts facing each other.

Axial symmetry is the same as reflection in a mirror or a lake.

The word 'axis' is used to describe the 'mirror line'.

Object

axis

Image

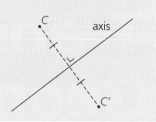

Key Points

To construct the image of a point by axial symmetry:
The point moves in a direction **perpendicular** to the axis until it reaches the axis and then it moves across the other side by **the same distance**.
Think of the axis as if it were a mirror.
In this diagram, point C can be referred to as the **object**.
Then C′ is known as the **image** of point C.

To find the image of a point under reflection in a line, we can use a set-square and compass. This construction is on the Higher Level course only. In this chapter we will find the images by drawing the objects on squared paper.

To construct the image of an object by axial symmetry:

- Pick all the points which define its shape.
- Reflect each point in the axis.
- Join up the corresponding (matching) image points to make the object's image.
- If a point is on the axis, then it is its own image.

Example 1

Draw the image of the F-shape under axial symmetry in the axis shown.

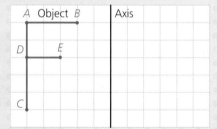

Solution

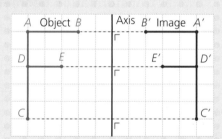

Note

Note that by axial symmetry:

> The object is 'flipped over'.
> The image is the same shape and size as the object, but back-to-front.

Axes of Symmetry

Some shapes are mapped onto themselves by axial symmetry in a line. In these cases the line is called an **axis of symmetry** of the shape.

As you can see, different shapes or objects can have more than one axis of symmetry.
Some shapes have no axes of symmetry, such as the letter G.

Example 2

Sketch each of the following capital letters. Draw the axis/axes of symmetry for each letter, if it has any.

(i) **B**   (ii) **P**   (iii) **H**

Solution

(i) --B--   B has 1 axis of symmetry.

(ii) P   P has no axes of symmetry.

(iii) -H-   H has 2 axes of symmetry.

Activity 10.1

1 (i) Copy the diagram into your copybook. Fill in the co-ordinates of points *P* and *Q* on your diagram.

(ii) Draw *P′* and *Q′*, the images of points *P* and *Q*, under axial symmetry in the *x*-axis.

(iii) Write the co-ordinates of *P′* and *Q′* on your diagram.

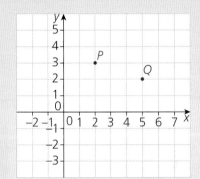

2 (i) Copy the triangle *ABC* onto squared paper and construct its image under axial symmetry in the *x*-axis.

(ii) Copy and complete the table below by writing down the co-ordinates of each point from part (i).

Object △ABC	A(,)	B(,)	C(,)
Image △A′B′C′	A′(,)	B′(,)	C′(,)

(iii) What do you notice about the co-ordinates of the vertices of the object compared with the co-ordinates of the vertices of its image?

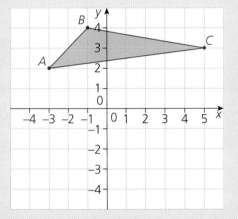

3 (i) Copy the triangle *MNQ* onto squared paper and construct its image under axial symmetry in the *y*-axis.

(ii) Copy and complete the table below by writing down the co-ordinates of each point from part (i).

Object △MNQ	M(,)	N(,)	Q(,)
Image △M′N′Q′	M′(,)	N′(,)	Q′(,)

(iii) What do you notice about the co-ordinates of the vertices of the object compared with the co-ordinates of the vertices of its image?

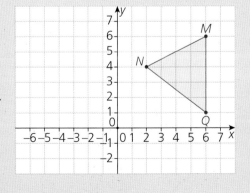

4 The diagram shows the letter F on the co-ordinate plane.

(i) Copy the diagram and draw in the image of the letter F under an axial symmetry in the *y*-axis.

(ii) Write down the co-ordinates of points *B* and *C*.

(iii) *A*, *B* and *C* are mapped onto *A′*, *B′* and *C′* under the transformation above. Write down the co-ordinates of *A′*, *B′* and *C′*.

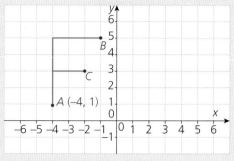

5 Copy (i) the rectangle and (ii) the square and draw in the axes of symmetry on each.

(i)

(ii)

6 How many axes of symmetry do these flags have?

(i)

(iii)

(v)

(ii)

(iv)

(vi)

7 Identify which of these capital letters have no axis of symmetry.

A B C D E F G H I J K L M N O P Q R S T U V W X Y Z

8 On squared paper, draw a shape that has:

(i) one axis of symmetry

(iii) three axes of symmetry

(ii) two axes of symmetry

(iv) four axes of symmetry.

9 The shape here is called a parallelogram because its opposite sides are parallel. None of the angles in this parallelogram is a right angle.

Draw a similar one and cut it out. Then by folding along, show that it has **no axes of symmetry**.

10 Draw a sketch of the image of each of these shapes under axial symmetry in the given axis.

(i)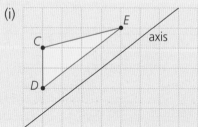

(ii)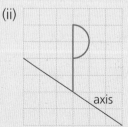

Section 10B Central Symmetry

A **central symmetry** in a point M is a transformation where each point in the plane moves to M and then out the other side the **same distance** and in the **same direction**.

Key Points

To construct the image of a point P under central symmetry in the point M:

1. Join P to M and extend the line segment $[PM]$.
2. Place the point of your compass at M and the pencil at P.
3. Swing the compass around so that the pencil cuts an arc on the line PM at P'. Then P' is the image of P by central symmetry in the point M.

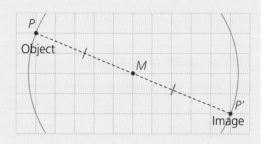

Example

Construct the image of the F-shape under central symmetry in the point O.

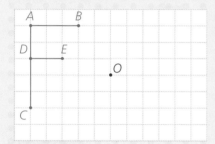

- Make sure that each point in the plane moves to O and then out the other side the **same distance** and in the **same direction**.
- Join up the corresponding points to make the image.
- The point O would be its own image.

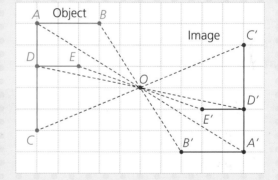

Solution

To construct the image of an object by central symmetry in a point O:

- Choose all the main points which define its shape.
- Reflect them in the point O.

Note

By central symmetry:

› The object is 'flipped over' and turned upside down.

› The image is the same shape and size as the object.

› The image of a line under central symmetry is a parallel line.

Centre of Symmetry

Some shapes are mapped onto themselves under central symmetry in a point.

If you were to draw the image of the capital letter H under central symmetry in the point P, you would find that you have the same shape that you started with.

The point P is called the **centre of symmetry** of the shape.

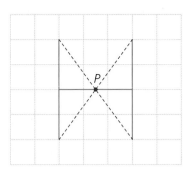

Test for Centre of Symmetry

To find out if an object has a centre of symmetry:

- Choose a point which you think is the centre of symmetry.
- Rotate the object around this point by 180 degrees.
- If the image after rotating is identical to the object, then the object has a centre of symmetry.

For example:

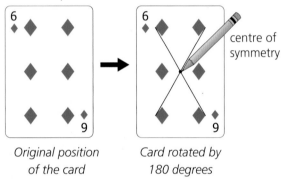

Original position of the card *Card rotated by 180 degrees*

Another example:

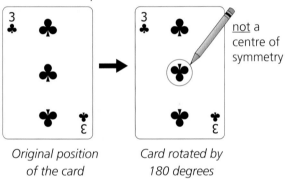

Original position of the card *Card rotated by 180 degrees*

The image is identical to the object when the card is rotated by 180 degrees, so this card **has a centre of symmetry**.

The image is not identical to the object when the card is rotated by 180 degrees, so this card **does not** have a centre of symmetry.

Activity 10.2

1 (i) Copy the diagram below into your copybook. Use your ruler and compass to draw the image of the line segment [*MN*] under central symmetry in the point *C*.

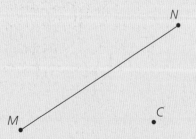

(ii) Label the image [*M′N′*]. What is the relationship between the lines *MN* and *M′N′*?

2 (i) Use your ruler and compass to draw the image of the line segment [*RS*] under central symmetry in the point *P*.

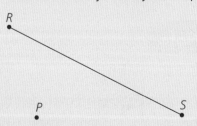

(ii) Label the image [*R′S′*]. What is the relationship between lines *RS* and *R′S′*?

3 Use your ruler and compass to draw the image of the triangle *ABC* under central symmetry in the point *Q*.

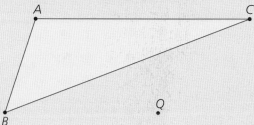

4 Identify the correct image of each object under central symmetry in the point *A*.

(i)

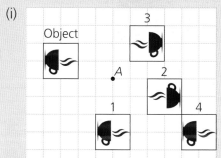

(ii)

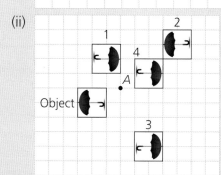

(iii)

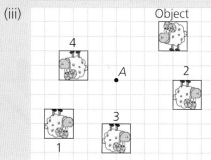

(iv)

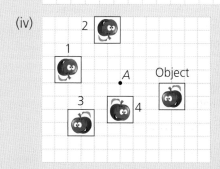

5 Copy each of the following onto squared paper and draw the image of each object under central symmetry in the point *P*:

(i)

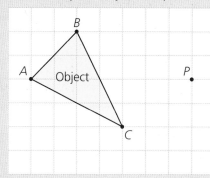

(ii)

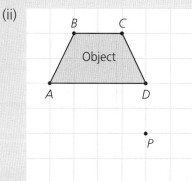

(iii)

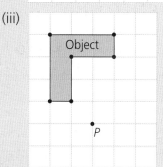

6 (i) Copy the diagram below on a co-ordinate plane.

(ii) Fill in the co-ordinates of points *A*, *B* and *C*.

(iii) Draw *A′B′C′*, the image of △*ABC* under central symmetry in the point *P*.

(iv) Fill in the co-ordinates of *A′*, *B′* and *C′* on your diagram.

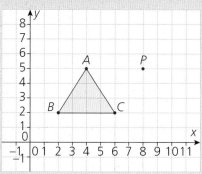

7 Use your ruler and compass to draw the image of the letter A under central symmetry in the point *R*.

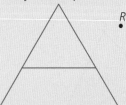

8 (i) Copy the diagram on a co-ordinate plane.

   (ii) Fill in the co-ordinates of points *M, N* and *Q*.

   (iii) Draw △*M′N′Q′*, the image of △*MNQ* under central symmetry in the point *O* (the origin).

   (iv) Fill in the co-ordinates of *M′, N′* and *Q′* on your diagram.

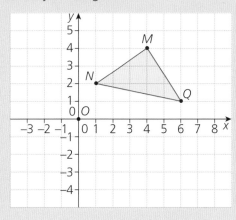

9 (i) Name the following playing cards.

   (ii) State which of the cards has a centre of symmetry.

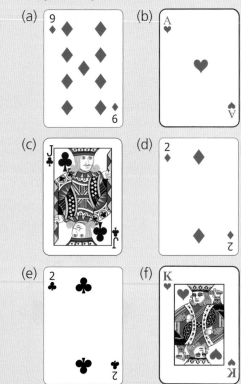

10 List the capital letters that have a centre of symmetry.

A B C D E F G
H I J K L M N
O P Q R S T U
V W X Y Z

Section 10C Translations

When you translate a word from one language to another, you 'carry across' the word into another language without changing its meaning.

An escalator carries everybody the same distance in the same direction without changing them in any way.

In geometry, a **translation** carries an object from one position in the plane to another position without changing it in any way.

The **direction** is indicated by an arrow on a line segment.
The **distance** is indicated by the length of the line segment.

The translation shown is called translation $\overrightarrow{AB}$.

It moves a point 6 units to the right and 2 units up.

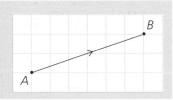

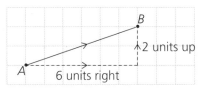

Under the translation $\overrightarrow{AB}$, every point in the plane moves 6 units to the right and 2 units up.

The diagram shows the image of three other points in the plane and their images under the translation $\overrightarrow{AB}$.

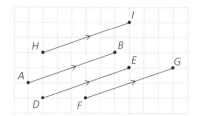

Example

(i) Describe the translation $\overrightarrow{PQ}$ in the diagram.

(ii) Draw the image of the F-shape under the translation $\overrightarrow{PQ}$.

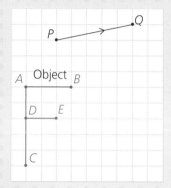

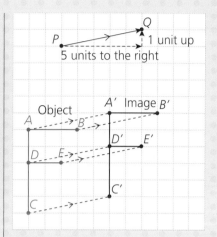

Notice that the image is the same size as the object and **faces the same way**. Only its position has changed.

Solution

(i) The translation $\overrightarrow{PQ}$ moves every point 5 units to the right and 1 unit up.

(ii) The points A, B, C, D and E all move in this direction and this distance.

The **orientation** of an object after a transformation is the relative direction in which it is facing.

See how these three transformations change the orientation of an object:

> **Key Point**
>
> You can also find the image of an object under a translation using your geometry instruments. This involves using your ruler and a set-square together to draw a line parallel to another line. The construction of this is done in Chapter 16.

Axial symmetry (back-to-front)	Central symmetry (upside down and back-to-front)	Translation (no change in orientation)

1 Identify the correct image for each of the following objects under the given translation.

(i)

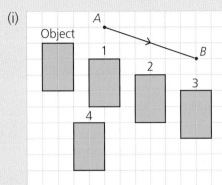

(ii)

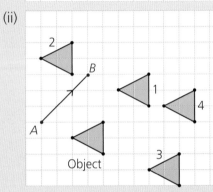

2 Describe the translations that map each shaded shape onto its image using the words up, down, left and right in relation to the squared grid.

For example, **a** maps to **b** by moving 4 units down and 7 units to the right.

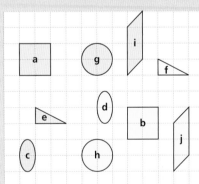

3 (i) Copy the diagram and fill in the co-ordinates of the points *A* and *B*.

(ii) Draw [*A′B′*], the image of [*AB*] under the translation $\overrightarrow{PQ}$.

(iii) Fill in the co-ordinates of *A′* and *B′*.

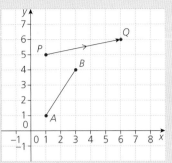

4 (i) Copy the diagram into your copybook and fill in the co-ordinates of points *D*, *E* and *F*.

(ii) Draw *D′E′F′*, the image of triangle *DEF* under the translation $\overrightarrow{PQ}$.

(iii) Fill in the co-ordinates of *D′*, *E′* and *F′*.

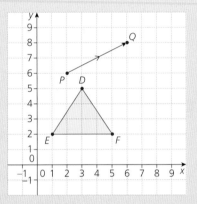

5 (i) Copy the diagram into your copybook.

(ii) Write down the co-ordinates of points *A*, *B* and *C*.

(iii) Draw *A′B′C′*, the image of triangle *ABC* under the translation $\overrightarrow{MN}$.

(iv) Write down the co-ordinates of *A′*, *B′* and *C′*.

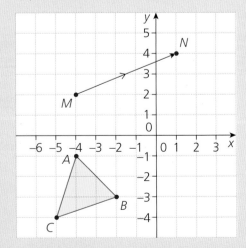

6 (i) Copy the diagram into your copybook.

(ii) Write down the co-ordinates of points *A*, *B* and *C*.

(iii) Draw *A'B'C'*, the image of triangle *ABC* under the translation $\overrightarrow{EF}$.

(iv) Write down the co-ordinates of *A'*, *B'* and *C'*.

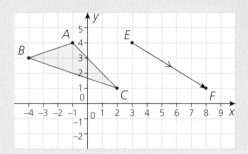

Section 10D Rotations

To **rotate** means to move in a circle around (about) a point.

This diagram shows a triangle *ABC* and its image, *A'B'C'*, by an **anti-clockwise** rotation of **90°** about a **point O**.

Notice that every point of the triangle *ABC* turns through the same angle (90° in this case).

This means that $|\angle AOA'| = 90°$,
$|\angle BOB'| = 90°$ and
$|\angle COC'| = 90°$.

The diagram below right shows a rectangle *ABCD* and its image, *A'B'C'D'*, by a **clockwise** rotation of **90°** about a **point O**.

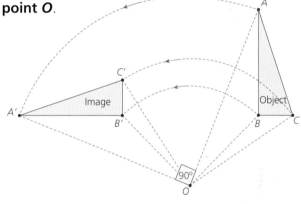

 Key Points

When we want to describe a rotation, we must name three things:

- The **centre of rotation**
- The **angle turned**
- The **direction** (clockwise or anti-clockwise).

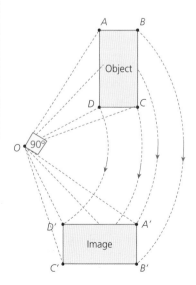

Note

We can see from the examples here that a rotation of a shape does not change the length of its sides, its area, or the size of any angles.

Example 1

Draw the image of the point *P* by a rotation of 60°
anti-clockwise about the point *A*.

Solution

- Draw a line joining *A* to *P*.
- With your compass point at *A* and radius = |*AP*|, draw a part of a circle.
- Use a protractor to draw an angle of 60° at point *A* to meet the part-circle at *P'*.
- *P'* is then the required image of *P*.

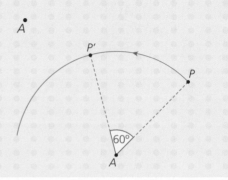

Example 2

Draw the image of the line segment [*CD*] by a rotation of 90° **clockwise** about the point *R*.

Solution

- Construct *C'*, the image of the point *C* by a rotation clockwise of 90° about *R*.

- Construct *D'*, the image of the point *D* by a rotation clockwise of 90° about *R*.
- Join *C'* to *D'*. [*C'D'*] is the required image.

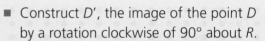

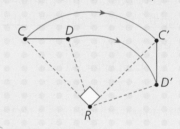

Example 3

(i) Draw the triangle *A*(0, 0), *B*(3, 4) and *C*(4, 2) on a co-ordinate plane.

(ii) Draw *A'B'C'*, the image of the triangle *ABC* by a rotation of 90° **anti-clockwise** about *A*.

(iii) Write down the co-ordinates *A'*, *B'* and *C'*.

Solution

(i) and (ii)

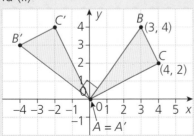

- Construct *B'*, the image of the point *B* by a rotation anti-clockwise of 90° about *A*.

- Construct *C'*, the image of the point *C* by a rotation anti-clockwise of 90° about *A*.

- *A* is its own image.

- Join *A'B'C'* to form the required triangle.

(iii) *A'* = *A* = (0, 0), *B'* = (–4, 3) and *C'* = (–2, 4).

For each of these activities, copy the given diagrams into your copybook and then draw the required images.

1 Draw the image of the point *P* by a rotation of 50° anti-clockwise about the point *O*.

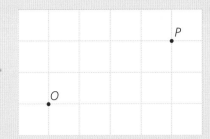

2 Draw the image of the point *Q* by a rotation of 60° clockwise about the point *O*.

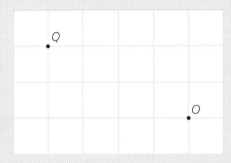

3 Draw the image of the point *Q* by a rotation of 120° clockwise about the point *O*.

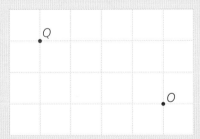

4 Draw the image of the line segment [*CD*] by a rotation of 90° clockwise about the point *R*.

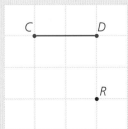

5 (i) Draw the shape below on a co-ordinate plane.

   (ii) Fill in the co-ordinates of *A*, *B* and *C* on your diagram.

   (iii) Draw the image of the L-shape by a rotation of 90° anti-clockwise about the point *O*.

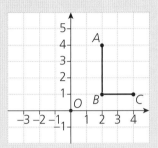

6 (i) Draw the triangle *ABC* as shown on a co-ordinate plane.

   (ii) Fill in the co-ordinates of *A*, *B* and *C*.

   (iii) Draw *A'B'C'*, the image of the triangle *ABC* by a rotation of 90° anti-clockwise about the point *O*.

   (iv) Fill in the co-ordinates of *A'*, *B'* and *C'* on your diagram.

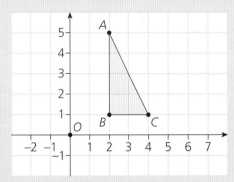

7 (i) Draw the triangle formed by the co-ordinates *A*(0, 0), *B*(2, 4) and *C*(3, 3) on a co-ordinate plane.

   (ii) Draw *A'B'C'*, the image of the triangle *ABC* by a rotation of 90° anti-clockwise about *A*.

   (iii) Write down the co-ordinates *A'*, *B'* and *C'*.

Transformation Geometry

1 A, B and C are images of the object under a transformation (translation, central symmetry, axial symmetry or rotation).

State what the transformation is for each image.

	Object	Image A	Image B	Image C
(a)				
(b)				
(c)				

2 (a) Copy the co-ordinate plane and plot the points A(1, 1), B(5, 1) and C(3, 6).

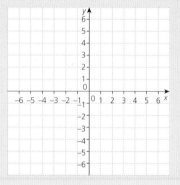

(b) Join the three points to form a triangle.

(c) On your diagram, draw the axis of symmetry of the triangle.

(d) On your diagram, draw the image of the triangle under an axial symmetry in the x-axis.

3 On squared paper, draw a co-ordinate plane showing values from –5 to 5 on both axes.

(a) On the graph, plot the following points: A(4, 1), B(1, 4) and C(2, 1). Join the points to form a triangle.

(b) On the same axes, draw the image of triangle ABC under the following transformations:

- Axial symmetry in the x-axis
- Central symmetry through the origin (0, 0)
- Axial symmetry in the y-axis.

4 A, B and C are images of the object under a transformation (translation, central symmetry, axial symmetry or rotation).

State what the transformation is for each image.

	Object	Image A	Image B	Image C
(a)				
(b)				
(c)				

5 Each of the three figures labelled A, B and C in the box is the image of the figure shown in the box on the left under a transformation. For each of A, B and C, state what the transformation is (translation, central symmetry, axial symmetry or rotation) and in the case of rotation, state the angle of rotation.

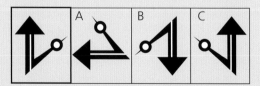

Exam-style Question

1 The diagram shows a triangle *A* on the co-ordinate plane and its image under a number of transformations.

Write down the co-ordinates of the vertices of the images of *A* under each of the transformations listed below.

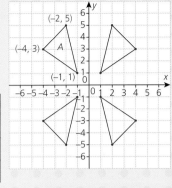

Transformation	Co-ordinates of vertices
Axial symmetry in the *y*-axis	(,), (,), (,)
Central symmetry in the point (0, 0)	
Axial symmetry in the *x*-axis	

JCOL 2011 Paper 2

KEY WORDS AND PHRASES

- **Transformation**
- **Axial symmetry**
- **Axis of symmetry**
- **Object**
- **Image**
- **Central symmetry**

- **Centre of symmetry**
- **Translation**
- **Rotation**
- **Map**
- **Symmetrical**

Chapter Summary 10

■ **Axial symmetry**

The axial symmetry of an image is its reflection of that image in a line. It is also known as a mirror reflection.

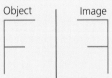

■ **Axis of symmetry**

The axis of symmetry of a shape is the line that divides the shape into two symmetrical parts, such that each part is the mirror image of the other.

■ **Translation**

A translation moves every point in the object the **same distance** in the **same direction**.

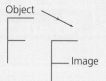

■ **Central symmetry**

Central symmetry is the reflection of an object through a point.

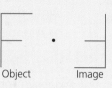

■ Some shapes are mapped onto themselves under central symmetry in a point. The point *P* is called the **centre of symmetry** of the shape.

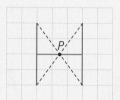

■ **Rotations**

When we want to describe a rotation, we must name three things:

- ■ The **centre of rotation**
- ■ The **angle turned**
- ■ The **direction** (clockwise or anti-clockwise).

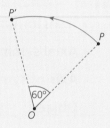

Applied Measure

Learning Intentions

In this chapter, you will learn about:

- Measure and time
- Finding the perimeter and area of rectangles, squares and figures made from combinations of these
- The nets of rectangular objects or solids
- The surface area of rectangular objects or solids

LO: GT.1, GT.2(b), U.5, U.6, U.13

Section 11A Time

Ever since humans first noticed the regular movement of the Sun and the stars, we have wondered about the passage of time. Down the centuries, time has been measured using sundials, oil lamps, water clocks and many other devices. Today we rely on atomic clocks for our most accurate time measurement.

There are two main ways to show the time: by using the '24-hour clock' or the 'am/pm' system.

- **24-hour clock** – The time is shown as how many hours and minutes have passed since midnight.
- **am/pm or 12-hour clock** – The day is split into the 12 hours running from midnight to noon (the 'am' hours) and the other 12 hours running from noon to midnight (the 'pm' hours).
  'am' stands for *ante meridiem* (Latin for 'before midday') and 'pm' stands for *post meridiem* ('after midday').

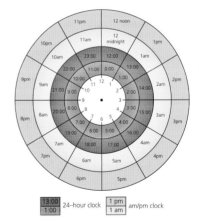

Example 1

How many seconds are there in 6 hours?

Solution

- 1 hour = 60 minutes
  6 × 1 hour = 6 × 60 minutes
  = 360 minutes

- 1 minute = 60 seconds
  360 × 1 minute = 360 × 60 seconds
  = 21 600 seconds

So, there are 21 600 seconds in 6 hours.

Example 2

A movie starts at 14.15 and ends at 16.08. What is the running time of the movie?

Solution

Method 1

End time	16.08
Start time	– 14.15

As the minutes to be subtracted are greater, we need to borrow 60 minutes from 16 hours.

So 16.08 changes to 15.68.

End time	15.68
Start time	– 14.15
	1.53

Running time is 1 hour and 53 minutes.

Method 2

Use the calculator:

Press 16 ⏺ 08 ⏺ – 14 ⏺ 15 ⏺

Answer that appears is 1°53'0"

We read this as 1 hour and 53 minutes.

Example 3

The following is an extract from a train timetable.

DUBLIN Connolly 🄻 🄰	Dep	07.35	09.35	11.00	13.20
Drogheda MacBride	Dep	08.08	10.06	11.36	13.50
Dundalk Clarke	Dep	08.30	10.30	11.58	14.15
Newry	Dep	08.48	10.48	12.16	14.33
Portadown	Dep	09.09	11.09	12.37	14.56
Lurgan	Dep	. . .	. . .	. . .	. . .
Lisburn	Dep	. . .	11.33	. . .	15.22
BELFAST Central	Arr	09.45	11.50	13.15	15.35

 (i) How long does the 07.35 train take to get to Belfast Central?

 (ii) How long does it take the train that leaves Dublin at 13.20 to get from Newry to Lisburn?

(iii) If Susan gets the 07.35 train from Dublin to Dundalk and then walks for 15 minutes to work, how long does it take her to get to work?

(iv) If Adam arrives at Newry train station at 2.10 pm, how long will he have to wait for the next train?

Solution

(i) 07.35 train from Dublin to Belfast:

Arrival time (Belfast)	09.45
Departure time (Dublin)	– 07.35
	2.10

Therefore the train will take 2 hours and 10 minutes.

(ii)

Arrival time (Lisburn)	15.22
Departure time (Newry)	– 14.33

Use the calculator:

Press 15 ⏺ 22 ⏺ – 14 ⏺ 33 ⏺ .

Answer that appears is 0°49'0"

We read this as 0 hours, 49 minutes.

(iii) 7.35 train from Dublin to Dundalk:

Arrival time (Dundalk)   08.30

Departure time (Dublin)   07.35

Subtract these times using a calculator:

Press 8 🔲 30 🔲 – 7 🔲 35 🔲 .

Answer that appears is 0°55'0"

We read this as 0 hours and 55 minutes.

Add on 15 minutes walking time.

Therefore it will take Susan 1 hour and 10 minutes to get to work.

(iv) Adam arrives at Newry train station at 2.10 pm. Convert 2.10 pm to the 24-hour clock by adding 12 hours = 14.10.

Departure time of the next train	14.33
Arrival time (Newry train station)	– 14.10
	0.23

Therefore, Adam will have to wait 23 minutes for the next train.

Activity 11.1

1 Express each of the following in 24-hour clock time.

(i) 4.30 pm
(ii) 2.45 am
(iii) 8.15 pm
(iv) 12.20 am

(v) 9.25 pm
(vi) 1.46 am
(vii) 11.55 pm
(viii) 10.59 am

2 Convert the following 24-hour clock times to am/pm times.

(i) 13.25
(ii) 06.40
(iii) 11.30
(iv) 17.50

(v) 08.15
(vi) 23.45
(vii) 00.10
(viii) 6.29

3 Express the following times in minutes:

(i) 2 hours 20 min
(ii) $\frac{1}{2}$ an hour
(iii) 0.75 hours
(iv) 2.2 hours

(v) 3 hours 55 min
(vi) $\frac{1}{6}$ of an hour
(vii) 1.4 hours
(viii) 2.5 hours

4 Paul is starting a new part-time job. He works on Thursdays from 6.30 pm to 9.00 pm. On Saturdays, his hours are from 10.30 am to 1 pm, and 2.30 pm to 5.30 pm. Paul gets paid €9.50 per hour.

(i) How many hours does Paul work in a week?

(ii) What is Paul's pay for the week?

5 The following is an extract from an Irish Rail timetable on the Dublin to Sligo route.

DUBLIN Connolly Ⓛ Ⓐ	Dep	08.00	11.05	13.05	15.05	16.00	17.05	17.15	18.05	19.05
Drumcondra	Dep	...	...	...	...	16.05	...	17.19	...	...
Maynooth	Dep	08.30	11.36	13.35	15.3 5	16.29	17.34	17.58	18.35	19.37
Kilcock	Dep	08.36	11.42	13.41	15.41	16.35	17.40	18.06	18.41	19.43
Enfield	Dep	08.45	11.51	13.51	15.50	16.44	17.50	18.16	18.50	19.53
Mullingar	Dep	09.10	12.16	14.16	16.15	17.15	18.15	18.44	19.19	20.23
Edgeworthstown	Dep	09.30	12.36	14.34	16.35	17.33	18.34	19.04	19.39	20.41
LONGFORD	Dep	09.42	12.47	14.45	16.46	17.45	18.46	19.16	19.50	20.52
Dromod	Dep	10.00	12.59	14.57	16.58	17.59	19.01	...	...	21.04
Carrick-on-Shannon	Dep	10.16	13.14	15.13	17.13	18.15	19.18	...	...	21.21
Boyle	Dep	10.28	13.34	15.34	17.27	18.34	19.31	...	...	21.33
Ballymote	Dep	10.43	13.49	15.49	17.42	18.49	19.46	...	...	21.48
Collooney	Dep	10.52	13.59	15.59	17.51	18.58	19.55	...	...	21.58
SLIGO MacDiarmada	Arr	11.09	14.10	16.10	18.06	19.09	20.06	...	...	22.09

(i) Calculate the journey time for each train from Dublin to Sligo.

(ii) How many trains arrive in Ballymote after 3 pm?

(iii) How many trains depart from Maynooth before 10 am?

(iv) If John arrives at the train station in Dublin Connolly at 1.55 pm, how long will he have to wait until the next train to Sligo?

(v) It takes John 20 minutes to walk from his house to the train station in Maynooth. He has to be in Carrick-on-Shannon for 2 pm to meet some friends.

   (a) At what time does John need to leave the house?

   (b) How long will he have to wait in Carrick-on-Shannon to meet his friends?

6 A plane takes $7\frac{1}{2}$ hours to fly from Dublin to Dubai.

The plane leaves Dublin at 8.20 am.

The time in Dubai is two hours ahead of Dublin time. What will be the local (Dubai) time when the plane lands?

7 The following is Ciara's school timetable:

Time	Monday	Tuesday	Wednesday	Thursday	Friday
9.20–9.30	Roll Call	Roll Call	Roll Call	Roll Call	Roll Call
9.30–10.10	Maths	Woodwork	Art	P.E.	Geography
10.10–10.50	Geography	Woodwork	Maths	P.E.	English
10.50–11.10	Break	Break	Break	Break	Break
11.10–11.50	Irish	Maths	Geography	Irish	Irish
11.50–12.30	History	History	Science	History	Art
12.30–1.10	Science	English	Science	English	French
1.10–1.50	Lunch	Lunch	Lunch	Lunch	Lunch
1.50–2.25	English	Irish	English	Maths	Maths
2.25–3.00	Art	French	Irish	Geography	Woodwork
3.00–3.35	Art	French	French	Woodwork	
3.35–4.05	C.S.P.E.	Science	History	S.P.H.E.	

(i) For how long is Ciara in school each day?

(ii) How many different subjects does Ciara study?

(iii) How many class periods are given to each subject during a week?

(iv) What is the time difference between double P.E. and double Art?

(v) For how long in total is Ciara in Maths class over the week?

8 (i) Write one million in figures.

(ii) How many days, hours and seconds have elapsed after 1 million seconds have passed? (Give your answer to the nearest hour.)

9 (i) One billion is one thousand million. Write one billion in figures.

(ii) How many years and days have elapsed after 1 billion seconds have passed? (Give your answer to the nearest day and take the number of days in a year to be 365.)

Section 11B Length and Distance

Human beings have been measuring the length of things with great accuracy for more than 5000 years. Some of the oldest structures in the world like Newgrange and the Egyptian pyramids remind us that our ancestors understood the concept of length measurement very well.

Newgrange, Co. Meath

Some of the earliest units of measurement of length were based on the human body. One of the most important was the cubit, the length from a person's elbow to the tip of their middle finger. Units such as feet and hands are still used; the hand is the unit of measure for the height of a horse.

There are two primary systems of measurement for length and distance.

1. The imperial system

The units for this system are:

- Inches (in)

- Feet (ft)

  An A4 sheet of paper is approximately 1 foot long.

- Yards (yd)

  The length from a door handle to the bottom of the door is approximately 1 yard.

- Miles (mi)

  When you are out for a walk, after your right foot has hit the ground 1000 times you have travelled approximately 1 mile.

2. The metric system

The units for the metric system are based on one metre (m).

Examples:

1 metre	= 1000 millimetres (mm)
	= 100 centimetres (cm)
	= 10 decimetres (dm)
10 metres	= 1 decametre
100 metres	= 1 hectometre
1000 metres	= 1 kilometre

Example 1

Convert each of the following measurements to the required unit.

(i) 340 cm to metres   (ii) 2.2 km to metres

Solution

(i) 100 cm = 1 metre

$1 \text{ cm} = \frac{1}{100}$ metre ... unitary method

(Start with 1 cm.)

$340 \times 1 \text{ cm} = 340 \times \frac{1}{100} \text{ m} = 3.4 \text{ m}$

(ii) 1 km = 1000 m ... unitary method

(Start with 1 km.)

$2.2 \times 1 \text{ km} = 2.2 \times 1000 \text{ m} = 2200 \text{ m}$

Example 2

A carpenter needs 15 pieces of timber, each measuring 60 cm. He can buy the timber in 2 m lengths.
How many 2 m lengths of timber will he need to buy?

Solution

Always convert all quantities to the same unit.

The carpenter needs to find how many lengths of 60 cm he can get from one 2 m length of timber.

Given that:

1 metre = 100 cm

   2 m = 200 cm

$\frac{200}{60} = 3\frac{1}{3}$, so 3 full lengths of 60 cm can be made from each 2 m length, with some timber left over.

$\frac{15}{3} = 5$, therefore he will need to buy

5 lengths of 2 m.

Connections

Your knowledge of measuring line segments in geometry will come in very useful in the following activities. Some measurements can also be used in statistics.

Activity 11.2

1 Construct line segments with the following lengths:
   (i) 56 mm   (iii) 0.12 m
   (ii) 8.5 cm   (iv) 105 mm

2 Construct line segments with the following lengths:
   (i) 6.8 cm   (iii) 4.9 mm
   (ii) 0.07 m   (iv) 130 mm

3 Change these measurements to cm:
   (i) 300 mm   (v) 1 km
   (ii) 1.2 m   (vi) 34 m
   (iii) 19 mm   (vii) 2000 mm
   (iv) 2 m 35 cm   (viii) $\frac{1}{2}$ metre

4 What is the most appropriate unit to use when measuring each of the following?
   (i) The distance from the Earth to the Moon
   (ii) The length of a running track
   (iii) The length of a pencil
   (iv) The thickness of a piece of wood
   (v) The height of a student
   (vi) The length of your fingernails

5 Convert these measurements to metres:
   (i) 240 cm   (v) 2.8 km
   (ii) 1.5 km   (vi) $\frac{3}{4}$ km
   (iii) 3000 mm   (vii) 0.35 km
   (iv) 7000 cm   (viii) 99 cm

6 Change these measurements to kilometres:
   (i) 2300 m   (v) 10 000 m
   (ii) 500 m   (vi) 250 m
   (iii) 4 km 200 m   (vii) 3 km 600 m
   (iv) 30 000 cm   (viii) 9000 m

7 A standard ruler is 30 cm long.
   How many complete rulers can be made from a 5 m length of plastic?

8 A runner completes 8.25 laps of a running track. The total length of the running track is 400 m.
   What distance did the runner travel? Give your answer in
   (i) metres
   (ii) kilometres.

9 A delivery van travels from Dublin to Galway and back 4 times a week. The distance from Dublin to Galway is 225 km. How many km will the delivery van travel in one week?

10 A farmer wants to construct a straight timber fence of length 650 m. The timber comes in 350 cm lengths. Each length of timber needs to have a stake at each end to support it.

How many lengths of timber and how many stakes will the farmer need?

11 A forester chops down a tree which is 35 metres in height. The top 5 metres of the tree are unsuitable for use, but the rest of the tree can be cut into logs.

How many logs of length 20 cm can be cut from the tree?

12 A cyclist completes a race in 6 hours. There were 10 watering points on the route.

The first watering point is 30 km from the start and the last is 30 km from the finish line. All watering points are 20 km apart from each other. How long was the race?

Section 11C Mass

The **mass** of an object is the measure of the matter in that object.

In everyday language, mass is referred to as weight. For instance, we speak of the weight of your school bag. However, the weight of an object in scientific terms refers to the **force** of the Earth's **gravity** acting on it.

The unit for this is the newton. For example, when you step on scales and get your weight you are actually getting your mass.

In this chapter, what we refer to as **weight** would be referred to as **mass** by your science teacher, which is more accurate.

This is the conversion table for different standard units of weight:

1 gram (g)	=	1000 milligrams
1 kilogram (kg)	=	1000 grams
1 tonne (t)	=	1000 kilograms

Example 1

Convert each of the following measurements to the required unit.

(i) 3600 g to kg   (ii) 5.4 kg to g

Solution

(i) 3600 g to kg

$$1000 \text{ g} = 1 \text{ kg}$$
$$\Rightarrow \quad 1 \text{ g} = \frac{1}{1000} \text{ kg} \ldots \text{ unitary method}$$
$$3600 \text{ g} = \left(\frac{1}{1000} \times 3600\right) \text{ kg}$$
$$= 3.6 \text{ kg}$$

(ii) 5.4 kg to g

$$1 \text{ kg} = 1000 \text{ g} \ldots \text{ unitary method}$$
$$\Rightarrow 5.4 \text{ kg} = (5.4 \times 1000) \text{ g}$$
$$= 5400 \text{ g}$$

Example 2

Balance the scales by adding the correct weight to the correct side.

800 g   1.7 kg

Leave your answer in grams.

Solution

■ To balance the scales, the weight needs to be the same on both sides.

■ Always convert the quantities to the same unit.

Convert 1.7 kg to grams.

1 kg = 1000 g

1.7 kg = (1000 × 1.7) g

= 1700 g

To balance the scales:

■ Find the difference between the two weights.

1700 g – 800 g = 900 g

■ 900 g needs to be added to the left side to balance the scales.

Activity 11.3

1 (i) Copy the following table into your copybook.

(ii) Convert each quantity to the required unit.

		milligrams (mg)			grams (g)			kilograms (kg)
(a)	20 g		(h)	2 kg		(o)	3500 g	
(b)	6.2 g		(i)	4500 mg		(p)	2 tonne	
(c)	0.7 g		(j)	1.8 kg		(q)	500 g	
(d)	100 g		(k)	$\frac{1}{2}$ kg		(r)	1.1 tonne	
(e)	3 g		(l)	500 mg		(s)	50 g	
(f)	$\frac{1}{2}$ g		(m)	3.1 kg		(t)	$\frac{3}{4}$ tonne	
(g)	2.1 g		(n)	8500 mg		(u)	1250 g	

2 What is the most suitable unit of weight when measuring each of the following?

(i) A spoon of sugar   (iv) A cement lorry   (vii) A packet of crisps

(ii) An elephant   (v) A baby   (viii) A car

(iii) A hamster   (vi) A feather   (ix) A bowl of cornflakes

3 A builder needs to move 35 tonnes of rock from one site to another. He has two lorries that can each carry 5000 kg per run. How many runs will each lorry need to do to move all the rock?

4 A shopkeeper buys a 10 kg bag of apples. He packs 32 separate bags of apples from the large bag. What is the weight in each bag?

5 Balance the scales.

(i)
750 g   1.2 kg

(ii)
150 g   650 g

(iii)
1 kg 450 g   2.6 kg

(iv)
4 kg 620 g   6 kg 95 g

6 A farmer grows a crop of potatoes. He sells them in 10 kg bags. His total crop weighs 7.45 tonnes. He expects that there will be 745 kg of wastage.

How many bags of potatoes will the farmer be able to fill?

7 The following recipe is for 20 cupcakes.

- 175 g self-raising flour
- 140 g butter (room temperature)
- 125 g caster sugar
- 2 eggs (room temperature)

Calculate how much of each ingredient is needed to make 150 cupcakes.

8 Add the following weights and give all your answers in kilograms.

(i) $150 \text{ g} + \frac{1}{2} \text{ kg} + 1.6 \text{ kg}$

(ii) $70 \text{ g} + 0.030 \text{ kg} + 55\,000 \text{ mg}$

(iii) $600 \text{ g} + 1.2 \text{ kg} + \frac{3}{4} \text{ kg}$

(iv) $80 \text{ g} + 0.7 \text{ kg} + 6000 \text{ mg}$

9 Beef needs to be roasted at a rate of 30 minutes per 450 g, plus 30 minutes extra. A roast beef joint weighing 2.7 kg is put into the oven at 11 am. At what time will the beef be cooked?

Section 11D Rectangles – Perimeter and Area

The **perimeter** of a shape is the sum of its sides.

If I start at one corner and walk around the edge of a rectangle until I am back at the start, I have walked the **perimeter** of that rectangle.

Example 1

These rectangles have been drawn on squares of side 1 cm. Find the perimeter of each of these rectangles.

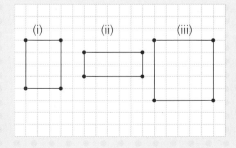

Solution

Add up the lengths of all the sides.

(i) Two sides are of length 3 cm and two sides are of length 4 cm so the perimeter = 3 + 4 + 3 + 4 = 14 cm.

(ii) Two sides are of length 2 cm and two sides are of length 5 cm so the perimeter = 2 + 5 + 2 + 5 = 14 cm.

(iii) Four sides are of length 5 cm so the perimeter = 5 + 5 + 5 + 5 = 20 cm.

The **area** of a given shape is the amount of surface enclosed within that shape.

- Area is a **2-dimensional** quantity and can be measured on a flat surface or on a curved surface.

- A simple way to think of area is 'if you can paint it, then it has area'. So we can talk about the area of the wall of a room or the area of a floor or the area of the side of a tin can.

- We can also speak about the area of very large surfaces like a field or a farm or the surface area of Ireland.

- The unit of area is a square of side 1 unit long. For example:

    1 mm × 1 mm = 1 mm²   1 m × 1 m = 1 m²

    1 cm × 1 cm = 1 cm²   1 km × 1 km = 1 km²

1 unit

1 unit | Area = 1 square unit (1 unit²)

- The standard unit of area is the square metre (m²).

    Large areas are measured in hectares (1 hectare = 10 000 m²).

Class Discussion

Think about the difference between **length** and **area**. Suppose you wanted to decorate your room. What items would you buy which would be priced by **length**? What items would you buy which would be concerned with **area**?

Area of a Rectangle

The rectangle on the right has length 3 units and width 2 units. We can see by counting that its area is 6 square units.

We could also get its area by multiplying 3 × 2 since multiplication is really a quick way of adding.

This leads us to a formula for the area of a rectangle:

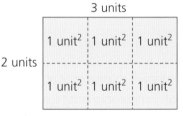

3 units

2 units

| 1 unit² | 1 unit² | 1 unit² |
| 1 unit² | 1 unit² | 1 unit² |

The area of a rectangle = length × width.

Example 2

Find the area of each of the following rectangles which are drawn on squares of side 1 cm.

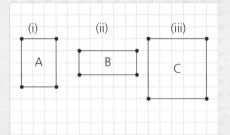

Solution

Each small square is 1 cm in length, so the area of each of these small squares is 1 cm².

Method 1

Add up all the squares inside the rectangle.

(i) Rectangle A: 12 cm²

(ii) Rectangle B: 10 cm²

(iii) Rectangle C: 25 cm²

Method 2

Multiply length by height for each rectangle.

(i) Rectangle A: 3 × 4 = 12 cm²

(ii) Rectangle B: 2 × 5 = 10 cm²

(iii) Rectangle C: 5 × 5 = 25 cm²

Example 3

Find the perimeter and area of the following shape.

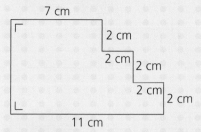

Solution

- The missing side is 2 + 2 + 2 = 6 cm.
- To find the perimeter of the shape, add all the sides:

  6 + 7 + 2 + 2 + 2 + 2 + 2 + 11 = 34 cm

- To find the area, break the shape into rectangles and then add all the areas together to get the total area.

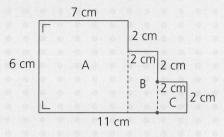

Area of A = 6 cm × 7 cm = 42 cm²

Area of B = 2 cm × 4 cm = 8 cm²

Area of C = 2 cm × 2 cm = 4 cm²

Total area = 42 + 8 + 4 = 54 cm²

Example 4

Find the area of the shaded region in the diagram below.

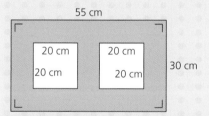

Solution

- Find the area of the full shape.

  55 cm × 30 cm = 1650 cm²

- Find the area of the unshaded regions.

  Region 1:

  20 cm × 20 cm = 400 cm²

  Region 2:

  20 cm × 20 cm = 400 cm²

  Total area unshaded = 400 cm² + 400 cm²

  = 800 cm²

- Subtract the unshaded regions from the full area to get the shaded region.

  1650 cm² − 800 cm² = 850 cm²

Example 5

Find the length of the missing side of this rectangle, given the perimeter.

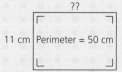

Solution

- Perimeter = 50 cm = the sum of all 4 sides.

  As we know one side is 11 cm, we also know that the opposite side is 11 cm.

- The perimeter − (11 + 11) = the sum of the 2 equal sides we don't know.

  50 cm − 22 cm = 28 cm

  ⇒ sum of other 2 equal sides = 28 cm

  1 side = $\frac{1}{2}$ × 28 cm = 14 cm

- Check your answer by getting the perimeter and comparing with the value given.

  11 + 11 + 14 + 14 = 50 cm ✓

Activity 11.4

1 Find the perimeter and area of the following rectangles.

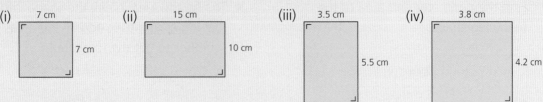

(i) 7 cm 7 cm

(ii) 15 cm 10 cm

(iii) 3.5 cm 5.5 cm

(iv) 3.8 cm 4.2 cm

2 Find the perimeter and area of the following shapes.

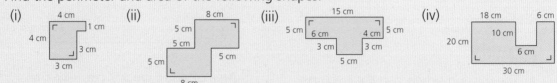

(i) 4 cm 1 cm 4 cm 3 cm 3 cm

(ii) 8 cm 5 cm 5 cm 5 cm 5 cm 8 cm

(iii) 15 cm 5 cm 6 cm 4 cm 5 cm 3 cm 3 cm 5 cm

(iv) 18 cm 6 cm 20 cm 10 cm 6 cm 30 cm

3 Find the perimeter and area of each of the following shapes.

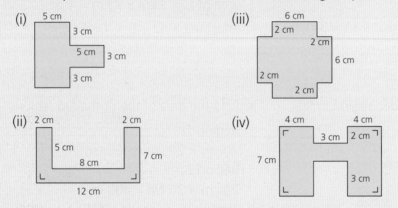

(i) 5 cm 3 cm 5 cm 3 cm 3 cm

(iii) 6 cm 2 cm 2 cm 6 cm 2 cm 2 cm

(ii) 2 cm 2 cm 5 cm 8 cm 7 cm 12 cm

(iv) 4 cm 4 cm 3 cm 2 cm 7 cm 3 cm

4 Find the area of the shaded region in each of the following shapes.

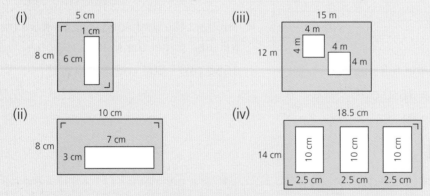

(i) 5 cm 1 cm 8 cm 6 cm

(iii) 15 m 4 m 4 m 12 m 4 m 4 m

(ii) 10 cm 7 cm 8 cm 3 cm

(iv) 18.5 cm 14 cm 10 cm 10 cm 10 cm 2.5 cm 2.5 cm 2.5 cm

5 Find the area of the shaded region in each of the following shapes.

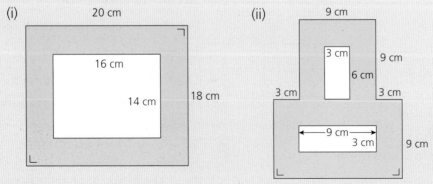

(i) 20 cm 16 cm 14 cm 18 cm

(ii) 9 cm 3 cm 9 cm 6 cm 3 cm 3 cm 9 cm 3 cm 9 cm

6 (i) Find the length of the missing side of each of the following rectangles, given the perimeter.

(a) Perimeter = 30 m

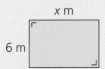

x m

6 m

(b) Perimeter = 40 cm

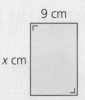

9 cm

x cm

(c) Perimeter = 44 m

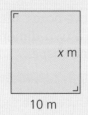

x m

10 m

(d) Perimeter = 76 cm

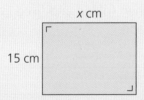

x cm

15 cm

(ii) Find the area of each rectangle.

7 A gardener is making 3 flower beds in his rectangular garden as in the diagram below. The rest of the garden is a lawn.

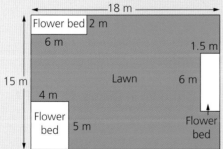

18 m

Flower bed 2 m

6 m

1.5 m

15 m

Lawn

6 m

4 m

Flower bed

5 m

Flower bed

Find the area of the lawn.

8 An A4 sheet of paper has dimensions: length 296 mm, width 210 mm.

(i) What is the perimeter of the sheet?

(ii) What is the area of the sheet?

The sheet is cut into two halves. Then each of these halves is cut into halves again. There are now 4 sheets of equal area.

(iii) What is the difference between the combined areas of the 4 pieces of paper and the area of the original sheet of paper? Explain your answer.

9 A garden measuring 16 m by 8 m is shown. It is surrounded by a path 1 m wide. Find the area of the path.

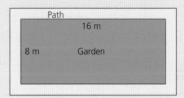

Path

16 m

8 m

Garden

10 A tiler is tiling a rectangular bathroom floor which measures 2.5 m by 3.6 m. She decides to use a border of wood 25 cm wide around the edges of the floor.

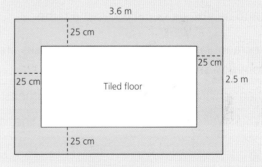

3.6 m

25 cm

25 cm

25 cm

Tiled floor

2.5 m

25 cm

(i) What is the area of the tiled part of the floor?

(ii) The tiles are squares of side 20 cm. Find the area of one tile in m².

(iii) How many tiles are needed to tile the floor?

11 The perimeter of a square is 96 cm.

(i) Draw a sketch of the square.

(ii) Find its area.

12 A rectangle has length 20 m. Its perimeter is 72 m.

(i) Draw a sketch of the rectangle.

(ii) Find its area.

13 The area of a square room is 36 m².

   (i) Draw a sketch of the room.

   (ii) Find its perimeter.

14 (i) Draw a square 1 cm long as accurately as you can.

   (ii) How many mm² are there in this square?

15 A square measures 1 m long.

   (i) Write the dimensions of the square in cm.

   (ii) How many cm² are there in this square?

Section 11E Nets and Surface Area of Rectangular Solids

The figure below is a **rectangular solid**. Rectangular solids can also be called cuboids.

A rectangular solid has six faces.

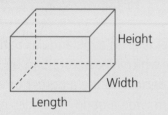

A rectangular solid where the length, width and height are equal is called a **cube**.

Rectangular objects or rectangular boxes are common shapes that we see every day.

To make all of the above boxes, the manufacturers create a **two-dimensional net** of the required size and shape.

> A **net** is a two-dimensional (2-D) representation of a three-dimensional (3-D) solid or object.

This net is then folded and fixed into the required shape.

Diagram 1 below is a net of a three-dimensional rectangular box.

When we fold the net along the dotted lines it forms Diagram 2 which is a 3-D rectangular object.

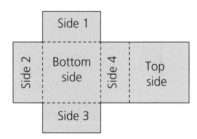

Diagram 1

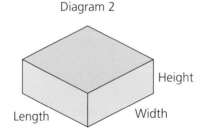

Diagram 2

We can have different nets of the same rectangular object, as shown in Diagrams 3 and 4.

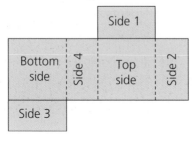

Diagram 3

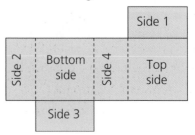

Diagram 4

These are some nets for a cube:

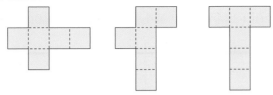

There are 11 different nets for a cube.

Total Surface Area of a Rectangular Solid

We can use a net to help find the **total surface area** of a rectangular object or solid.

Example 1

Find the total surface area of this rectangular box using the net shown.

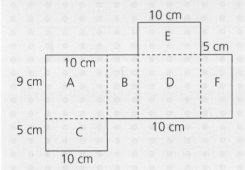

Solution

Method 1

Find the area of each side and add them together.

Area of A = 10 cm × 9 cm = 90 cm²

Area of B = 5 cm × 9 cm = 45 cm²

Area of C = 5 cm × 10 cm = 50 cm²

Area of D = 10 cm × 9 cm = 90 cm²

Area of E = 5 cm × 10 cm = 50 cm²

Area of F = 5 cm × 9 cm = 45 cm²

Total surface area

= 90 + 45 + 50 + 90 + 50 + 45 = 370 cm²

Method 2

Label the values given as height, width and length:

height = 5 cm, width = 9 cm, length = 10 cm

Total surface area

$$= 2(l \times w) + 2(l \times h) + 2(w \times h)$$

Total surface area

$$= 2(10 \times 9) + 2(10 \times 5) + 2(9 \times 5)$$

$$= 180 + 100 + 90$$

$$= 370 \text{ cm}^2$$

Example 2

The surface area of a cube is 96 cm². What is the length of each side?

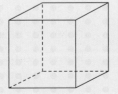

Solution

All 6 sides of a cube have the same area. To get the area of one side we divide the surface area by the number of sides.

Area of one side = $\frac{96}{6}$ = 16 cm²

Area = length × height

$$l \times l = 16 \text{ cm}^2$$

$$(l)^2 = 16 \text{ cm}^2$$

$$l = \sqrt{16} = 4 \text{ cm}$$

1 The following are nets of rectangular solids. Find the total surface area of each.

(i)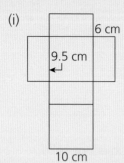

(iii)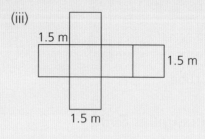

(v)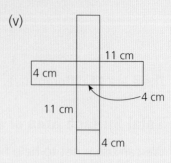

(ii)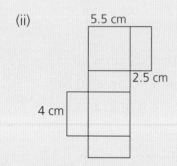

(iv)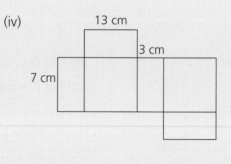

2 (i) Draw a net of each of the following solids.

(ii) Use the nets to find the total surface area of each solid.

(a)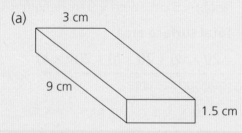

(b)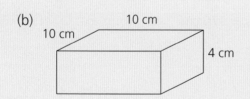

(c)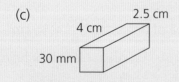

(d)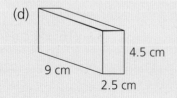

3 (i) Draw a net of a cube of side length 4 cm.

(ii) Use your net to find the surface area of the cube.

4 Find the surface area of each of the following rectangular solids.

Rectangular solid	Length	Width	Height
(i)	5 m	2 m	4 m
(ii)	17 cm	11 cm	7 cm
(iii)	1.25 m	1.75 m	1.5 m
(iv)	35 cm	15 cm	35 cm
(v)	65 mm	40 mm	70 mm
(vi)	1.5 m	750 cm	500 cm

5 A company produces two different-size boxes for packaging cereal:

Box A: length = 19 cm, height = 26 cm, width = 6 cm

Box B: length = 14.5 cm, height = 23 cm, width = 5 cm

(i) Sketch the nets for the two different cereal boxes.

(ii) Find the total surface area of each box.

(iii) If the company produces 200 units of Box A and 150 units of Box B, how much cardboard is used?

6 The diagram shows a net of a cube with the faces named by letter.

(i) When the cube is formed, which face is opposite face A?

(ii) Which faces are opposite faces B and C?

7 When this net is formed into a cube, find the side that is opposite:

(i) side A

(ii) side B

(iii) side D.

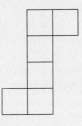

8 The numbers on opposite faces of a die add to 7.

The diagram on the right is a net for a die.

Draw a sketch of the net and number the sides so that the opposite faces add to 7.

9 (i) Which of the sketches below is a net of a cube?

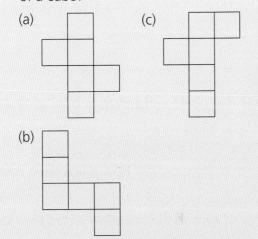

(a)

(c)

(b)

(ii) Draw a sketch of the net(s) which are nets of a cube and number the faces so that the opposite faces add to 7.

10 For each of the following cubes, find the length of each side.

(i) Total surface area 150 cm²

(ii) Total surface area 294 cm²

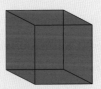

(iii) Total surface area 6 m²

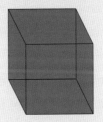

(iv) Total surface area 54 cm²

11 A company produces three different-sized boxes for packaging three different sizes of toothpaste tubes:

Box A: length = 15 cm, height = 4 cm, width = 4 cm

Box B: length = 18 cm, height = 5 cm, width = 5 cm

Box C: length = 10 cm, height = 3 cm, width = 3 cm

(i) Sketch the nets for the three different toothpaste boxes.

(ii) Find the total surface area of each box.

(iii) If the company produces 300 units of each type, how much cardboard is used?

1 The following is an extract from Irish Rail Cork to Dublin train services.

Kildare		Dep	06.02	06.15	06.35	06.49	06.58
Newbridge		Dep	06.08	06.22	06.42	06.56	07.04
Sallins & Naas		Dep	. . .	06.30	06.50	07.05	07.11
Hazelhatch & Celbridge		Dep	. . .	06.39	06.59	07.14	07.20
Adamstown		Dep	. . .	. . .	07.04	. . .	07.25
Clondalkin Fonthill		Dep	. . .	. . .	07.09	07.22	. . .
Park West & Cherry Orchard		Dep	. . .	. . .	07.13	. . .	. . .
DUBLIN Heuston **B L A**	Arr	06.38	07.00	07.24	07.35	07.40

Using the information from the timetable above, answer the following questions:

(a) How long is the journey from Kildare to Heuston station for each train?

(b) How many trains stop in Sallins and Naas?

(c) There are 56 minutes between the times of the first and last trains leaving Kildare. How long is there between the times of the first and last trains arriving in Heuston station?

(d) What time would you expect the 06.15 train from Kildare to pass through Adamstown?

(e) Mary lives in Newbridge and her place of work is a 15-minute walk from Clondalkin Fonthill. What train must she get from Newbridge station in order to be in work by 7.30 am?

2 A carpenter needs 24 pieces of wood 12 cm long. He can buy the timber in metre lengths.

(a) How many lengths of timber does the carpenter need to buy?

(b) How much timber will the carpenter have left over?

3 The following is a diagram of a park:

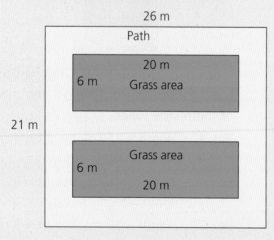

(a) Find the area of the grass in the park.

(b) What is the width of the path?

(c) Find the area of the path.

4 Aoife drove from Dublin to Cork. She left Dublin at 08.45 and arrived in Cork at 12.21.

(a) How long did it take Aoife to drive from Dublin to Cork?

(b) The distance from Dublin to Cork is 252 km. Calculate Aoife's average speed in km/h.

(c) Aoife estimates that it costs 25 cent per km to drive her car. How much did it cost her to drive her car from Dublin to Cork?

5 Using a net or otherwise, find the surface area of each of the following rectangular solids.

(a) Length = 12 cm, width = 10 cm, height = 14 cm

(b) Length = 4 cm, width = 3 cm, height = 2 cm

(c) Length = 25 cm, width = 15 cm, height = 10 cm

(d) Length = 20 cm, width = 18 cm, height = 15 cm

Exam-style Question

1 A gardener wants to build a patio in her garden and a space for a barbeque. Below is a plan of the patio and barbeque she wants to build.

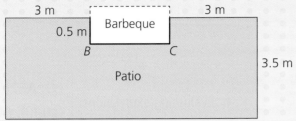

(a) Find the length of [BC].

(b) Find the perimeter of the patio.

(c) The owner wants to cover the patio with slabs. Find the area to be covered.

(d) The slabs are squares of side 0.5 m. Find the number of slabs required.

(e) She has €500 to spend on slabs. The slabs cost €4.50 each. Does she have enough money to cover the entire patio? Explain your answer.

JCOL 2012 Paper 2

KEY WORDS AND PHRASES

- Time
- 24-hour clock
- 12-hour clock
- Timetable
- Length
- Distance
- Imperial units
- Metric units
- Unitary method
- Mass
- Weight
- Force of gravity
- Perimeter
- Area
- Net
- Surface area net
- Rectangular solid
- Cuboid
- Cube

Chapter Summary 11

- Clocks can be 12-hour or 24-hour.
- Length can be measured in metres, centimetres, millimetres or kilometres.
- Measurement can be in imperial or metric units.
- The weight of an object is measured in grams, milligrams or kilograms.

- The perimeter of a rectangle is the sum of its side lengths.
- The area of a rectangle = length × width.
- We use nets to help find the surface area of rectangular objects or solids.

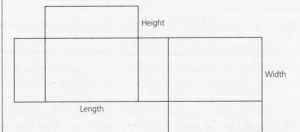

Algebra 1

Learning Intentions

In this chapter, you will learn about:

- The use of letters to represent quantities that are variables
- Indices in algebra
- Terms, coefficients and expressions
- Adding and subtracting terms

- Evaluating expressions
- Simplifying terms
- Multiplying terms
- Multiplying expressions including the use of brackets and the distributive law

LO: AF.2(a, b), AF.3 (a(I-II)), AF.3 (b(I-II)), U.5, U.6, U.13

Historical background

The word 'algebra' comes from the Arabic word 'al-jabr', which comes from the title of a book written in 825 AD by a famous Arabic mathematician named Al-Khwarizmi.

Section 12A Variables and Constants

Peter works in a busy restaurant at weekends. He is paid €30 per evening plus tips. So Peter's pay is €(30 + tips).

The amount he gets from tips **varies** a lot from day to day. So we would call this a **variable.** But the €30 is **constant** (never changing).

We could just use the letter t to stand for the word 'tips' and so we would write Peter's pay as:

Pay = €(30 + t). Here, t is variable and 30 is a constant.

Key Points

Variables are quantities that can take on different values.
In algebra, letters are commonly used to stand for variables.
A **constant** always has the same value.

The use of variables is hugely important. We call this branch of mathematics **algebra**.

Class Activity

This example is for class discussion. Write down each step as you go along.

1. Think of a number, any number.
2. Double it.
3. Add 4 to the result.
4. Now divide this by 2.

5. Finally, subtract your original number from the number you now have.
6. The answer is 2, right?

Solution

The example above can be written in words or can be represented algebraically using variables and constants. It is much simpler to represent it algebraically.

Step in words	Step using variables and constants	Explanation
Think of a number.	Let x = the number.	You can use any letter you like.
Double it.	$2x$	'Double' means multiply by 2. $2x$ means '2 times x'.
Add 4 to the result.	$2x + 4$	Is this the same as $6x$? Check it out.
Divide by 2.	$x + 2$	Divide both terms by 2.
Subtract the original number from the number you now have.	2 Everyone is at 2 now, no matter what x they took at the start.	Subtract x.

We can see that a complicated problem can be represented much more easily using variables and constants rather than words.

Key Point

When we represent information using variables and constants we are representing the information **algebraically**.

Things you must know:

	Meaning/Explanation
	Remember that multiplication is indicated by one or more sets of brackets.
$2(3)$	means '2 times 3'
$(2)(3)$	means '2 times 3'
$(x)(y)$	means 'x times y'
	Note: There are no signs between the brackets, so make sure you understand the difference between $(2)(3) = 6$ and $(2) + (3) = 5$.
x	$+1x$
$-x$	$-1x$, which means '-1 times x'
$5x$	5 times x, or 5 multiplied by x
$5 + x$	5 add x, or 5 plus x
$x - 3$	x less 3, or 3 less than x

Things you must know:

	Meaning/Explanation
xy	x multiplied by y
$2xy$	2 multiplied by x multiplied by y
$\dfrac{x}{2}$	x divided by 2
	Order of operations applies in algebra (**BIRDMAS**).

Terms, Coefficients and Expressions

A **term** is made when a constant and a set of variables are multiplied together. Examples of terms are: $4x$, $-8y$, $6x^3$, $-3xy$, a^3b^2, $6abcd$.

The **constant** in a term is known as the **coefficient** of the variable in that term.

Examples:

- In the term $6x^3$, the coefficient of x^3 is 6.
- In the term $-3xy$, the coefficient of xy is -3.

An **expression** is a set of terms which are added or subtracted.

For example: $4x^2 + 2x - 7$ is an expression with three terms.

Expressions which can be written in different forms can be called **equivalent expressions**. For example: $2x + 2 = x + x + 2 = x + x + 1 + 1$

Like terms have the same variables with equal powers.

For example:

- $2y$, $7y$, $-9y$ are like terms.
- $3xz$, $-2xz$ and $12xz$ are like terms.
- $3abc^2$ and $5abc^2$ are like terms.

Unlike terms may have different variables or the same variables with different powers.

For example:

- $2x$ and $5y$ are unlike terms.
- $3abc$ and $6acd$ are unlike terms.
- $3x^2$ and $3x$ are unlike terms.

Letters in an expression are normally written in alphabetical order.

For example: write **2xyz**, not $2yzx$ or $2zyx$ or $2xzy$.

Example 1

$5x^2 - 2x - 6$ is an **expression** of three **terms**.

(i) Write down the terms in the expression.

(ii) Write down the coefficient of the variable in each term.

Solution

(i) The three terms are: $5x^2$, $-2x$ and -6.

(ii) The coefficient of x^2 is 5, the coefficient of x is -2, and the constant is -6.

Evaluating Expressions

To find the value of an expression for particular value(s) of the variables, **substitute** the value(s) into the variables in the expression. Remember to use **BIRDMAS** to decide on the order of operations.

Algebra 1

Example 2

If $x = 3$, find the value of the following:

(i) $5x$ (ii) $2x - 4$ (iii) $\dfrac{5x}{3}$ (iv) $x^2 + 3x + 6$

Solution

Method
> First, replace the variable with a bracket.
> Then put the value into the bracket.

(i) $5x = 5(3) = 15$

(ii) $2x - 4 = 2(3) - 4 = 6 - 4 = 2$

(iii) $\dfrac{5x}{3} = \dfrac{5(3)}{3} = \dfrac{15}{3} = 5$

(iv) $x^2 + 3x + 6 = (3)^2 + 3(3) + 6$
$= 9 + 9 + 6$
$= 24$

Example 3

If $p = 4$ and $q = -2$, find the value of the following:

(i) $3pq$ (ii) $p^2 - p - 6$ (iii) $q^2 - 3q + 4$ (iv) $\dfrac{4p - 2q}{3p + q}$

(handwritten) $= \dfrac{4(4) - 2(-2)}{3(4) -2} = \dfrac{16+4}{12-2} = \dfrac{20}{10} = \dfrac{2}{1} = 2$

Solution

(i) $3pq = 3(4)(-2) = 3(-8) = -24$

(ii) $p^2 - p - 6 = (4)^2 - (4) - 6$
$= 16 - 4 - 6 = 6$

(iii) $q^2 - 3q + 4 = (-2)^2 - 3(-2) + 4$
$= 4 + 6 + 4 = 14$

(iv) $\dfrac{4p - 2q}{3p + q} = \dfrac{4(4) - 2(-2)}{3(4) + 1(-2)}$
$= \dfrac{16 + 4}{12 - 2}$
$= \dfrac{20}{10} = 2$

Activity 12.1

1 Write each of the following using mathematical symbols and operations.

(i) 5 minus 3 *5 − 3*

(ii) 5 times q, minus $3r$ *5q − 3r*

(iii) 9 add 7 *9 + 7*

(iv) 9 multiplied by a, plus 7 *9a + 7*

(v) The difference of 21 and 11 *21 − 11*

(vi) 21 times b, minus 11 *21b − 11*

(vii) The product of 4 and 2 *4 × 2*

(viii) 4 times d, multiplied by 2 times d *(4d)(2d)*

(ix) 7 times x, multiplied by 16

(x) 7 times k, multiplied by k

(xi) n multiplied by m multiplied by p

2 If $x = 2$ and $y = 3$ find the value of:

(i) $x + 3$ (vi) xy

(ii) $y - 2$ (vii) $3xy$

(iii) $5x$ (viii) $3x + 2y$

(iv) $3x + 4$ (ix) $4x - y$

(v) $2y + 1$ (x) $6x - 2y$

Algebra 1

3 Find the value of each of these expressions when $n = 5$.

   (i) $n + 5$ (vi) $2n$

   (ii) $n - 3$ (vii) $2n + 5$

   (iii) $5n$ (viii) $5 - n$

   (iv) $n + 6$ (ix) $20 - 3n$

   (v) $n + 2$ (x) $-2n + 7$

4 If $a = 1$, $b = 2$ and $c = 3$, find the value of:

   (i) $a + b + c$

   (ii) $2a + 4b + c$

   (iii) $a + 2b - c$

   (iv) $3a - 2b + 4ac$

5 (i) Copy and complete this table. The first column has been done for you.

Instruction	First number	Second number	Third number	Variable
Starting number	3	4	5	k
Multiply by 4	4(3) = 12			
Subtract 5 from your answer	12 − 5			
Result	7			

(ii) What starting number would give a result of 3?

6 (i) Copy and complete the following table giving values of $2n$ for different values of n:

Value of n	$2n$
1	2(1) = 2
2	
3	
4	
5	
6	

(ii) Look at the pattern of numbers in the second column. What type of number does $2n$ always give?

7 (i) Copy and complete the following table giving values of $(2n - 1)$ for different values of n:

Value of n	$2n - 1$
1	2(1) − 1 = 2 − 1 = 1
2	
3	
4	
5	
6	

(ii) Look at the pattern of numbers in the second column. What type of number does $(2n - 1)$ always give?

8 (i) Copy and complete the following table giving values of n^2 for different values of n:

Value of n	n^2
1	$1^2 = (1)(1) = 1$
2	
3	
4	
5	
6	

(ii) Look at the pattern of numbers in the second column. These are called square numbers. Write down the next four square numbers.

9 The letter F stands for Frank's age, in years. Fill in the table to match each description. Each of your answers will contain the letter F.

Description	Algebraic term
Frank's age	F
Frank's age in 4 years' time	
Frank's age in 10 years' time	
Frank's age 3 years ago	
Twice Franks' age	
Half of Franks' age	

10 If $x = 2$, find the value of the following:

   (i) $3x$ *6*

   (ii) $7x$ *14*

   (iii) $2x + 4$ *8*

   (iv) $5x - 3$ *7*

   (v) x^2 *4*

   (vi) $5x^2$ *(5×2)²*

   (vii) x^3 *2³ = 8*

   (viii) $3x^2 + 5$

11 If $a = 3$, find the value of the following:

   (i) $5a + 2$

   (ii) $3a - 5$

   (iii) $a - 7$

   (iv) $5 - 2a$

   (v) $5a^2 + 4a$

   (vi) $(a + 4)^2$

12 If $p = 2$ and $q = 1$, find the value of the following:

   (i) $4p + 2q$

   (ii) $p + q$

   (iii) $p - q$

   (iv) $5p - 3q$

   (v) pq

   (vi) $6pq$

13 If $x = 2$ and $y = -3$, find the value of the following:

   (i) $3x + y$

   (ii) $x - 4y$

   (iii) $-3x + 4y$

   (iv) $-x - y$

   (v) $y^2 + 3y$

   (vi) $5y^2 + 2x$

   (vii) xy

   (viii) $(x - 6)^2$

   (ix) $x^2 - 6$

> **Recall:**
> $(+) \times (+) = +$
> $(-) \times (-) = +$
> $(-) \times (+) = -$
> $(+) \times (-) = -$

14 Sean has a number trick where he asks the class to 'think of a number'. He calls this number 'x'. He gives the class the instructions in the table below and 'magically' tells them the answer they got.

   (i) Copy and complete the table to show the effect of these instructions:

Instruction	Result of instruction
Think of a number	x
Multiply the number by 4	
Add 6 to this answer	
Subtract your original number (x)	
Divide your answer by 3	
Subtract your original number	

   (ii) Now try this for a couple of values of x and see if it works for any number. This is an example of how a variable works.

15 If $a = 3$ and $b = -4$, find the value of the following:

   (i) $5ab$ *5×3×-4*

   (ii) $a^2 - a - 2$

   (iii) $b^2 + b + 2$

   (iv) $\dfrac{5a - 3b}{a + b}$

16 If $x = -2$ and $y = -5$, find the value of the following:

   (i) $-3xy$

   (ii) $x^2 - xy$

   (iii) $y^2 - 3y + 5$

   (iv) $\dfrac{5x + y}{3x - 2y}$

   (v) $\dfrac{4x - 3y}{-2x - y}$

   (vi) $\dfrac{3x + 2y}{-x + 2y}$

17 If $m = -2$, $p = -4$ and $q = -3$, find the value of the following:

   (i) mpq

   (ii) $3pq$

   (iii) $2p^2 + 3q^2$

   (iv) $p^3 + q^3$

   (v) $q^3 + q^2 - q$

   (vi) $p^3 - q^3$

18 If $a = -2$, $b = -3$ and $c = -1$, find the value of the following:

   (i) $a^2 - bc$

   (ii) $2a^2c$

   (iii) $2b^2 - 4c^2$

   (iv) $2a - 3b + c$

   (v) $3a^2b^2c^2$

   (vi) $a^2 + b^2 + c^2$

19 Find the value of the following expressions if $x = -3$:

   (i) $x^2 - 5x + 4$ (iii) $3x^2 + 2$

   (ii) $x^2 - 4x + 2$ (iv) $5 - 4x - 3x^2$

20 If $a = -2$, $b = 4$ and $c = 5$, find the value of the following:

   (i) $\dfrac{a^2}{bc}$ (iii) $\dfrac{a + c}{4bc}$

   (ii) $\dfrac{a^2 - b}{c + 3}$ (iv) $\dfrac{a + b^3}{b^3 + c}$

Section 12B Adding and Subtracting Terms

 Key Points

- Only terms that have the same variable(s) raised to the same power can be added or subtracted. These terms are known as **like terms**.
- When adding or subtracting like terms, the powers of the variables do not change.

Expressions which can be written in different forms can be called **equivalent expressions**.

Example 1

Simplify the following:

 (i) $3x + 5x - 2x$

(ii) $3a + 5b - 2a + 4b$

(iii) $3x^2 + 5x^2 - 2x^2$

Solution

 (i) $3x + 5x - 2x$

    $= 8x - 2x$

    $= 6x$

(ii) $3a + 5b - 2a + 4b$

    $= 3a - 2a + 5b + 4b$ ...regrouping

    $= a + 9b$

(iii) $3x^2 + 5x^2 - 2x^2$

    $= 8x^2 - 2x^2$

    $= 6x^2$

Example 2

Add $2x^2 - 3x + 3x^2 + 4 + 4x$. $= 5x^2 + 1x + 4$

Solution

$2x^2 - 3x + 3x^2 + 4 + 4x$

$= 2x^2 + 3x^2 - 3x + 4x + 4$

$= \quad 5x^2 \quad + \quad x \quad + 4$

Algebra 1

Example 3

Evaluate the following:

(i) $2x + 5y - 2 + 4x - 7y - 5$

(ii) $4a^3 + 5a^2 - 2 + 5a^3 + 5 + 3a^2$

(iii) $3x^2 + 5x^3$

Solution

(i) $2x + 5y - 2 + 4x - 7y - 5$

$= 2x + 4x + 5y - 7y - 2 - 5$ ...regrouping

$= 6x - 2y - 7$

(ii) $4a^3 + 5a^2 - 2 + 5a^3 + 5 + 3a^2$

$= 4a^3 + 5a^3 + 5a^2 + 3a^2 - 2 + 5$

$= 9a^3 + 8a^2 + 3$

(iii) $3x^2 + 5x^3$

These are unlike terms and so this expression cannot be made any simpler.

Example 4

(i) Copy and complete the diagram by writing $(3m + 6)$ in ten different ways.

(ii) Which expression is the simplest?

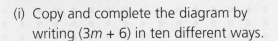

Solution

(i)

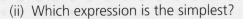

(ii) $(3m + 6)$ is the simplest.

Algebra 1

1 Simplify each of the following by adding like terms:

(i) $2x + 4x + 5x$ $11x$

(ii) $5a + 3a + a$ $9a$

(iii) $4x + 3x + 2 + 7$ $7x + 9$

(iv) $3a + 3 + a + 4$

(v) $5b + 6a + a + 2b$

(vi) $3y + 3a + 6a + 8y$ $11y + 9a$

2 Simplify each of these:

(i) $5x - 3x$ (iv) $7a + 3 - 3a - 4$

(ii) $6a - a$ (v) $5x + 6y - 2x - 8y$

(iii) $9x - 5x$ (vi) $5y - 10y + 6 + 2y$

3 Simplify each of the following:

(i) $2a + 5a$ (vi) $11m - 8m$

(ii) $6x + 11x$ (vii) $p + 3p + 4p$

(iii) $3x + x$ (viii) $5t - t$

(iv) $4y - 2y$ (ix) $9x^2 + 2x^2$

(v) $p + 8p$ (x) $3xy + 2xy$

4 Simplify the following:

(i) $15x - 3x - x$

(ii) $3ab - a + 4ab + 2a$

(iii) $7x^2 - 4x^2$

(iv) $14a^2 + 12 - 12a^2 - 3$

(v) $3xy + 4y - 7xy - y$

(vi) $10y^3 - 4y + 6 + 2y^3$

5 Simplify as far as possible:

(i) $3x^2 + 6x^2 - x^2$

(ii) $-x - x$

(iii) $3a + 2b + 4a + 5b$

(iv) $2x^2 + 6x + 3x^2 + 3x$

(v) $2x^2 + 3x^3 + 4x^2 + 5x^3$

(vi) $7w - 2v - w - v$

(vii) $5ab - xy + 3ab + 3xy$

(viii) $3a - b - c + 2a + 4b + 3c$

(ix) $\dfrac{x}{2} + 2y + \dfrac{x}{2} - y$

(x) $4ab + 2cd - 3ab + cd$

6 (i) Copy and complete the diagram, by writing $(3x + 4y)$ in ten different ways.

(ii) Which expression is the simplest?

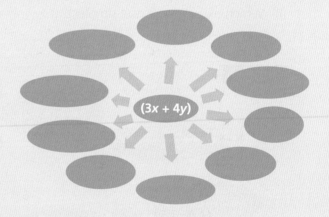

7 Simplify the following:

(i) $3x^2 + 10x - x^2 - 12x + 1$

(ii) $6a^2 - a + 5a - 3 + 3a^2$

(iii) $8x^3 + 2x^2 - 6x^3 - 15$

(iv) $14a^2 + 5 - 3a - 4a^2$

(v) $5xy + 4y - 2xy - 8y$

(vi) $5y^3 - 10y^2 + 6 + 2y^3 + 4y - 8$

8 Find the perimeter of (total distance around) these shapes. Your answers will contain the variable a and numbers.

(i)

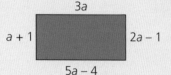

(ii)

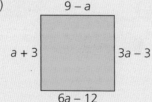

(iii)

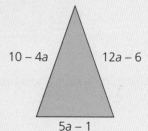

$= 3 + 13a$

Section 12C Multiplication of Terms

Algebra Rules

 Key Points

- Only like terms may be added or subtracted, but **any terms** may be multiplied.
- To multiply terms: number × number, variable × variable.
- Recall: When we write a^m, a is called the **base** and m is the **index**.
- When multiplying powers with the same base, add the indices: $a^m a^n = a^{m+n}$
  Examples: $(2^3)(2^5) = 2^8$ and $(x^3)(x^5) = x^8$
- When dividing powers with the same base, subtract the indices: $a^m \div a^n = a^{m-n}$
  Examples: $(2^5) \div (2^2) = 2^3$ and $x^5 \div x^2 = x^3$
- When raising a power to another power, multiply the indices: $(a^m)^n = a^{mn}$.
  Examples: $(2^3)^2 = 2^6$ and $(x^3)^2 = x^6$

Example 1

Simplify $(3x)(4y)$.

Solution

$(3x)(4y) = (3)(4)(x)(y) = 12xy$

> ❯ Recall: The **associative law** says that we can multiply terms in any order.

We say that $(3x)$ and $(4y)$ are two **factors** of $12xy$.

Example 2

Simplify $(4a)(a^3)$.

Solution

$(4a)(a^3) = (4a^1)(1a^3) = (4)(1)(a^1)(a^3)$
$$= 4a^{1+3} = 4a^4$$

> ❯ Recall: a is really $1a^1$

We say that $(4a)$ and (a^3) are two **factors** of $4a^4$.

Example 3

Simplify:

(i) $(5x^2)(4x^3) = 20x^5$

(ii) $(-2xy)(6xy) = -12x^2y^2$

(iii) $(a^2)(4a^2)(6) = 24a^4$

Solution

(i) $(5x^2)(4x^3)$

$= (5)(4)(x^2)(x^3)$

$= 20x^5$

(ii) $(-2xy)(6xy)$

$= (-2)(6)(x)(x)(y)(y)$

$= -12x^2y^2$

(iii) $(a^2)(4a^2)(6)$

$= (4)(6)(a^2)(a^2)$

$= 24a^4$

Algebra 1

1 Simplify each of the following by multiplication:

(i) $5(3x)$ $15x$ (iv) $2x(10x)$ $20x^2$

(ii) $(3a)(4)$ $12a$ (v) $2a(3x)$ $6ax$

(iii) $6(3m^2)$ $18m^2$ (vi) $5m^3(3m)$ $15m^4$

2 Simplify these by multiplication:

(i) $(-5x)(3)$ (iv) $9x(-10x)$

(ii) $(3)(-4m)$ (v) $(-2a)(5x)$

(iii) $(-6)(-4m^2)$ (vi) $7m^2(-3m^3)$

3 Simplify each of the following by multiplication:

(i) $xy(x)$ (iv) $2x(10x)$

(ii) $(3ab)(4b)$ (v) $4a(7x)$

(iii) $6mn(3mn)$ (vi) $8m^3(2m^2)$

4 Multiply these:

(i) $(-5ab)(4)$ (iv) $(mn)(-10mn)(m)$

(ii) $(2mn)(-4mn)$ (v) $(-3ab)(5a^2b^2)$

(iii) $(-6x)(-4x^2y)$ (vi) $12m^2(-5m^4)$

5 Simplify each of the following:

(i) $(x^2)(x^3)$ (iv) $(a^3)(a)$

(ii) $(x^4)(x^7)$ (v) $(3a)(5a^2)$

(iii) $(a^5)(a^{10})$

6 Simplify each of the following:

(i) $(5x^3)(2x^2)$ (iv) $(x)(x)(x)$

(ii) $(4b^5)(3b^3)$ (v) $(x)(y)(x)(y)$

(iii) $(4y^2)(6y^3)$

7 Simplify each of the following:

(i) $(3)(6x)$ (iv) $(4xy)(3xy)$

(ii) $(3y)(9)$ (v) $(-3x)(4)$

(iii) $(4y)(3y)$

8 Simplify each of the following:

(i) $(3a^4)(5a^2)$ (iv) $(9m)(-4m)$

(ii) $(6y^2)(6y^3)$ (v) $(8p)(-5p)$

(iii) $(3x)(5x)$

9 Simplify each of the following:

(i) $(-4t)(6t)$ (iv) $(5x)(3x^3)$

(ii) $(-6t)(-2t)$ (v) $(10b^3)(b^5)$

(iii) $(-3w^2)(2w^3)$

10 Simplify each of the following:

(i) $(4x)^2$ (iv) $(5m^2y^3)^2$

(ii) $(3x^2y)^2$ (v) $(10a^2b^2)^2$

(iii) $(-2x)^3$

11 Simplify each of the following:

(i) $(-2x)(-x)(-8x)$ (iii) $(-4x)(x)(3y)$ (v) $(3x^2)(4xy)(-6y^2)$ $= -72x^3y^3$

(ii) $(3x)(-2y)(-6x)$ (iv) $(-4xy)(x)(y)$

> Recall: **only like terms** may be **added**, but you can **multiply** any term by any term.

12 The expressions below are a mixture of additions, subtractions and multiplications. Simplify them where possible. If you cannot simplify, then write it down and put a tick ✓ beside it.

(i) $3xy + 4xy$ (vi) $5p - 6q$ (xi) $(5x^2)(6x)$

(ii) $(3xy)(4xy)$ (vii) $4a^2b + 6a^2b$ (xii) $5x^2 - 6x$

(iii) $3xy - 4xy$ (viii) $(4a^2b)(6a^2b)$ (xiii) $6x^3 + x^3$

(iv) $5p + 6q$ (ix) $4a^2b - 6a^2b$ (xiv) $(6x^3)(x^3)$ $6x^6$

(v) $(5p)(6q)$ (x) $5x^2 + 6x$ (xv) $6x^3 - x^3$ $+5x^6$

Section 12D Multiplication of Expressions

- Multiplication with brackets can be done by two methods:
  - the **array** method
  - the **distributive** method
- Both methods apply the **distributive law**, which says that multiplication is **distributive** over addition and subtraction.

Example 1

Multiply: (i) $3(5x + 3y + 4)$ (ii) $5(2x^2 - 7x + 3)$ (iii) $4x(5x^2 - 10)$

Solution

Method 1	Method 2
Rearrange the question into an array (grid).	Distribute the number across the three terms inside the bracket.
(i) 	×	5x	+3y	+4	 	3	15x	+9y	+12	 $3(5x + 3y + 4) = 15x + 9y + 12$	$3 (5x + 3y + 4)$ $= 15x + 9y + 12$
(ii) 	×	2x²	−7x	+3	 	5	10x²	−35x	+15	 $5(2x^2 - 7x + 3) = 10x^2 - 35x + 15$	$5 (2x^2 - 7x + 3)$ $= 10x^2 - 35y + 12$
(iii) 	×	5x²	−10	 	4x	20x³	−40x	 $4x(5x^2 - 10) = 20x^3 - 40x$	$4x (5x^2 - 10)$ $= 20x^3 - 40x$

Example 2

Simplify $3(x + 2y + 3) + 2(3x - 4y - 1)$.

Solution

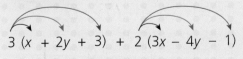

$3 (x + 2y + 3) + 2 (3x - 4y - 1)$ ... distribute the number across the terms inside the brackets

$= 3x + 6y + 9 + 6x - 8y - 2$ ... write out all terms

$= 3x + 6x + 6y - 8y + 9 - 2$ ... collect like terms together

$= 9x - 2y + 7$ ... add/subtract like terms, and simplify the expression

Algebra 1

Key Points

1. To remove the brackets, you are multiplying so you use the rules for multiplication.
2. When the brackets are gone you are adding/subtracting, so you use the rules for addition/subtraction.

Example 3

Simplify $x(2x^2 + 3x + 1) - (x^2 - x - 2)$.

Solution

$x (2x^2 + 3x + 1) + 1 (x^2 - x - 2)$ ... distribute the number across the terms inside the brackets

$= 2x^3 + 3x^2 + x - x^2 + x + 2$ ... be careful with signs

$= 2x^3 + 3x^2 - x^2 + x + x + 2$

$= 2x^3 + 2x^2 + 2x + 2$ ... simplify the expression

Activity 12.4

1 Multiply out the following arrays (grids). Then write your solutions below.

(i)
×	x	$+2$
3	$3x$	6

$3(x + 2) = 3x + 6$

(ii)
×	$2a$	$+3b$	-6
5	$10a$	$15b$	-30

$5(2a + 3b - 6) = 10a + 15b - 30$

(iii)
×	$5x$	$-y$	-6
4	$20x$	$-4y$	-24

$4(5x - y - 6) = 20x - 4y - 24$

(iv)
×	$2x^2$	$+5x$	-6
$3x$			

$3x(2x^2 + 5x - 6) =$

(v)
×	$4x^2$	$-5x$	-1
$-6x$			

$-6x(4x^2 - 5x - 1) =$

(vi)
×	$4x^2$	$-x$	-1
$-x$			

$-x(4x^2 - x - 1) =$

2 Multiply out the brackets and simplify:

(i) $3(x + 4)$ $3x + 12$ (v) $4(2x + 5)$ $8x + 20$

(ii) $5(a - 6)$ $5a - 30$ (vi) $8(3x - 1)$ $24x - 8$

(iii) $4(p - 3)$ $4p - 12$ (vii) $3(6x - 5)$ $18x - 15$

(iv) $8(x - 8)$ $8x - 64$ (viii) $2(3x - 12)$ $6x - 24$

3 Multiply out the brackets and simplify. Be careful with signs.

(i) $-5(x + 3)$ $-5x - 15$ (v) $-1(3x - 3)$

(ii) $-2(a - 5)$ $-2a + 10$ (vi) $-(5x - 5)$

(iii) $-6(p + 4)$ $-6p - 24$ (vii) $4(-6x + 2)$

(iv) $-8a(a - 1)$ $-8a^2 + 8a$ (viii) $-2(5 - 3y)$

4 Multiply out the following.

(i) $5(3x - 2y - 1)$ $15x - 10y - 5$

(ii) $4x(3x^2 - 7x - 2)$

(iii) $3(x - y - 2)$

(iv) $3x^2(4x + 7)$

(v) $-6x^2(7x - 2)$

(vi) $6x(3x^2 + 2x + 10)$

(vii) $-x(x - y - 1)$

(viii) $3x(3x + 2y - 7)$ $9x^2 + 6xy - 21x$

5 Multiply out the brackets and simplify where possible.

   (i) $3(x + 2) + 5(2x + 3)$ $3x + 6 + 10x + 15$

  (ii) $2(x - 1) + 3(4x + 2)$

 (iii) $4(2p - 5) + 3(3p + 1)$

 (iv) $5(m - 4) - 2(3m + 6)$

  (v) $3(x + 2y - 3) + 2(2x - y - 1)$

 (vi) $4(2a - b + 4) - 3(a + 2b - 5)$

 (vii) $2(3p + 2q + 6) + 3(2p + 4q - 5)$

(viii) $6(x - 2y - 1) - 3(2x + y - 4)$

6 Multiply out the brackets and simplify where possible.

   (i) $2(x^2 - 4x + 5) - 5(x^2 + x - 2)$

  (ii) $4(3x^2 + 4x - 1) - (3x^2 - 3x - 7)$

 (iii) $x(4x^2 - 5x - 2) - (4x + 6)$

 (iv) $3x(x^2 - 1) - (x^2 + 2)$

  (v) $2(6x^2 - 4x + 6) - 3x(5x - 2)$

 (vi) $5m(m - 3) - 2(m^2 - m - 1)$

 (vii) $p^2(p - 1) + p(p - 1) + (p - 1)$

(viii) $4a^2(2a + 1) - 2a(2a + 1) + (2a - 3)$

$$= 8a^3 + 4a^2 - 4a^2 - 2a + 2a - 3$$
$$= 8a^3 - 3$$

Section 12E **Binomial Multiplication**

A **binomial** is an expression with two terms, for example: $3x + 4$

Example 1

Multiply: $(x + 2)(x + 3)$.

Solution

To multiply out the expression, the array method or the distributive law can be used.

Method 1

Multiply $(x + 2)(x + 3)$ by completing the array below.

×	x	$+3$
x	x^2	$+3x$
$+2$	$+2x$	$+6$

Collect terms from the highlighted boxes: $x^2 + 2x + 3x + 6$, and then simplify.

Answer: $x^2 + 5x + 6$

Method 2

$(x + 2)(x + 3) = x\,(x + 3) + 2\,(x + 3)$ ... the distributive law

             $= x^2 + 3x + 2x + 6$ ... add/subtract like terms and simplify

Answer: $x^2 + 5x + 6$

Example 2

 (i) 3 and 4 are factors of a certain number. What is that number?

(ii) $(3x - 4)$ and $(2x + 3)$ are factors of an expression.
     Find the expression in its simplest form.

Solution

(i) We get the number by multiplying the factors: $(3)(4) = 12$

(ii) We get the expression by multiplying the factors:

$(3x - 4)(2x + 3)$

$= 3x(2x + 3) - 4(2x + 3)$

$= 6x^2 + 9x - 8x - 12$

$= 6x^2 + x - 12$

[handwritten: 9¼]

[handwritten: $x^2 + xa + 2x + 2a = x^2 + 5x + 6$]

[handwritten: $= ax + 2x - 5x = 6$]

Activity 12.5

1 Complete the following multiplication arrays. Simplify your answers as far as possible.

(i)

×	x	−3
x	x^2	$-3x$
+2	$+2x$	-6

$(x + 2)(x - 3) =$

(ii)

×	$2x$	+5
x		
−1		

$(x - 1)(2x + 5) =$

(iii)

×	$2a$	−1
a		
+5		

$(a + 5)(2a - 1) =$

(iv)

×	p	−6
p		
+7		

$(p + 7)(p - 6) =$

(v)

×	m	+3
$3m$		
−2		

$(3m - 2)(m + 3) =$

(vi)

×	y	−6
y		
+3		

$(y + 3)(y - 6) =$

2 Multiply out and simplify.

(i) $(x + 1)(x + 5)$ (iv) $(y + 6)(y + 5)$

(ii) $(a + 3)(a + 2)$ (v) $(p + 4)(p + 4)$

(iii) $(b + 5)(b + 7)$ (vi) $(x + 6)(x + 8)$

3 Multiply out and simplify.

(i) $(x + 1)(x - 4)$ (iv) $(y + 2)(y - 1)$

(ii) $(a - 2)(a + 7)$ (v) $(p - 10)(p + 2)$

(iii) $(b - 2)(b - 4)$ (vi) $(x - 6)(x - 3)$

4 Multiply out and simplify.

(i) $(3x + 1)(2x - 4)$

(ii) $(5a - 2)(3a + 5)$

(iii) $(4b - 2)(5b - 4)$

(iv) $(3y + 2)(2y - 4)$

(v) $(p - 6)(2p + 2)$

(vi) $(4x - 6)(2x - 2)$

5 Multiply these out and simplify.

(i) $(5p + 2)(2p + 5)$

(ii) $(2x - 7)(3x - 5)$

(iii) $(7x - 2)(3x + 4)$

(iv) $(2p + 3)(p + 4)$

(v) $(4a + 3)(2a + 1)$

(vi) $(2y - 3)(4y + 5)$

(vii) $(2a + 1)(a - 5)$

(viii) $(x - 4)(x - 6)$

6 (i) 2 and 5 are factors of a certain number. What is the number?

(ii) $(x + 2)$ and $(x + 5)$ are factors of some expression. Find the expression in its simplest form.

7 The factors of some expressions are given below. Find each expression in its simplest form.

(i) $(x - 2)$ and $(x + 1)$

(ii) $(3x + 1)$ and $(x - 4)$

(iii) $(a + 2)$ and $(3a + 1)$

(iv) $(5a - 1)$ and $(a + 2)$

8 Find the area of this rectangle (in terms of x).

$x + 3$

$2x + 1$

9 Find the area of this rectangle (in terms of x).

$x - 3$

$3x + 2$

10 Multiply out the expressions below, using a method of your choice.

(i) $(x + 2)^2$

(ii) $(b - 4)^2$

(iii) $(2m + 1)^2$

(iv) $(3n - 4)^2$

11 Find the area of this square (in terms of x).

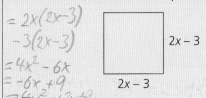

$2x - 3$

$2x - 3$

$= 2x(2x-3)$
$-3(2x-3)$
$= 4x^2 - 6x$
$= -6x + 9$
$= 4x^2 - 12x + 9$

12 If $(x + 3)$ is one factor of $x^2 + 7x + 12$, find the other factor.

13 If $(x + 1)(x + a) = x^2 + 8x + 7$, find a by filling in the array.

×	?	?
x	x^2	?
$+1$	?	$+a$

14 If $(x + 2)(x + a) = x^2 + 5x + 6$, find the value of a.

$x(x+a) = x^2 + xa$
$2(x+a) = 2x + 2a$ $a = 3$

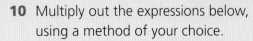

Algebra 1

Revision Activity 12

1 Simplify each of the following:

(a) $2ab + 7ab$

(b) $(2x)(7x)$

(c) $(x^2)(x^7)$

(d) $(5y)(3y)$

(e) $3x^2 - 7x^2$

(f) $(2x)^2$

(g) $(a^{-2})(a^3)$

2 Simplify each of the following:

(a) $3x^2 - 6x + 7 + 2x - 3 - 5x^2$

(b) $a + 7b - 6a + 13b$

(c) $x + z + y + 2x$

(d) $2x^2 - 25 - 7x + 6 - 2$

(e) $14 - 6x^2 - 7 + 5x^2 - x$

(f) $9d - 7e + 3d + 4e$

(g) $-5x^2 - 3x^2 + 5x - 7x + 11$

(h) $-13x^2 + 5x + 8x^2 - 2 - 6x + 9$

3 Find the value of each of the following expressions when $a = -5$ and $b = 4$.

(a) $4a - 2b$

(b) $-a - 3b$

(c) $3ab - 5b$

(d) $a^2b + 6ab^2 - 3$

4 Find the value of each of the following expressions when $x = 7$.

(a) $x^2 + 2x - 4$

(b) $6x^2 - x + 8$

(c) $2x^2 + 5x + 2$

(d) $8x^2 - 7x + 4$

5 Expand and simplify these expressions:

(a) $a(a - b) + b(a - b) + b^2$

(b) $-6(a - 2) + 5(-6a - 3)$

(c) $3(2x - 2y) - 2(x - 3y)$

(d) $-4(3y + 2a) - 3(2y + 2a)$

(e) $-3(d - 6e - 4) - 2(4d + 3e + 5)$

(f) $3x(2x^2 - x + 1) - 2(x^2 - 2x - 1)$

(g) $y(6y^2 - 3y - 1) + 3(y^2 - 2y - 1)$

6 Write down, in its simplest form, an expression for the perimeter of the shapes below.

(a)

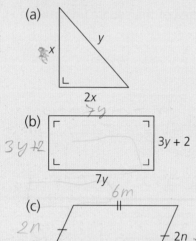

(b)

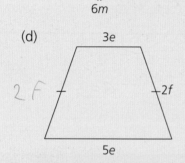

(c)

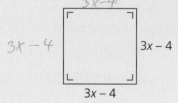

(d)

3e

2f   2f

5e

(e) Find both the perimeter and the area of the square below.

3x − 4

$3x − 4$ $3x − 4$

$3x − 4$

7 Multiply out the brackets below using the array method.

(a) $(2x + 5)(x + 4)$

(b) $(y - 1)(y - 3)$

(c) $(2a - 3)(5a + 1)$

(d) $(3z - 6)(2z - 5)$

8 Multiply each of the following and simplify.

(a) $(5x - 2)(4x + 3)$ (d) $(2a - 1)(5a + 4)$

(b) $(2a - b)(3a + 2b)$ (e) $(3x + 5)(2x - 2)$

(c) $(2x + 5y)(2x - 5y)$

9 Write out the instructions given below using a variable and constants.

Steps in words	Steps in letters
Think of a number	4
Add 6	10
Multiply the answer by 3	30
Subtract 12	18
Add 6	24
Divide by 3	8
Subtract the original number	4
What is the answer?	4

Exam-style Questions

1 If $a = 3$ and $b = 5$, find the value of:

(a) $a + 2b$ (b) $ab - 6$

$(3)(5) - 6 = 9$

$3 + 2(5)$

$= 13$

JCOL 2010 Paper 1

2 Multiply $(x - 2)$ by $(-3x + 11)$. Write your answer in its simplest form.

JCOL 2010 Paper 1

3 The factors of $t^2 + at + b$ are $(t + 7)$ and $(t + 9)$. Find the values of a and b.

KEY WORDS AND PHRASES

- **Algebra**
- **Term**
- **Coefficient**
- **Expression**
- **Like terms**
- **Unlike terms**
- **Factor**
- **Indices**
- **Distributive law**
- **Array**
- **Binomials**
- **Substitution**

Chapter Summary 12

Things you must know:	
	Meaning/Explanation
	Remember that multiplication is indicated by one or more sets of brackets.
$2(3)$	means '2 times 3'
$(2)(3)$	means '2 times 3'
$(x)(y)$	means 'x times y'
	Note: There are no signs between the brackets, so make sure you understand the difference between $(2)(3) = 6$ and $(2) + (3) = 5$.
x	$+1x$
$-x$	$-1x$, which means '-1 times x'
$5x$	5 times x, or 5 multiplied by x
$5 + x$	5 add x, or 5 plus x
$x - 3$	x less 3, or 3 less than x
xy	x multiplied by y
$2xy$	2 multiplied by x multiplied by y
$\dfrac{x}{2}$	means x divided by 2
Order of operations applies in algebra (**BIRDMAS**).	

Like terms have the same variables with equal powers, for example:

- $2y$, $7y$, $-9y$ are like terms.
- $3xz$, $-2xz$ and $12xz$ are like terms.
- $3abc^2$ and $5abc^2$ are like terms.

■ Only like terms may be added or subtracted.

- When adding like terms, the powers of the variables do not change.

■ Both like and unlike terms can be multiplied and divided.

■ When we write a^m, **a** is called the base and **m** is the index.

■ If the bases are the same:

- add the indices to multiply:

$$a^m a^n = a^{m+n}$$

- subtract the indices to divide:

$$\frac{a^m}{a^n} = a^{m-n}$$

■ $(a^m)^n = a^{m \times n}$

■ Expressions can be multiplied using the distributive law: $a(b + c) = ab + ac$

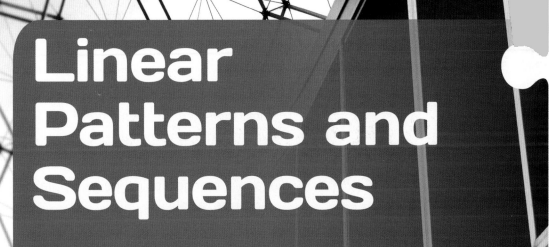

Chapter 13

Linear Patterns and Sequences

Learning Intentions

In this chapter, you will learn about:

- Sequences
- Patterns in sequences – relationships
- Recognising linear relationships
- The use of variables to make rules for a pattern
- Predicting terms of a sequence with variables

LO: N.4, AF.1(a-b),
U.4, U.5, U.6, U.13

 ## Section 13A Patterns

In the BBC television series, *The Story of Maths*, the narrator, Marcus du Sautoy, says in his introduction:

'I am a mathematician. I see myself as a pattern searcher, hunting down the hidden structures that lie behind the apparent chaos and complexity of the world around us.'

In this section we will look at ways to see **patterns** in numbers and situations. The aim is to **generalise** and **predict** from the pattern what will happen next.

A **pattern** is a set of objects, numbers, letters, shapes, pictures, symbols or diagrams which repeat in a set way.

Below are some images of repeating patterns found in nature.

Snowflake   DNA spirals   Peacock   Sunflower   Butterfly

Let's have a look at some patterns in Example 1 and see if you can be a pattern searcher like Marcus du Sautoy.

Example 1

Write down the next three items in each of the patterns below:

(i) 5, 10, 15, 20

(ii) apple, orange, apple, orange

(iii) Sue, Bob, Tom, Sue, Bob, Tom, Sue

(iv) ■ ▲ ■ ▲

(v) 100, 90, 80

(vi) green, amber, red, green, amber

(vii) a, b, c, d, e, a, b, c

(viii) x, y, z, x, y, z, x

(ix) cat, dog, mouse, cat, dog, mouse

Solution

The next three items in each pattern are shown in bold or underlined:

(i) 5, 10, 15, 20, **25**, **30**, **35**

(ii) apple, orange, apple, orange, **apple**, **orange**, **apple**

(iii) Sue, Bob, Tom, Sue, Bob, Tom, Sue, **Bob**, **Tom**, **Sue**

(iv) ■ ▲ ■ ▲ ■ ▲ ■

(v) 100, 90, 80, **70**, **60**, **50**

(vi) green, amber, red, green, amber, **red**, **green**, **amber**

(vii) a, b, c, d, e, a, b, c, **d**, **e**, **a**

(viii) x, y, z, x, y, z, x, **y**, **z**, **x**

(ix) cat, dog, mouse, cat, dog, mouse, **cat**, **dog**, **mouse**

Example 2

A three-shape repeating pattern is shown below:

(i) If the pattern continued, what would the 28th shape be?

(ii) If the pattern continued, what would the 72nd shape be?

(iii) If the pattern continued, what would the 300th shape be?

(iv) If the pattern continued, what would the 2000th shape be?

Solution

(i) ■ The first shape in the pattern is ▬.

■ The second shape in the pattern is ▢.

■ The third shape in the pattern is ●.

■ The pattern is repeated every three shapes.

To find the 28th shape, we can use two methods.

Method 1

We could find the shape by drawing a table as shown below:

Pattern number	Shape	Pattern number	Shape	Pattern number	Shape	Pattern number	Shape	Pattern number	Shape
1	▬	7	▬	13	▬	19	▬	25	▬
2	▢	8	▢	14	▢	20	▢	26	▢
3	●	9	●	15	●	21	●	27	●
4	▬	10	▬	16	▬	22	▬	28	▬
5	▢	11	▢	17	▢	23	▢	29	▢
6	●	12	●	18	●	24	●	30	●

From the table we can see that the 28th shape is .

Method 2

Alternatively, we could find the shape by looking closely at how the pattern repeats:

- The pattern is repeated every three shapes: ▬ ▢ ●.
- To find the 28th shape, divide 28 by 3 (as the pattern repeats every three shapes).

  This gives $\frac{28}{3}$ = 9 with remainder 1.

  This means that the pattern has repeated 9 times, with 1 shape extra.

  The first shape is: ▬.

- So the 28th shape is the first shape in the repeated pattern, i.e. the green rectangle.

You can see that method 2 is much quicker and can be used to solve problems where we need to predict a shape much further along in the pattern.

(ii) $\frac{72}{3}$ = 24, so the 72nd shape is ●.

  Note: If there is no remainder then the shape is the last one in the repeated pattern.

(iii) $\frac{300}{3}$ = 100, so the 300th shape is also a ●.

(iv) $\frac{2000}{3}$ = 666, remainder 2.

  The 2000th shape is the second shape in the repeated pattern: ▢.

1 Write down the next three items in each of the patterns below.

(i) 2, 6, 10, 14

(ii) banana, pear, orange, peach, banana, pear, orange

(iii) Jack, Katie, Conor, Jack, Katie, Conor

(iv)

(v) −6, −4, −2, 0, 2

(vi) pink, purple, blue, pink, purple, blue, pink

(vii) e, g, b, d, a, e, g

(viii) horse, cow, pig, horse, cow, pig

(ix)

(x) sun, moon, star, sun, moon, star

2 Here is a four-shape repeating pattern:

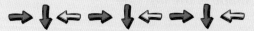

(i) Describe how the pattern repeats in words.

(ii) Find out what the 9th shape is, by drawing a table to show how the pattern repeats.

(iii) From the repeating pattern, write down the 16th shape in the pattern.

(iv) If the pattern continued, what would the 61st shape be?

(v) If the pattern continued, what would the 142nd shape be?

3 Here is a four arrow repeating pattern:

(i) Describe how the pattern repeats in words.

(ii) Find out what the 15th arrow is, by drawing a table to show how the pattern repeats.

(iii) Use the pattern to find the 50th arrow in the pattern.

(iv) If the pattern continued, what would the 673rd arrow be?

(v) If the pattern continued, what would the 1500th arrow be?

4 Here is a repeating sticker pattern:

(i) Describe how the pattern repeats in words.

(ii) What symbol would the 13th sticker be?

(iii) What symbol would the 24th sticker be?

(iv) What symbol would the 26th sticker be?

(v) What symbol would the 43rd sticker be?

(vi) What symbol would the 3467th sticker be?

5 Here is a four-arrow repeating pattern:

(i) Predict which arrow the 12th arrow in the pattern would be.

(ii) Predict which arrow the 54th arrow in the pattern would be.

(iii) If the pattern continued, what colour would the 233rd arrow be?

(iv) If the pattern continued, what colour would the 503rd arrow be?

(v) Predict what colour the 5000th arrow in the pattern would be.

6 In the 100-square grid below, some of the squares are coloured blue.

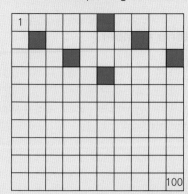

(i) Copy the grid and continue the pattern.

(ii) Write down the numbers that represent the blue squares.

(iii) In words, write down what you notice about the blue square numbers.

(iv) What colour would the 102nd square be?

(v) What colour would the 240th square be?

(vi) What colour would the 223rd square be?

7 For each sequence of patterns, draw the next three shapes and thus find the next three numbers in the sequence.

(a)

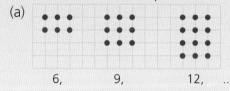

6,   9,   12,   ...

(b)

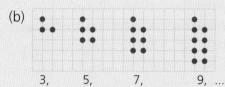

3,   5,   7,   9, ...

(c)

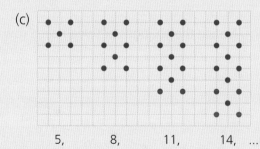

5,   8,   11,   14,   ...

(d)

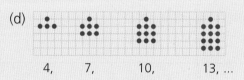

4,   7,   10,   13, ...

8 Find the next three numbers in each sequence:

(a) 3, 5, 7, 9, 11, ...

(b) 12, 17, 22, ...

(c) 50, 47, 44, 41, 38, ...

(d) 5, 8, 11, 14, 17, ...

(e) 6, 8, 10, 12, 14, ...

(f) 20, 19, 18, 17, 16, ...

(g) 47, 41, 35, 29, 23, ...

(h) 9, 6, 3, 0, ...

(i) −17, −13, −9, ...

9 Copy each sequence and fill in the missing number.

(a) 4, 7, ☐, 13, 16, ...

(b) 7, ☐, 15, 19, 23, ...

(c) 89, 80, 71, ☐, 53, ...

(d) 3, 11, ☐, 27, 35, ...

(e) 15, ☐, 27, 33, 39, ...

(f) 88, 77, 66, ☐, 44, 33, ...

(g) −72, −60, −48, ☐, −24, −12, ...

Section 13B **Sequences**

A **sequence** is an ordered list of items.

> A **number sequence** is an ordered list of numbers separated by commas which are connected by a rule in some way. Examples are:
>
> $$1, 2, 3, 4, 5, 6, \ldots$$
>
> $$1, 4, 7, 10, 13, \ldots$$
>
> $$1, 4, 9, 16, \ldots$$
>
> The numbers in the sequence are called **terms**.

Linear Patterns and Sequences

- We can describe a sequence by saying how to get from one term to the next. This is called the **term-to-term rule**.
- Each term's place in the sequence is called its **position** or **term number**.

    Example: the sequence that starts 3, 5, 7, 9, …

Position (Term number)	1	2	3	4
Sequence	3	5	7	9

- The term-to-term rule is 'add 2'.
- We can use the letter T for the word 'Term'.

    Here $T_1 = 3$, $T_2 = 5$, $T_3 = 7$, etc.

Example: The following is the famous Fibonacci sequence which describes many natural happenings in nature: 1, 1, 2, 3, 5, 8, 13, ….

Here $T_1 = 1$, $T_2 = 1$, $T_3 = 2$, $T_4 = 3$, etc.

Here the term-to-term rule is 'add the two previous terms to get the next one'.

Linear Sequences

In a cinema there are 6 seats in the first row. Each row after the first row contains 4 more seats than the row before it. Below is a diagram of the first three rows of seats in the cinema:

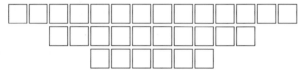

We can draw a table and a graph to see this pattern. Notice the changes between each row in the Number of Seats column of the table.

Row	Number of Seats (S)	Change
1	6	
2	10	+4
3	14	+4
4	18	+4
5	22	+4
6	26	+4

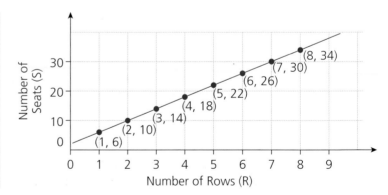

This is an example of a **linear pattern or sequence**.

It is called a linear sequence because the graph of this pattern is a straight line.

A sequence where a constant (the **same** number) is added each time to get the next term is called a **linear sequence** (also called an arithmetic sequence).

The number added each time is called the **common difference** or **first difference**.

Examples :   6, 10, 14, 18, … the common difference is +4

30, 25, 20, 15, … the common difference is −5

Finding Any Term of a Linear Sequence

We would really like to be able to say what the 10th term or the 20th term of a sequence is without having to list all the terms.

This means we need to link the value of a term to its position in the sequence by using a **position-to-term** rule.

This is often referred to as getting the **nth term** or T_n of the sequence.

Example

(i) Write down the next five terms of the sequence 2, 4, 6, 8, 10, ….

(ii) Give the term-to-term rule.

(iii) Complete the following table:

Position (Term number)	1	2			5
Term	2	4			10
Difference		+2			

(iv) Write down the relationship between the position number and the value of the term in each stage of the pattern using a variable.

Solution

(i) 12, 14, 16, 18, 20

(ii) The term-to-term rule is 'add 2'.

(iii)

Position (Term number)	1	2	3	4	5
Term	2	4	6	8	10
Difference		+2	+2	+2	+2

This is a linear sequence. The common difference between each term is 2.

(iv) The sequence is in fact the 2 times tables:

$2 \times 1, 2 \times 2, 2 \times 3, 2 \times 4, …$ etc.

so T_n = '2 times n' = **$2n$**

Key Points

In the Example above:
- 'Every even number' can be written as '2 times (any Natural number)'.
- If we let the letter n stand for the phrase 'any Natural number', then 'every even number' can be written as:
  - $2 \times n$, or
  - $2(n)$, or
  - $2n$, where n is any Natural number.
- As n could be any Natural number, n **varies**. So n is called a **variable**.

Remember

Variables are quantities that can take on different values.

In maths, n, x, y and other letters are commonly used to stand for variables.

The opposite of a variable is a **constant**, which always has the same value.

For example: 2, 56, 2000, 27.789 and $\frac{1}{2}$ are all constants.

1 Sophie started this sequence of numbers: 3, 6, 9, 12, …

  (i) Write down the next five terms in this sequence.

  (ii) Describe the sequence in words.

  (iii) Copy and complete the sentences: 'These numbers are all divisible by _____. They are also multiples of _____.'

  (iv) Copy and complete this table.

Term number	Term	Pattern
1	3	3(1)
2	6	3(2)
3	9	
4	12	
	…	
	24	
	99	

  (v) Write a rule in words which defines all of these numbers.

  (vi) Sophie's rule to work out any term of the sequence is 3n, where n is the term number. Explain how she knows this.

2 Here is a strip of red and green blocks:

    `1 2 3 4 5 6`

  (i) Assume that the pattern continues indefinitely. Copy and complete this table.

Block position	Colour
1	Red
2	Green
3	
4	
5	
6	
7	
8	
9	
10	

  (ii) (a) List the position numbers of the first ten red blocks.

(b) What do you notice about these numbers?

(c) List the position numbers of the first ten green blocks.

(d) What do you notice about these numbers?

(e) What colour is the 50th block? How do you know?

(f) What colour is the 51st block? How do you know?

(g) What position number is the 100th green block? Explain your answer.

(h) What position number is the 100th red block? Explain your answer.

  (iii) Gillian said: 'To find the position number for a green block, I just have to work out 2n, where n is any Natural number.' Explain what Gillian meant.

  (iv) Barry said: 'To find the position number for a red block, you work out 2n – 1, where n is any Natural number.' Does this work? Explain what 2n – 1 means in this context.

3 Look at this strip of coloured blocks:

    `1 2 3 4 5 6`

  (i) Assume that the pattern continues indefinitely. Copy and complete this table.

Block position		
Red	Yellow	Green
1	2	3
4		6

(ii) (a) What is the pattern in the position numbers for the red blocks?

(b) What is the pattern in the position numbers for the yellow blocks?

(c) What is the pattern in the position numbers for the green blocks?

(d) Which number pattern is easiest to predict?

(e) What colour is the 12th block?

(f) What colour is the 24th block? How do you know?

(g) What colour is the 25th block? How do you know?

(h) What colour is the 23rd block? How do you know?

(i) What colour is the 100th block? How do you know?

(j) What colour is the 1000th block? How do you know?

(iii) Make a rule to work out the position number of a green block.

(iv) Make a rule to work out the position number of a yellow block.

(v) Make a rule to work out the position number of a red block.

4 Adi made these patterns with coloured squares.

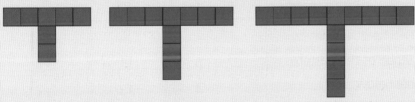

(i) Copy and complete this table.

Pattern number	Number of blue squares	Number of red squares	Total number of squares
1			
2			
3			
4			
5			
6			

(ii) Give a rule for the number of blue squares in any pattern.

(iii) Give a rule in words for the number of red squares in any pattern.

(iv) Give a rule for the number of red squares in any pattern using a variable.

(v) Give a rule in words for the total number of squares in any pattern.

(vi) Adi's rule to work out the total number of squares in any pattern is $3n + 4$, where n is the number of the pattern.

(a) What does the 4 stand for in this rule?

(b) What does the $3n$ stand for in this rule?

(vii) Adi wants to make pattern number 10.

(a) How many squares does she need?

(b) How many of these are red?

(viii) Adi made a pattern using a total of 28 squares.

(a) What number pattern is this?

(b) How many red squares are in it?

(ix) If Adi had just 12 blue squares and 42 red squares, what is:

(a) the biggest pattern number possible

(b) the total number of squares for this pattern?

Section 13C Deriving a Method for Finding Any Term in a Linear Sequence

From our work in Activity 12.2, we can observe the following rule:

> Any term T_n in a linear sequence = (common difference) × n ± some number

This means that we just need to figure out what number to add to or subtract from the (common difference) × n.

Example

The first three stages of a pattern of squares are shown below.

Stage 1   Stage 2   Stage 3

(i) Draw the fourth stage of the pattern.

(ii) Complete the table below:

Stage number	Number of squares	Difference
1		
2		
3		
4		
5		

(iii) Describe in words how the number of squares is growing.

(iv) Find T_n, the relationship between the stage number and the number of squares in each stage of the pattern.

Solution

(i)
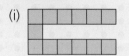

(ii)

Stage number	Number of squares	Difference
1	7	
2	9	+2
3	11	+2
4	13	+2
5	15	+2

(iii) 2 extra squares are added each time.

(iv) The common difference is 2, so the sequence is linked to the 2 times tables: 2 × 1, 2 × 2, 2 × 3, 2 × 4 … etc = 2, 4, 6, 8, 10, …

so the $T_n = 2n \pm b$, where b is some number.

To work out b, compare $T_n = 2n$ and the given sequence 7, 9, 11, 13, …

For $T_n = 2n$, $T_1 = 2(1) = 2$.

We have to add 5 in order to get 7 which is the first term of the sequence.

So $T_n = 2n + 5$

Check for T_2 and T_3:

$T_2 = 2(1) + 5 = 2 + 5 = 7$ ✓
$T_3 = 2(2) + 5 = 4 + 5 = 9$ ✓

1 The first three stages of a pattern of squares are shown below:

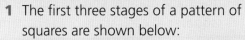

Stage 1 Stage 2 Stage 3

(i) Copy the three stages above into your copybook and draw the fourth stage.

(ii) Complete the table below:

Stage number	Number of squares	Difference
1		
2		
3		
4		
5		

(iii) How many squares do you add each time?

(iv) The first five multiples of 2 are: 2, 4, 6, 8, 10. What do you add to these numbers to get the numbers of squares in each stage?

(v) Copy and complete:
number of squares = ... × stage number + ...

(vi) Write down the formula using S for the number of squares and n for stage number.

(vii) How many squares are in the 10th stage of the pattern?

2 The first four stages of a pattern of stars are shown below:

(i) Draw the fifth and sixth stages.

(ii) Complete the table below:

Stage number	Number of stars
1	
2	
3	
4	
5	
6	
7	

(iii) Describe in words how the number of stars is growing.

(iv) Write down the relationship between the stage number and the number of stars in each stage of the pattern.

(v) How many stars are there in the 12th stage of the pattern?

3 The first four stages of a pattern of yellow squares and blue squares are shown below:

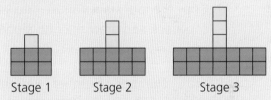

Stage 1 Stage 2 Stage 3

(i) Draw the fourth stage of the pattern.

(ii) Complete the table below:

Stage number	Number of yellow squares	Number of blue squares
1		
2		
3		
4		
5		

(iii) Describe in words how the number of yellow squares is growing.

(iv) Describe in words how the number of blue squares is growing.

(v) Write down the relationship between the stage number and the number of **yellow** squares in each stage of the pattern.

(vi) Write down the relationship between the stage number and the number of **blue** squares in each stage of the pattern.

(vii) Write down the relationship between the stage number and the **total** number of squares in each stage of the pattern.

4 Cora is making a pattern of triangles and squares with matches. The first four stages of her pattern are shown below:

Stage 1

Stage 2

Stage 3

Stage 4

(i) Copy the four stages above into your copybook and draw the fifth stage.

(ii) Complete the table below:

Stage number	Number of triangles	Number of squares	Number of matches
1	1	1	6
2			
3			
4			
5			
6			

(iii) Describe in words how the number of **triangles** is growing.

(iv) Describe in words how the number of **squares** is growing.

(v) Describe in words how the number of **matches** is growing.

(vi) Write down the relationship between the stage number and the number of **triangles** in each stage of the pattern.

(vii) Write down the relationship between the stage number and the number of **squares** in each stage of the pattern.

(viii) Write down the relationship between the stage number and the number of **matches** in each stage of the pattern.

(ix) How many matches will Cora need for stage 10 of her pattern?

5 The first four stages of a pattern of yellow squares and green squares are shown below:

Stage 1   Stage 2   Stage 3   Stage 4

(i) Copy the four stages above into your copybook and draw the fifth stage.

(ii) Complete the table below:

Stage number	Number of yellow squares	Number of green squares
1		
2		
3		
4		
5		
6		

(iii) Describe in words how the number of yellow squares is growing.

(iv) Describe in words how the number of green squares is growing.

(v) Write down the relationship between the stage number and the number of **yellow** squares in each stage of the pattern.

(vi) Write down the relationship between the stage number and the number of **green** squares in each stage of the pattern.

(vii) (Write down the relationship between the stage number and the **total** number of squares in each stage of the pattern.

6 The first three stages of a pattern of red squares and blue squares are shown below:

Stage 1   Stage 2   Stage 3

(i) Draw the fourth stage.

(ii) Complete the table below:

Stage number	Number of red squares	Number of blue squares
1		
2		
3		
4		
5		
6		

(iii) Describe in words how the number of red squares is growing.

(iv) Describe in words how the number of blue squares is growing.

(v) Write down the relationship between the stage number and the number of **red** squares in each stage of the pattern.

(vi) Write down the relationship between the stage number and the number of **blue** squares in each stage of the pattern.

(vii) Write down the relationship between the stage number and the **total** number of squares in each stage of the pattern.

Revision Activity 13

1 The first three stages of a pattern of tiles are shown below:

Stage 1   Stage 2   Stage 3   Stage 4

(i) Copy the four stages above into your copybook and draw the fifth and sixth stages.

(ii) Complete the table below:

Stage number	Number of tiles
1	
2	
3	
4	
5	
6	
7	

(iii) Describe in words how the number of tiles is growing.

(iv) Write down the relationship between the stage number and the number of tiles in each stage of the pattern.

2 The first three stages of a pattern are shown below:

  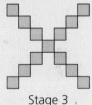

Stage 1   Stage 2   Stage 3

(i) Copy the three stages above into your copybook and draw the fourth stage.

(ii) Complete the table below:

Stage number	Number of squares
1	
2	
3	
4	
5	

(iii) Describe in words how the number of squares is growing.

(iv) Write down the relationship between the stage number and the number of squares in each stage of the pattern.

3 (i) Sketch the fifth stage of the pattern of red and white tiles below:

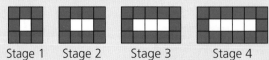

Stage 1   Stage 2   Stage 3   Stage 4

(ii) How many red tiles are needed for the 6th stage?

(iii) For *n* white tiles, how many red tiles will be required?

4 Here are some of Sean's matchstick patterns.

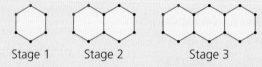

Stage 1   Stage 2   Stage 3

(i) Draw a sketch of Stage 4 and Stage 5 of the patterns.

(ii) Find the relationship between the stage number and the number of matches in Sean's patterns.

(iii) How many matches would it take to make Stage 8 of the patterns?

(iv) Which stage of the patterns takes 51 matches?

Exam-style Question

1 The first three stages of a pattern are shown below.
Each stage is made up of a certain number of shaded discs and a certain number of white discs.

1st Stage   2nd Stage   3rd Stage

(i) Shade in the appropriate discs below to show the 4th stage of the pattern.

(ii) Complete the table below to show how the pattern continues.

Number of shaded discs	Number of white discs
1	5
2	
3	
4	
5	
6	

(iii) In a particular stage of the pattern, there are 21 white discs. How many shaded discs are there in this stage of the pattern?

(iv) Write down the relationship between the number of shaded discs and the number of white discs in each stage of the pattern. State clearly the meaning of any letters you use.

JCOL 2014

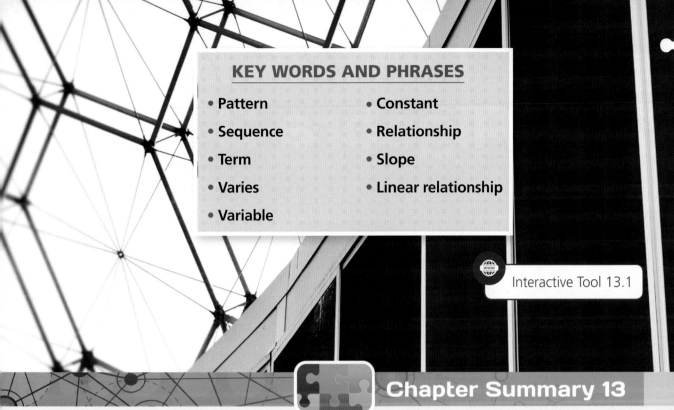

- A **sequence** is an ordered list.
- A **number sequence** is a list of numbers separated by commas which are connected by a rule in some way.
- A **pattern** is a set of objects, numbers, letters, shapes, pictures, symbols or diagrams which repeat in a set way.
- The numbers in a sequence are called **terms.**
- **Variables** are quantities that can take on different values. So, in maths, *n, x, y* and other letters are commonly used to stand for variables.
- The opposite of a variable is a **constant**, which always has the same value.
  For example: 2, 56, 2000, 27.789 and $\frac{1}{2}$ are all constants.
- To find the T_n of the sequence: 1,   3,   5,   7,   9, ...

  Difference = 2

  The multiples of 2 are: 2,   4,   6,   8,   10, ...   2n

  Compare these to the given sequence:

  We need to **subtract 1** to get the given sequence.

  $T_n = 2n - 1$ where n = any term number

Algebra 2

In this chapter, you will learn about:

- The concept of equality
- What is meant by a linear equation
- Solving linear equations in one variable:
  - with one operation
  - with more than one operation
  - with one variable on either side of the equals sign
  - containing brackets
- Using linear equations to solve word problems

LO: AF.2(c), U.3, U.5, U.6, U.13

Section 14A Introducing Linear Equations

Life is all about balance. Real-life examples include:

Justice scales

Work–life balance

Night and day

See-saw

Maths is no different; linear **equations** behave like a balance.

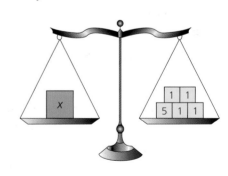

In an **equation**, a term or expression is equal (=) to another term or expression. We say that the equation is **balanced**.

The equals sign divides an equation into two sides: left (LHS) and right (RHS). So for the balance here we know that $x = 5 + 1 + 1 + 1 + 1 = 9$.

When we **solve an equation**, we find the value of the unknown variable or variables (i.e. the letters in the equation).

To keep an equation balanced, any operation applied to one side of the equation must also be applied to the other side. This means that:

- If I add a number to one side of an equation, I must add the **same** number to the other side of the equation.
- If I subtract a number from one side of an equation, I must subtract the **same** number from the other side of the equation.
- If I multiply one side of an equation by a number, I must multiply the other side of the equation by the **same** number.
- If I divide one side of an equation by a number, I must divide the other side of the equation by the **same** number.

Key Point

To solve an equation, whatever you do to one side you must do exactly the same to the other side. This is called balancing the equation.

Section 14B Solving Linear Equations with One Variable

An equation like $h = 5 + 2d$ can represent the height of a sunflower which was 5 cm tall at the start and grew by 2 cm per day. The graph of this equation is a line, so we call it a **linear** equation.

Key Point

In a linear equation containing only x terms (or any variable) and numbers, we must rearrange the equation as follows:

x terms = numbers <u>or</u> **numbers = x terms**

Example 1

Solve $x + 6 = 13$ for x.

Solution

Rearrange the equation so
x terms = numbers:

$$x + 6 = 13$$

$$x + 6 - 6 = 13 - 6 \quad \ldots \text{subtract 6 from both sides}$$

$$\Rightarrow x = 7$$

$$x + 6 = 13$$

$$7 + 6 = 13$$

$$13 = 13 \checkmark \quad \ldots \text{the equation is balanced. So } x = 7.$$

Example 2

Solve $x - 2 = 8$ for x.

Solution

$$x - 2 = 8$$

$$x - 2 + 2 = 8 + 2 \quad \ldots \text{add 2 to both sides to get } x \text{ on the LHS only}$$

$$\Rightarrow x = 10$$

$$x - 2 = 8$$

$$10 - 2 = 8$$

$$8 = 8 \checkmark \quad \ldots \text{the equation is balanced. So } x = 10.$$

Example 3

Solve $-3x = 9$ for x.

Solution

$$-3x = 9$$

$$\frac{-3x}{-3} = \frac{9}{-3} \quad \text{... divide both sides by } -3 \text{ to get } x \text{ on the LHS only}$$

$$\Rightarrow x = -3$$

$$-3x = 9$$

$$-3(-3) = 9$$

$$9 = 9 \checkmark \quad \text{... the equation is balanced. So } x = -3.$$

Example 4

Solve $\frac{x}{7} = 5$ for x.

Solution

$$\frac{x}{7} = 5$$

$$\frac{7(x)}{7} = 7(5) \quad \text{... multiply both sides by 7}$$

$$\Rightarrow x = 35$$

$$\frac{x}{7} = 5$$

$$\frac{35}{7} = 5$$

$$5 = 5 \checkmark \quad \text{... the equation is balanced. So } x = 7.$$

Activity 14.1

Solve for the unknown variable:

1 $a + 9 = 4$

2 $x - 11 = -12$

3 $d + 4 = -6$

4 $y - 2 = 1$

5 $b + 7 = 11$

6 $h - 7 = -4$

7 $h + 14 = 14$

8 $y + 7 = 12$

9 $c + 2 = -5$

10 $b - 9 = 2$

11 $d - 2 = 6$

$= d = 6 + 2$
$= d = 8$

$d = 8$

12 $s - 1 = 6$

13 $m + 5 = -8$

14 $-g - 3 = -6$

15 $x - 1 = -9$

16 $x + 13 = 3$

17 $x - 3 = 3$

18 $-w + 7 = 15$

19 $c - 23 = -20$

20 $-x - 4 = -10$

21 $13n = 39$

22 $6x = -42$

$= \frac{-42}{6} = -7$

23 $-3a = 12$

24 $5d = -25$

25 $-25k = -125$

26 $9y = -63$

27 $12x = 144$

28 $7h = 21$

29 $4m = -16$

30 $8b = -32$

31 $\frac{h}{11} = -2$

32 $\frac{x}{10} = 12$

$x = 120$

33 $\frac{n}{2} = -6$

34 $\frac{p}{4} = 9$

35 $\frac{d}{-6} = 7$

36 $\frac{x}{2} = 8$

37 $\frac{m}{5} = -4$

38 $\frac{y}{-8} = -5$ $\quad y = 40$

39 $\frac{k}{-3} = -1$ $\quad k = 3$

40 $\frac{a}{7} = -3$

$a = -21$

Section 14C Linear Equations with More Than One Operation

Example 1

Solve $7x + 3 = 31$ for x.

Solution

$$7x + 3 = 31$$
$$7x + 3 - 3 = 31 - 3 \quad \text{... subtract 3 from both sides}$$
$$7x = 28$$
$$\frac{7x}{7} = \frac{28}{7} \quad \text{... divide both sides by 7}$$
$$\Rightarrow x = 4$$

Check the answer by substituting $x = 4$ into the original equation:
$$7x + 3 = 31$$
$$7(4) + 3 = 31$$
$$28 + 3 = 31$$
$$31 = 31 \checkmark \quad \text{... the equation is balanced. So } x = 4.$$

Example 2

Solve $2p - 8 = 20$ for p.

Solution

$$2p - 8 = 20$$
$$2p - 8 + 8 = 20 + 8 \quad \text{... add 8 to both sides to get } p \text{ on the LHS only}$$
$$2p = 28$$
$$\frac{2p}{2} = \frac{28}{2} \quad \text{... divide both sides by 2}$$
$$\Rightarrow p = 14$$

Check the answer by substituting $p = 14$ into the original equation:
$$2p - 8 = 20$$
$$2(14) - 8 = 20$$
$$28 - 8 = 20$$
$$20 = 20 \checkmark \quad \text{... the equation is balanced. So } p = 14.$$

Algebra 2

Activity 14.2

Solve the following equations.

1. $20a - 11 = 149$
2. $3y - 1 = 8$
3. $4a + 12 = -16$
4. $3b - 100 = -1$
5. $7d + 45 = -18$
6. $13t + 7 = 150$
7. $441 = 7z + 21$
8. $-5y + 2 = -8$
9. $6k - 2 = 40$
10. $8x - 15 = 65$
11. $2p + 36 = -8$
12. $17m + 5 = 39$
13. $11q - 14 = -135$
14. $39 = 2h - 21$
15. $14x + 34 = 230$
16. $5p + 7 = 232$
17. $16h + 24 = 136$
18. $50w - 2 = -252$
19. $19c + 21 = 382$
20. $36n - 31 = 149$

(handwritten working)

$= 36n = 149 + 31$
$= 36n = 180$
$n = 5$

$= 441 - 21 = 7z$
$= 420 = 7z$
$= 60 = 2z$
$z = 60$

Section 14D Solving Linear Equations with One Variable on Either Side of the Equals Sign

Example 1

Solve $11x - 24 = 3x + 8$ for x.

Solution

$$11x - 24 = 3x + 8$$
$$11x - 24 - 3x = 8 \qquad \text{... subtract } 3x \text{ from both sides}$$
$$8x - 24 = 8$$
$$8x = 8 + 24 \qquad \text{... add 24 to both sides}$$
$$8x = 32$$
$$\frac{8x}{8} = \frac{32}{8} \qquad \text{... divide both sides by 8}$$
$$\Rightarrow x = 4$$

Check the answer by substituting $x = 4$ into both sides of the original equation:

LHS: $11x - 24 = 11(4) - 24 = 44 - 24 = 20$

RHS: $3x + 8 = 3(4) + 8 = 12 + 8 = 20$

As LHS = RHS, the equation is balanced. So $x = 4$.

Example 2

Solve $13 - 3y = 2y - 7$ for y.

Solution

To find y, rearrange the equation so 'numbers = y terms', as there are more 'y's on the RHS ($2y > -3y$):

$$13 - 3y = 2y - 7$$
$$13 = 2y - 7 + 3y \qquad \text{... add } 3y \text{ to both sides}$$
$$13 = 5y - 7$$
$$13 + 7 = 5y \qquad \text{... add 7 to both sides}$$
$$20 = 5y$$
$$\frac{20}{5} = \frac{5y}{5} \qquad \text{... divide both sides by 5}$$
$$\Rightarrow 4 = y$$

Check the answer by substituting $y = 4$ into both sides of the original equation:

LHS: $13 - 3y = 13 - 3(4) = 13 - 12 = 1$

RHS: $2y - 7 = 2(4) - 7 = 8 - 7 = 1 \qquad \text{... the equation is balanced. So } y = 4.$

For each question below:

(i) Solve for the unknown variable, showing all steps.

(ii) Check your answer.

1 $5a - 9 = 54 - 4a$

2 $4h + 6 = 2h + 10$

3 $4x - 12 = -2x$

4 $5d - 13 = 11 - 3d$

5 $t + 5 = 16 - 10t$

6 $3y - 2 = -2y - 37$

7 $6s + 2 = 3s + 5$

8 $9x + 15 = 3x - 3$

9 $-3x - 9 = -7x + 11$

10 $6q - 3 = 3q + 3$

11 $y + 7 = 2y - 1$

12 $2b - 15 = -3b + 10$

13 $-2x - 6 = 4x + 6$

14 $6g + 2 = 2g + 10$

15 $7b + 4 - 5 = 14 - 5b - 3b$

16 $-2h + 6 = -h + 76$

17 $8 - 7x = -5x + 18$

18 $9w - 11 = 2w + 3$

19 $12x - 22 = 55 + x$

20 $6r + 9 = 29 - 4r$

$= 6r + 4r = 29 - 9$

$= 10r = 20$

$r = 2$

$6s - 3s = 5 - 2$

$= 3s = 3 \quad s = 1$

$= 6g - 2g = 10 - 2$

$= 4g = 8 \quad g = 2$

Section 14E Linear Equations with Brackets

Example 1

Solve $4(p + 3) = 36$ for p.

Solution

$4(p + 3) = 36$

$\quad 4p + 12 = 36$ … expand using the distributive law

$\quad\quad 4p = 36 - 12$ … subtract 12 from both sides

$\quad\quad 4p = 24$

$\quad\quad \dfrac{4p}{4} = \dfrac{24}{4}$ … divide both sides by 4

$\quad \Rightarrow p = 6$

Check the answer by substituting $p = 6$ into the original equation:

$4(p + 3) = 36$

$4(6 + 3) = 36$

$\quad 4(9) = 36$

$\quad\quad 36 = 36 \checkmark$ … as LHS = RHS, the equation is balanced.

So $p = 6$.

Example 2

Solve $2(2 - y) = y + 3 - 8(y - 2)$ for y.

Solution

$$2(2 - y) = y + 3 - 8(y - 2)$$
$$4 - 2y = y + 3 - 8y + 16 \qquad \text{... expand using the distributive law}$$
$$4 - 2y = -7y + 19$$
$$4 - 2y + 7y = 19 \qquad \text{... add } 7y \text{ to both sides}$$
$$4 + 5y = 19$$
$$5y = 19 - 4 \qquad \text{... subtract 4 from both sides}$$
$$5y = 15$$
$$\frac{5y}{5} = \frac{15}{5} \qquad \text{... divide both sides by 5}$$
$$\Rightarrow y = 3$$

Check the answer by substituting $y = 3$ into both sides of the original equation:

LHS: $2(2 - y) = 2(2 - 3) = 2(-1) = -2$

RHS: $y + 3 - 8(y - 2) = 3 + 3 - 8(3 - 2) = 6 - 8(1) = 6 - 8 = -2$

As the LHS = RHS, the equation is balanced. So $y = 3$.

Activity 14.4

For each question below:

 (i) Solve for the unknown variable, showing all steps.

(ii) Check your answer.

1 $5(y - 2) = -25$

2 $3(2s - 7) = 9$

3 $3(x - 2) = 5(x - 2)$

4 $5d + 5 = 2(2d + 5)$

5 $2(2x - 5) = 2x + 10$

6 $3(a - 2) = a + 4$

7 $2(h + 2) - 3(h - 3) = h + 7$

8 $17 = 24 + 7(1 - y)$

9 $3(b - 1) = 18 - 5(b + 1)$

10 $-1 - (1 - c) = 2c - 11$

11 $6(s - 2) = 5(s + 10)$

12 $2 - 6(2 - y) = 5(y + 3)$

13 $3(g - 2) - 12 = 2(g - 3) - 5$

14 $3(w - 5) - 2(1 - w) = 3 - 3(4 - w)$

15 $2(k + 3) = 8 - 4(k - 1)$

16 $4(1 + 3b) = 2(b - 3)$

17 $9(x - 2) = 3(x + 7) - 3$

18 $3(-y - 5) + 4 = 2(y + 13) + 3$

19 $100 - 9(m - 1) = m - 1$

20 $3(n + 4) - 5(n - 1) = 9n - 5$

(handwritten working)
$= -1 - 1 - 1c = 2c - 11$
$= -1c - 2c = -11 + 1 + 1$
$= -3c = -9$
$c = 3$

$= -1 - 1 + 1c = 2c - 11$
$= -1 - 1 + 11 = 2c - 1c$
$= 9 = 1c \quad c = 9 \Leftarrow 9$

Section 14F Using Linear Equations to Solve Word Problems

Real-life problems can be written as simple linear equations.

Example 1

(i) What number is 1 bigger than x?

(ii) The sum of two consecutive numbers is 47. Find the two numbers

Solution

(i) $(x + 1)$ is one bigger than x.

(ii) Let x = the smaller number.

Then $(x + 1)$ is the bigger number.

Sum of the 2 numbers is $x + (x + 1)$.

$x + (x + 1) = 47$

$\Rightarrow x + x + 1 = 47$

$\Rightarrow \qquad 2x = 47 - 1$

$\Rightarrow 2x = 46$

$\Rightarrow \quad x = 23$

So 23 is the smaller number and 24 the bigger.

Example 2

Pádraig and Paul have a combined age of 111 and Pádraig's age is twice Paul's age. Find out how old Paul and Pádraig are.

Solution

Let x be Paul's age.

$\Rightarrow$ Pádraig = $2x$ years old.

$x + 2x = 111$ ... we know their combined age is 111

$3x = 111$

$\dfrac{3x}{3} = \dfrac{111}{3}$ ... divide by 3

$\Rightarrow x = 37$

- Paul = x years old. So Paul is 37 years old.

Pádraig = $2x = 2(37) = 74$ years old.

- Check the solution:

Sum of ages = $37 + 74 = 111$ ✓

Example 3

An electrician charges €30 per hour and spends €20 a day on diesel for his van.

(i) Write an algebraic expression to represent his earnings for one day.

(ii) The electrican earns €160 in one day. How many hours has he worked?

Solution

(i) Let x represent the number of hours the electrician works in one day.
His earnings can be represented by the expression: $30x - 20$

(ii) If he earns €160, then:

$30x - 20 = 160$

$30x = 160 + 20$ ... add 20 to both sides

$30x = 180$

$\dfrac{30x}{30} = \dfrac{180}{30}$ ... divide both sides by 30

$\Rightarrow x = 6$

- Answer: The electrician worked 6 hours.
- Check solution: 6 hours × €30 = €180; then take away €20 for diesel = €160 ✓

Activity 14.5

1 Write each statement as a linear equation, then solve.

(i) Four times a number plus 6 is 50. Find the number. $4x + 6 = 50$

(ii) A number plus 12 is 87. Find the number. $4x = 50 - 6$ $x = 11$

(iii) A number divided by 7 is 9. Find the number.

(iv) A number is multiplied by 5 and then 6 is added to the result. The result is 36. Find the number.

(v) 9 is added to a number. The result is multiplied by −4. The answer is −16. Find the number.

(vi) One number is greater than another number by 7. If the two numbers add to 59, find both numbers.

2 Masha is y years old.

(i) How old was she 6 years ago? Give your answer in terms of y.

(ii) If Masha was 14 years old 6 years ago, find the value of y.

3 The perimeter of the right-angled triangle shown is 36 cm. Find the value of y, then find the length of each side.

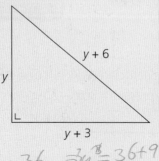

$y + 6$

y

L

$y + 3$

$3y + 9 = 36$ $3y = 36 + 9$

$3y = 45$ $y = 15$ $36 - 9$

$= 27 - 3 = 9$

4 Eileen is y years old.

(i) How old will she be in 13 years' time? Give your answer in terms of y.

(ii) If Eileen will then be 42 years old, write an equation to find the value of y.

5 Cora says, "I am thinking of a number. When 13 is added to 4 times the number, the result is the same as when 20 is subtracted from 7 times the number".

Let x be the number. Form an equation in x and use it to find Cora's number.

6 The perimeter of a square is 16 m. What is the length of each side?

7 n, $n + 1$ and $n + 2$ are three **consecutive** Natural numbers. Find the three numbers if their sum is 102.

8 Rachel, Jack, DJ, Katie and Conor share a bag of jelly sweets. Jack and DJ each get x sweets, Rachel gets $x + 2$ sweets, Katie gets $x + 1$ sweets and Conor gets $x + 3$ sweets. How many sweets does each child get if there are 36 sweets in the bag?

9 In an English test, the highest score was 39 points more than the lowest score. If the sum of the two scores is 137, find the lowest score.

10 The perimeter of a rectangle is 24 m and the length of the rectangle is 4 m longer than the width. Work out the length and width of the rectangle.

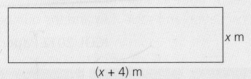

x m

(*x* + 4) m

11 (i) What number is 1 more than *y*?

(ii) The sum of two consecutive numbers is 87. Find the two numbers by forming an equation in *y*.

12 Tom says, "If you add 11 to my age and multiply the result by 3, the answer is 1 more than 7 times my age". How old is Tom?

13 A hurling team scored 18 times, with a mixture of goals and points. A goal is worth 3 points. If the team's total score was 28, how many goals did they get?

> **Hint**
>
> › Let *x* = the number of goals. Then (18 − *x*) is the number of points.

14 Mick McDonald has a farm with hens and sheep, totalling 21 animals.

(i) If there are *x* sheep, how many hens are there?

(ii) The animals have a total of 52 legs altogether. How many hens and how many sheep are on Mick's farm?

$(x+11)3 = 7x + 11$

$= 3x + 33 = 7x + 1$ $= 3x - 7x = 1 - 33$ $= -4x = -32$ $= -8 = -32$

Revision Activity 14   *x* = 5

1 In each question, show all steps clearly and check your solutions.

(a) Solve:

(i) 9 = 2*y* + 5

(ii) 7*x* + 8 = −90

(b) Solve the equation 2*n* + 7 = *n* + 12.

(c) Solve the equation 4(*d* + 5) − 2(*d* + 3) = 12.

(d) The cost of two adults and three children attending the cinema is €36. If an adult ticket costs €3 more than a child ticket, what is the cost of each ticket?

2 In each part of the question, show all steps clearly and check your solutions.

(a) Solve:

(i) 5*h* − 42 = 8

(ii) 34 = 10*k* + 4

(b) Solve the equation *f* − 12 = −*f* − 14.

$= 1f + 1f = 12 - 14$

$= 2f = -2$

$f = -1$

(c) Solve the equation
2(*m* + 7) − 4(*m* + 3) = 15(*m* − 1).

(d) A triangle of perimeter 18 cm has sides of length *l* cm, (*l* + 2) cm and (2*l* − 4) cm.

What is the length of each side?

3 In each question, show all steps clearly and check your solutions.

(a) Find the value of the unknown variable in the following equations.

(i) 9*y* − 1 = −100

(ii) 162 = 13*b* − 7

(b) Solve the equation
−12 + 5*m* − 37 = −7*m* − 13.

(c) Solve the equation
8(5*h* − 1) − 2(3 − *h*) = 7(7*h* − 4).

(d) Seán is saving for college. He has €2500 in the credit union and saves €125 a week from his wages. How many weeks would he need to save to reach his target of €9000?

Exam-style Question

1 Jane sets Molly a word problem. 'If I multiply a number by seven and add four, the result is the same as multiplying the number by three and taking away eight.' Molly starts by writing $7x + 4 =$. Finish Molly's equation and solve it to find the number.

JCOL 2012 Paper 1

KEY WORDS AND PHRASES

- Algebra
- Balanced
- Equation

- Linear equation
- Variables
- Constants

- Consecutive
- Distributive law

Chapter Summary 14

- An **equation** has a term or expression equal (=) to another term or expression. We can say that the equation is **balanced**.

- A **linear equation** is an equation that makes a straight line when graphed.

- When we **solve an equation** we find the value of the unknown variable.

- To solve an equation, whatever you do on one side you must do exactly the same on the other side.

- We can use equations to solve word problems.

Geometry 2

Learning Intentions

In this chapter, you will learn about:

- Triangles and the categories of triangles
- The six parts of a triangle
- Congruent triangles
- Axiom 4: We can assume that two triangles are congruent if we have the minimum conditions:
  Side-Side-Side (SSS), Side-Angle-Side (SAS), or Angle-Side-Angle (ASA)
- Supplementary angles and vertically opposite angles
- Theorem 1: Vertically opposite angles are equal
- Theorem 2: In an isosceles triangle, the angles opposite the equal sides are equal (and converse)
- Alternate angles and Corresponding angles
- Theorems 3 and 5: The properties of alternate and corresponding angles
- Theorem 4: The angles in any triangle sum to 180°
- Theorem 6: Exterior angles of a triangle and their properties

LO: GT.3 b (i and ii),
U.5, U.6, U.11, U.12, U.13

You will need...

- a pencil
- a ruler
- a geometry set

Historical background

Euclid, who lived around 385–275 BC, is widely considered to be the father of geometric proofs. He started with a small number of terms which could be accepted without definition and some simple statements (axioms) which he accepted were true without proof. He then began to build on these using definitions and proofs.

Section 15A Congruent Triangles

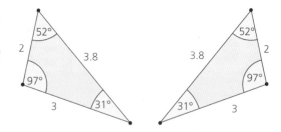

Looking at this diagram, we can see that each part of the first triangle is equal to the **corresponding** (**matching**) part of the second triangle. Each of the three angles in the first triangle has a matching angle in the second triangle, and the same goes for each of the three sides.

> If you were to cut these triangles out and put one on top of the other, they would fit exactly. These triangles are what we call **congruent triangles**. They are equal in every respect.

It will be very important to know when we have two congruent triangles in a diagram. So, what are the **minimum** requirements which will ensure that two triangles are congruent?

Congruent Triangles 1: Side-Side-Side (SSS)

In fact, it is true that two triangles are congruent if we have **just the three sides** (SSS) equal in each triangle, even though we may not have any information about the angles.

This can be proven, but we will accept it as a fact for our course. (Remember that we use the word 'axiom' for 'fact'.) You can use your constructions of SSS triangles to check for yourself.

This is part of another axiom:

> ## AXIOM 4(i)
>
> Two triangles are congruent if all three corresponding sides in each are equal (SSS).

Congruent Triangles 2: Side-Angle-Side (SAS)

It is true that two triangles are congruent if we have just **SAS** information about the two triangles.

We accept this without proof as another part of Axiom 4.

> ## AXIOM 4(ii)
>
> Two triangles are congruent if two sides and the included angle in each are equal (SAS).

Key Point

Be careful here: You can assume that two triangles are congruent only if you have the **included** angle between the two equal sides in each triangle. For example, you could not assume that these two triangles are congruent from the information given in the diagrams.

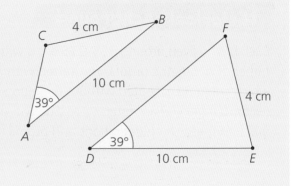

Geometry 2

Congruent Triangles 3: Angle-Side-Angle (ASA)

It is also sufficient to say that two triangles are congruent if we have just **ASA** information about the two triangles. This is the third part of the axiom:

AXIOM 4(iii)

Two triangles are congruent if two angles and the side between them are equal in each (ASA).

Key Point

Be careful here: Be sure that you have the side **between the equal angles** in each triangle before assuming that the triangles are congruent.

We now have three sets of minimum conditions for congruence.

This is the complete Axiom 4:

AXIOM 4

1. Two triangles are congruent if all three corresponding sides in each are equal (SSS).
2. Two triangles are congruent if two sides and the included angle in each are equal (SAS).
3. Two triangles are congruent if two angles and the side between them are equal in each (ASA).

Key Point

We use similar markings on each triangle to show which parts are equal.

Example

The equal parts in these triangles are indicated by similar markings.

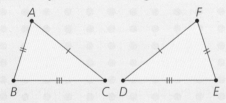

(i) State clearly why these two triangles are congruent.

(ii) Copy the triangles and complete the markings.

(iii) Copy and complete this statement:

Because these two triangles are congruent, I know that:

$|\angle ABC| =$

$|\angle ACB| =$

$|\angle CAB| =$

Solution

(i) These triangles are congruent because:
$|AB| = |FE|$, $|BC| = |DE|$, $|AC| = |FD|$ (SSS)

(ii) The three angles in $\triangle ABC$ are equal to the three matching angles of $\triangle DEF$.

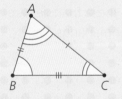 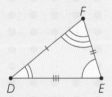

(iii) *Because these two triangles are congruent, I know that:*

$|\angle ABC| = |\angle FED|$

$|\angle ACB| = |\angle FDE|$

$|\angle CAB| = |\angle DFE|$

Geometry 2

1 What are the six parts of a triangle?

2 (i) Write down in your own words what it means to say that two triangles are congruent.

(ii) What do you know about the matching parts of two congruent triangles?

(iii) Give three conditions which allow us to assume that two triangles are congruent.

3 The equal parts of these triangles are indicated by similar markings.

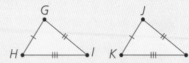

(i) State clearly in your own words why we can say for sure that these two triangles are congruent. (Your answer will contain SSS, SAS or ASA.)

(ii) What can we say about the other three parts of these triangles? Copy the triangles and complete the markings.

(iii) Copy and complete this statement:

Because these two triangles are congruent, I know that:

$|\angle HGI| =$

$|\angle HIG| =$

$|\angle GHI| =$

4 The equal parts of these triangles are indicated by similar markings.

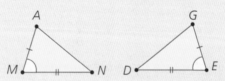

(i) State clearly in your own words why we can say for sure that these two triangles are congruent. (Your answer will contain SSS, SAS or ASA.)

(ii) What can we say about the other three parts of these triangles?

(iii) Copy and complete this statement:

Because these two triangles are congruent, I know that:

$|\angle MAN| =$

$|\angle ANM| =$

$|AN| =$

5 The equal parts of these triangles are indicated by similar markings.

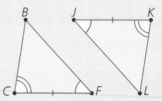

(i) State clearly in your own words why we can say for sure that these two triangles are congruent. (Your answer will contain SSS, SAS or ASA.)

(ii) What can we say about the other three parts of these triangles? Copy the triangles and complete the markings.

(iii) Copy and complete this statement:

Because these two triangles are congruent, I know that:

$|BC| =$

$|BF| =$

$|\angle CBF| =$

6 The equal parts of these triangles are indicated by similar markings.

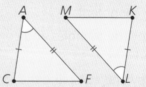

(i) State clearly in your own words why we can say for sure that these two triangles are congruent. (Your answer will contain SSS, SAS or ASA.)

(ii) What can we say about the other three parts of these triangles? Copy the triangles and complete the markings.

(iii) Copy and complete this statement:

Because these two triangles are congruent, I know that:

|FC| =

|∠ACF| =

|∠AFC| =

7 The equal parts of these triangles are indicated by similar markings.

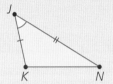 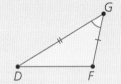

(i) State clearly in your own words why we can say for sure that these two triangles are congruent. (Your answer will contain SSS, SAS or ASA.)

(ii) What can we say about the other three parts of these triangles? Copy the triangles and complete the markings.

(iii) Copy and complete this statement:

Because these two triangles are congruent, I know that:

|∠JKN| =

|∠JNK| =

|KN| =

8 The triangles below have their three angles the same size (AAA).

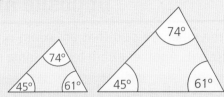

(i) Are the triangles congruent?

(ii) Draw two more pairs of triangles which have the same angles but are not congruent.

(iii) Copy and complete this sentence: 'I cannot assume that two triangles are _____ if I am told only that the three corresponding angles in each are equal.'

9 The two triangles below are 'stuck together'. They share a common side [TV]. The equal parts of these triangles are indicated by similar markings.

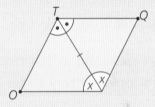

(i) Draw a sketch of the two triangles separately.

(ii) State clearly why we can say for sure that these two triangles are congruent. (Your answer will contain SSS, SAS or ASA.)

(iii) Explain how you know |∠TOV| = |∠TQV|.

Section 15B Supplementary Angles and Vertically Opposite Angles

Remember we said that an axiom is a statement which we take as true without having to prove it. Another axiom tells us some more very important facts about angles.

AXIOM 3

The properties of the degree measure of an angle:

1. A straight angle has 180°.

2. Given a ray [AB and a number *d* between 0 and 180, there is exactly one ray from A on either side of the line AB that makes an (ordinary) angle having *d* degrees with the ray [AB.

3. If *D* is a point inside an angle ∠BAC, then |∠BAC| = |∠BAD| + |∠DAC|.

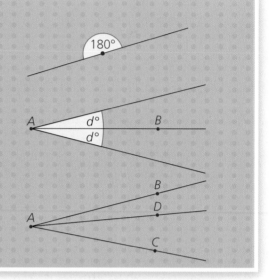

This means that the sum of all the angles around a point add to 360°.

> Two angles which add to give 180° are called **supplementary** angles.

In this diagram, |∠a| = 180°, so ∠b and ∠c are supplementary angles.

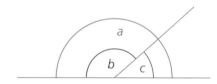

Example 1

Find the value of α and the value of β in the diagrams below.

(i)

(ii)

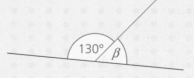

Solution

(i) α + 130° = 180°, so α = 180° − 130° = 50°

(ii) β + 130° = 180°, so β = 180° − 130° = 50°

Notice that α and β are both equal to 50° because the supplementary angle in each case is 130°.

Now we'll combine the two diagrams in Example 1 to make one diagram:

Can you see the two original diagrams in the new one?

The new diagram has an 'X' shape, and the 130° is still there.

What size is α now? What size is β now? Do you see that they are still equal? Notice that these angles are directly opposite each other in the 'X' shape.

We have, in fact, used what we call a 'logical argument' to come to a new fact, which we will see shortly.

This 'X' is a special shape which appears in many everyday objects.

There are four angles made around the point of intersection.

> The pairs of angles directly opposite each other are called **vertically opposite angles**.

There are two such pairs: $\angle 1$ and $\angle 3$
$\angle 2$ and $\angle 4$.

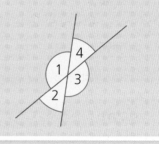

We showed above that the vertically opposite angles were equal.

This will always be true and this is important enough to be called a **theorem**.

You will hear a lot about theorems, and you need to know what they are.

> A **theorem** is a statement obtained by logical argument from an axiom (or previous theorems).

THEOREM 1

Vertically opposite angles are equal.

This means that, when two lines intersect at a point, the angles directly opposite each other are equal.

In the diagram, $|\angle 1| = |\angle 3|$
$|\angle 2| = |\angle 4|$

The 2018 revised syllabus requires students to display understanding of proofs.
We have already discussed how Theorem 1 works, but the following is the proof:

Proof of Theorem 1

Given: Two intersecting lines. Prove: $|\angle 1| = |\angle 2|$.

Proof:

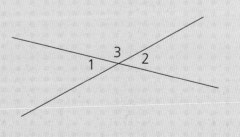

$|\angle 1| + |\angle 3| = 180°$ *and* $|\angle 2| + |\angle 3| = 180°$

$\Rightarrow |\angle 1| + |\angle 3| = |\angle 2| + |\angle 3|$

$\Rightarrow |\angle 1| = |\angle 2|$

Geometry 2

The next theorem is about the angles in an isosceles triangle.

THEOREM 2

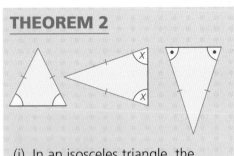

(i) In an isosceles triangle, the angles opposite the equal sides are equal.

(ii) Conversely, if two angles are equal, then the triangle is isosceles.

Example 2

ABC is an isosceles triangle. Name another angle equal to 72° in the diagram.

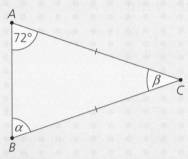

Solution

$\alpha = 72°$ because angles opposite equal sides in an isosceles triangle are equal.

The proof of Theorem 2 uses congruent triangles:

Proof of Theorem 2

Given: Isosceles triangle ABC.

Prove: $|\angle ABC| = |\angle ACB|$

Construction: Join A to D, the mid-point of [BC]

Proof:

In the triangles ABD and ADC,

$|AB| = |AC|$ … given

$|AD| = |AD|$

$|BD| = |DC|$

$\Rightarrow$ Triangles ABD and ADC are congruent (SSS)

$\Rightarrow |\angle ABC| = |\angle ACB|$

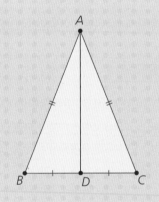

1 (i) What do you call two angles which add to give 180°?

(ii) Find the size of the angle α in each of the following diagrams:

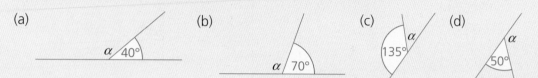

(a)   (b)   (c)   (d)

α 40° α 70°   135° α α 50°

2 Find the size of the angle θ in each of the following diagrams:

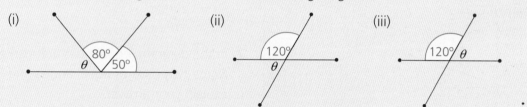

(i)   (ii)   (iii)

80° θ 50°   120° θ 120° θ

3 This diagram has two lines intersecting at a point.

(i) What is the value of β? How do you know?

(ii) What is the value of α? How do you know?

(iii) What can you say about α and β?

(iv) What size is the missing angle?

(v) What are the angles α and β called?

(vi) Write out in your own words the theorem which tells you about how these angles are related.

C

120° β

A ——————— B

α

D

4 Find the size of the angles marked with a letter.

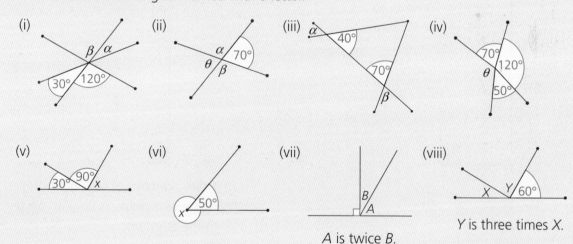

(i)   (ii)   (iii)   (iv)

β α α 70° α 40°   70° 120°

30° 120° θ β 70° θ 50°

   β

(v)   (vi)   (vii)   (viii)

30° 90° x 50° B X Y 60°

   x A

      A is twice *B*.   *Y* is three times *X*.

5 Name the equal angles in these isosceles triangles.

(i)
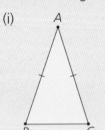

(ii)
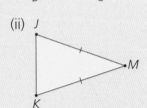

(iii)
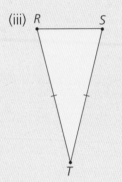

(iv)
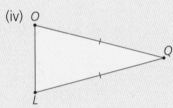

(v)
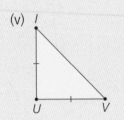

(vi)
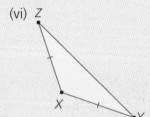

6 *ABC* is an isosceles triangle. Name another angle equal to 63° in the diagram. Explain your answer.

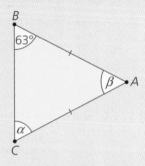

7 In the diagram, equal sides are marked. Name two pairs of equal angles and explain your answer.

8 A square has all four sides equal and all its angles are right angles. *PQRS* is a square.

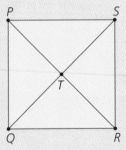

(i) Draw sketches of four right-angled isosceles triangles that you can see in the diagram.

(ii) Name four pairs of equal angles which are not right angles. Explain your answer.

Section 15C Alternate Angles and Corresponding Angles

In this section, we are going to look at angles which occur in a particular situation, for example the angles formed on a gate or on the hinges of a wooden door.

Transversals

A **transversal** is a line that cuts across two or more lines.

In this chapter, we will focus on transversals that cut across **parallel lines**.

Look at the diagram on the right. The two parallel lines *l* and *m* are both met by a transversal *t*.

We have used numbers to name the angles.

From the diagram, we can see that the transversal makes a lot of angles with the other two lines.

- You can see 'X'-shaped angles which we met before and which we call **vertically opposite** angles.
- How many pairs of these can you see?
- You can also see **supplementary** angles – remember those? (Check back if you've forgotten!) How many pairs of these can you see?

Interior Angles

The angles 2, 7, 3 and 6 are between the parallel lines. We call these **interior** angles. There are two on each side of the transversal.

Corresponding Angles

When two lines are crossed by the transversal, the angles in matching corners are called **corresponding** angles.

Here are all the corresponding angles from the diagram.

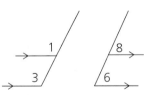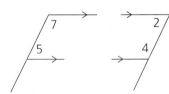

- We can see that all the corresponding angles form an 'F' shape.
- These pairs of angles are on the same side of the transversal in corresponding positions.
- Hence, when you see an 'F' shape formed, you have **corresponding angles.**

Alternate Angles

The pairs of angles on opposite sides of the transversal line but between the two lines are called **alternate angles**.

- We can see that alternate angles form a 'Z' shape.
- The angle pairs are in 'alternate' (opposite) sides of the transversal line, and they are in the 'interior' of the two parallel lines.
- Hence when you see a 'Z' shape formed, you have alternate angles.

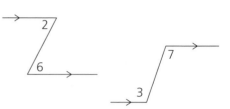

Key Points

Remember: **Z shape** – alternate angles
F shape – corresponding angles
X shape – vertically opposite angles

Example

The diagram shows two parallel lines and a transversal *t*.

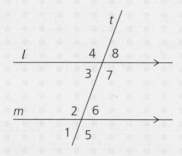

(i) Draw a sketch of four separate pairs of corresponding angles.

(ii) Draw a sketch of two separate pairs of alternate angles.

(iii) Draw a sketch of four separate pairs of vertically opposite angles.

(iv) Draw a sketch of eight separate pairs of supplementary angles.

(v) Name the four interior angles.

(vi) Copy and complete this table.

Pairs of corresponding angles	Pairs of alternate angles	Pairs of vertically opposite angles	Pairs of supplementary angles
∠3 and ∠1	∠3 and ∠6	∠3 and ∠8	∠3 and ∠4

Geometry 2

Solution

(i) The four pairs of corresponding angles are:

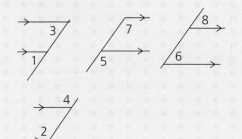

(ii) The two pairs of alternate angles are:

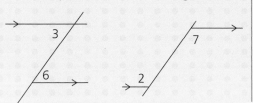

(iii) The four pairs of vertically opposite angles are:

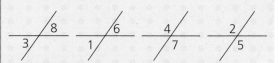

(iv) The eight pairs of supplementary angles are:

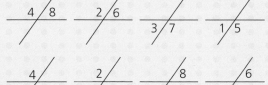

(v) The four interior angles are ∠2, ∠3, ∠6 and ∠7.

(vi)

Pairs of corresponding angles	Pairs of alternate angles	Pairs of vertically opposite angles	Pairs of supplementary angles
∠3 and ∠1	∠3 and ∠6	∠3 and ∠8	∠3 and ∠4
∠7 and ∠5	∠2 and ∠7	∠4 and ∠7	∠7 and ∠8
∠4 and ∠2		∠2 and ∠5	∠1 and ∠2
∠8 and ∠6		∠1 and ∠6	∠5 and ∠6
			∠4 and ∠8
			∠2 and ∠6
			∠3 and ∠7
			∠1 and ∠5

Activity 15.3

In all of the following activities there are two parallel lines with a transversal crossing them.

1 Draw a sketch of this gate in your copybook.

   (i) Identify two pairs of alternate angles.

   (ii) Identify two pairs of corresponding angles.

   (iii) Identify two pairs of vertically opposite angles.

2 (i) Draw a sketch of four separate pairs of corresponding angles.

(ii) Draw a sketch of two separate pairs of alternate angles.

(iii) Draw a sketch of four separate pairs of vertically opposite angles.

(iv) Draw a sketch of eight separate pairs of supplementary angles.

(v) Name the four interior angles.

(vi) Copy and complete this table:

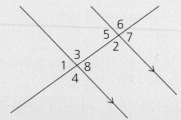

Pairs of corresponding angles	Pairs of alternate angles	Pairs of vertically opposite angles	Pairs of supplementary angles

3 The diagram at the right shows two lines crossed by a transversal. Copy and complete the table below.

Pairs of corresponding angles	Pairs of alternate angles	Pairs of vertically opposite angles	Pairs of supplementary angles

4 Draw this diagram in your copybook. You can use the lines in your copybook or the two edges of your ruler to draw the parallel lines. Construct the 50° angle accurately. You can have any distance between the lines.

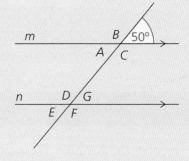

(i) Measure all the angles with your protractor, then copy and complete the table below.

Angle	A	B	C	D	E	F	G
Value							

(ii) From your table, what can you conclude about the pairs of alternate angles?

(iii) From your table, what can you conclude about the pairs of corresponding angles?

(iv) From your table, what can you conclude about the pairs of vertically opposite angles?

(v) What do you notice about $|\angle C| + |\angle G|$ and $|\angle A| + |\angle D|$?

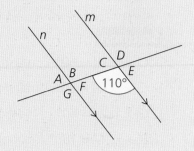

5 Draw this diagram in your copybook as accurately as you can. You can use the two edges of your ruler to draw the parallel lines. Construct the 110° angle accurately. You can have any distance between the lines.

(i) Measure all the angles with your protractor, then copy and complete the table below.

Angle	A	B	C	D	E	F	G
Value							

(ii) From your table, what can you conclude about the pairs of alternate angles?

(iii) From your table, what can you conclude about the pairs of corresponding angles?

(iv) From your table, what can you conclude about the pairs of vertically opposite angles?

(v) What do you notice about $|\angle C| + |\angle B|$?

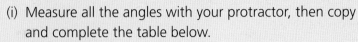

Section 15D Theorem 3 and Theorem 5

Our work in Activity 15.3 gives us a good idea of the properties of alternate and corresponding angles formed with parallel lines. These facts are stated in Theorem 3 and Theorem 5.

THEOREM 3

(i) If a transversal makes equal alternate angles on two lines, then the lines are parallel.

(ii) Conversely, if two lines are parallel, then any transversal will make equal alternate angles with them.

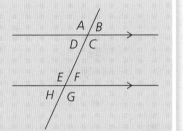

THEOREM 5

Two lines are parallel if and only if for any transversal, corresponding angles are equal.

 Key Point

We also noticed that the sum of two **interior angles** on the same side of the transversal add up to 180°.

Example

The diagram shows two parallel lines with a transversal crossing them. $|\angle A| = 60°$.

Find all the remaining angles in the diagram, and explain your answers.

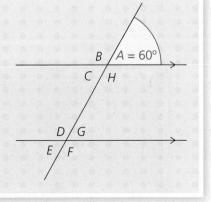

Geometry 2

Solution

$|\angle C| = |\angle A| = 60°$… vertically opposite angles ($\angle s$)

$|\angle C| = |\angle G| = 60°$… alternate $\angle s$

$|\angle G| = |\angle E| = 60°$… vertically opposite $\angle s$

$|\angle B| + |\angle A| = 180°$… supplementary angles $\Rightarrow |\angle B| = 120°$

$|\angle B| = |\angle H| = 120°$… vertically opposite $\angle s$

$|\angle H| = |\angle D| = 120°$… alternate $\angle s$

$|\angle D| = |\angle F| = 120°$… vertically opposite $\angle s$

Activity 15.4

1 Look at the diagram on the right.

  (i) What is the size of $\angle\alpha$? Why?

  (ii) What is the size of $\angle\beta$? Give two ways that you can find this.

  (iii) What is the size of $\angle\theta$? Give two ways that you can find this.

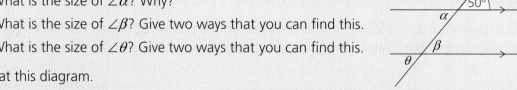

2 Look at this diagram.

  (i) Copy and complete this table.

Angle	A	B	C	D	E	F	G
Degrees							

  (ii) Find the value of $|\angle F| + |\angle G|$.

  (iii) Find the value of $|\angle B| + |\angle C|$.

3 Look at this diagram. There are two parallel lines and a transversal.

  (i) Copy and complete this table.

Angle	A	B	C	D	E	F	G
Degrees							

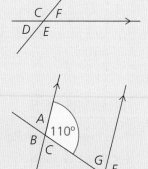

  (ii) Find the value of $|\angle C| + |\angle D|$.

  (iii) Can you give a rule about interior angles?

4 The path of a snooker ball is shown in this diagram. Find the angles A and B. Explain your answers.

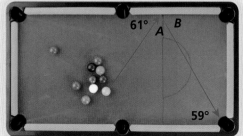

5 In the diagram, $p \parallel q$ and $m \parallel n$. $|\angle V| = 55°$. Find the values of all the other angles.

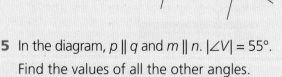
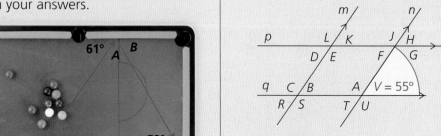

6 In the diagram, $p \parallel q$ and $m \parallel n$.

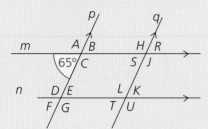

Find the values of all the angles in the diagram.

7 Find the value of each of the marked angles in the picture. Explain your answers.

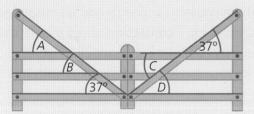

8 Study the diagram below and answer the following.

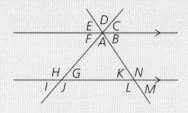

(i) Identify all pairs of vertically opposite angles.

(ii) Identify all pairs of corresponding angles.

(iii) Identify all pairs of alternate angles.

9 Peter is standing on top of a vertical cliff looking out to sea (see diagram). He observes a bird on the horizon, on the same level as his feet. He then looks down at a ship on the sea.

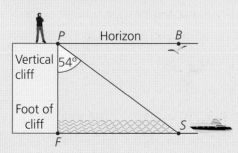

(i) Explain the words 'horizon' and 'vertical' in your own words.

(ii) Name a pair of alternate angles in the diagram.

(iii) If $|\angle FPS| = 54°$, find all the other angles in the diagram. Explain your answers.

10 In the diagram, $ST \parallel QR$.

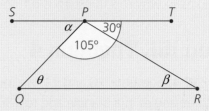

(i) What is $|\angle\alpha|$? Justify your answer.

(ii) What is $|\angle\theta|$? Justify your answer.

(iii) What is $|\angle\beta|$? Justify your answer.

(iv) Copy and complete this statement: 'The three angles of $\triangle PQR$ add up to _____.'

(v) Does this mean that this is true for all triangles? Explain your answer.

11 In the diagram, $PQ \parallel BC$.

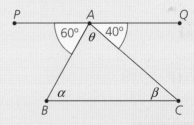

(i) What is $|\angle\theta|$? Justify your answer.

(ii) What is $|\angle\alpha|$? Justify your answer.

(iii) What is $|\angle\beta|$? Justify your answer.

(iv) What is $|\angle\theta| + |\angle\alpha| + |\angle\beta|$?

(v) Copy and complete this statement: 'The three angles of $\triangle ABC$ add up to _____.'

(vi) Does this mean that this is true for all triangles? Explain your answer.

12 In the diagram, $ST \parallel BC$.

Copy and complete the following statements.

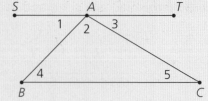

(i) $|\angle 1| + |\angle 2| + |\angle 3| = ?$

(ii) $|\angle 1| = |\angle ?|$ and $|\angle 3| = |\angle ?|$

(iii) Therefore, $|\angle 1| + |\angle 2| + |\angle 3| = |\angle 2| + |\angle ?| + |\angle ?| = $ _____.

(iv) The three angles of $\triangle ABC$ add up to _____.

(v) This proves that the three angles in **any triangle** add to 180°.
Explain why this question is different from questions **10** and **11**.

Section 15E Theorem 4

In Activity 15.4, questions 10 and 11, we investigated the angles in a triangle and we suspected that the three angles in a triangle add to 180°. That is, we made a **conjecture** about this because it is true for some triangles. Then, in question 12, we **proved** that it is true for all triangles. Make sure that you have done these two questions, as you are expected to engage with proofs.

THEOREM 4

The angles in any triangle add to 180°.

For this triangle $\angle A + \angle B + \angle C = 180°$, where $\angle A$, $\angle B$ and $\angle C$ are interior angles of the triangle.

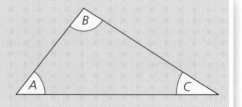

Example 1

Find the missing angle in this diagram.

Solution

$B + 75° + 61° = 180°$ … Theorem 4
$\Rightarrow B° = 180° - 75° - 61°$
$= 44°$

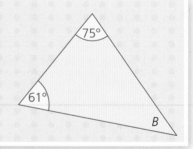

Example 2

Find the missing angles in the diagram.

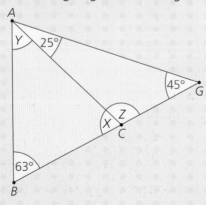

Solution

In triangle ACG,

$Z + 25° + 45° = 180°$ … Theorem 4
$\Rightarrow Z = 180° - 25° - 45°$
$\Rightarrow |\angle Z| = 110°$

$|\angle X| + |\angle Z| = 180° \Rightarrow |\angle X| = 70°$

In triangle ABC,

$Y + 63° + 70° = 180°$ … Theorem 4
$\Rightarrow Y = 180° - 63° - 70°$
$\Rightarrow |\angle Y| = 47°$

1 Find the missing angle A in these diagrams.

(i)
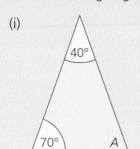
40°
70° A

(iii)
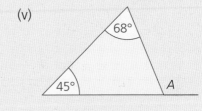
A
51° 79°

(v)
68°
45° A

(ii)
30°
90° A

(iv)
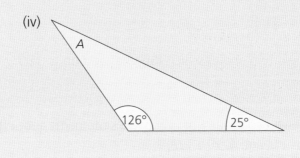
A
126° 25°

2 Find the missing angles in these diagrams.

(i)
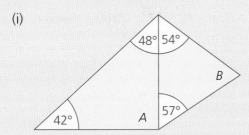
48° 54°
B
42° 57°
A

(ii)
B 46°
63°
A
34°

3 Find the size of the angle C in the bicycle frame shown.

41°
C 63°

4 Look at this diagram. The triangle PQT has one side extended to R, making the **exterior angle** ∠PTR.

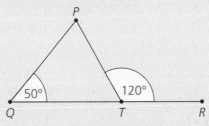
P
50° 120°
Q T R

(i) What is |∠PTQ|? Explain your answer.

(ii) What is |∠QPT|? Explain your answer.

(iii) Name two angles which together add up to the exterior angle ∠PTR.

5 The triangle *ABC* below has one side extended to *D*, making the **exterior angle** ∠*ACD*.

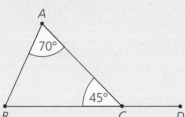

(i) What is |∠*ABC*|? Explain your answer.

(ii) What is |∠*ACD*|? Explain your answer.

(iii) Name two angles which together add up to the exterior angle ∠*ACD*.

6 (i) From the diagram on the right, write down three angles which together add up to 180°.

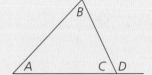

☐ + ☐ + ☐ = 180°

(ii) Write down two angles which together add up to 180°.

☐ + ☐ = 180°

(iii) What can you conclude from your two statements about the relationship between |∠*D*| and (|∠*A*| + |∠*B*|)?

Section 15F **Theorem 6**

Make sure that you have done questions 5 and 6 in Activity 15.5 which proves theorem 6, as you are expected to engage with the proofs of theorems.

> **THEOREM 6**
>
> Each exterior angle of a triangle is equal to the sum of the two interior opposite angles.
>
> For this triangle we can say that ∠*A* + ∠*B* = ∠*D*,
>
> where ∠*D* is the exterior angle and ∠*A* and ∠*B* are the interior opposite angles.

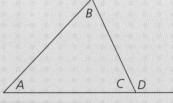

Activity 15.6

1 In each of the following, find the size of the angles marked with letters.

(i)

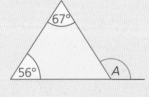

(iii)

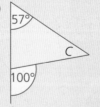

(v)

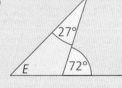

(ii)

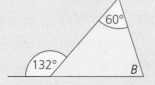

(iv)

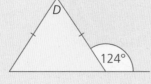

(vi)

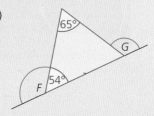

2 Find the value of each of the missing angles, giving a reason for each answer.

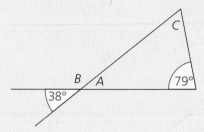

3 The diagram shows two isosceles triangles with equal sides marked. Find the six missing angles in the diagram. Explain your answers.

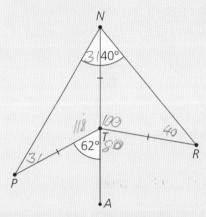

4 Find the size of the angles marked X, Y, Z, given that △ABC is isosceles with |CA| = |CB|, and AE is parallel to BD. Show how you worked out your answers.

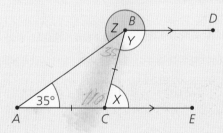

5 In the diagram, m ∥ n. Find all the missing angles in the diagram (there are five).

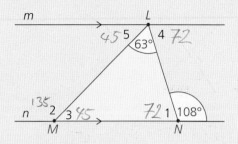

6 In the diagram, p ∥ q.

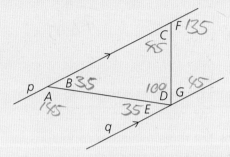

(i) Name two angles which together add up to |∠A|.

(ii) Name two angles which together add up to |∠F|.

(iii) If |∠B| = 35° and |∠F| = 135°, find all the other angles in the diagram.

7 In the diagram, l ∥ m. Find the size of the angles θ, β and α.

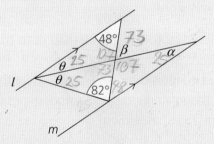

Revision Activity 15

1 (a) What are supplementary angles?

(b) Find the value of x in this diagram.

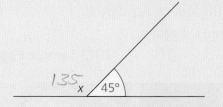

2 (a) State, in your own words and with the help of a diagram, what vertically opposite angles are.

(b) State a property of vertically opposite angles.

3 Find the size of the angles marked with a letter in the following diagram.

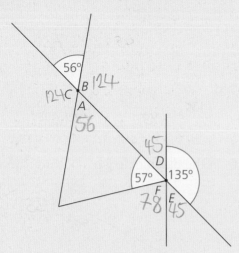

56°
B 124
124 C
A
56
45
D
57° 135°
F E
78 45

4 (a) Explain what it means to say that two triangles are congruent.

(b) List three minimum conditions for congruent triangles.

5 Write in your own words a theorem which gives a property of the angles in an isosceles triangle.

6 In a right-angled triangle, one of the acute angles is four times as large as the other acute angle.

Find the measures of the two acute angles in the triangle.

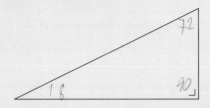

72
18 90

7 In the diagram below, the lines marked with arrows are parallel.

Find the size of the angles marked A, B, C and D.

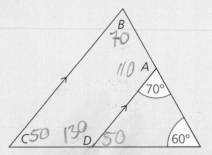

B
70
110 A
70°
C 50 130 D 50
60°

Exam-style Question

1 Seámus and Liz mark the positions of three particular towns from a map onto tracing paper. Seámus labels the towns A, B and C. Liz labels them D, E and F. They then measure some distances and angles on their diagrams, as shown.

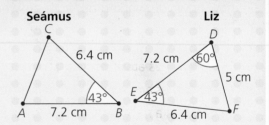

Seámus
C
6.4 cm
43°
A 7.2 cm B

Liz
D
7.2 cm 60°
5 cm
E 43°
6.4 cm F

Seámus says that the diagrams look different and that one of them must be incorrect. Liz says that does not matter because their triangles are congruent.

(a) Explain what it means to say that two triangles are congruent.

(b) Draw a sketch of each triangle in your copybook and mark in all the information given.

(c) Do you agree with Liz that the two triangles are congruent? Give reasons for your answer.

(d) Calculate the third angle in Liz's triangle and write it in on her diagram.

(e) Write the remaining angles and sides into Seámus's diagram.

2013 Sample Paper

KEY WORDS AND PHRASES

- **Triangle**
- **Scalene**
- **Isosceles**
- **Equilateral**
- **Right-angled**

- **Obtuse-angled**
- **Acute-angled**
- **Parts of a triangle**
- **Vertex**
- **Base**

- **SSS**
- **ASA**
- **SAS**
- **Included angle**
- **Congruent triangles**

Chapter Summary 15

- **Congruent triangles** are triangles which are equal in every respect.

- **Axiom 3:**

  a. A straight angle has 180°.

  b. $|\angle a| = |\angle b| + |\angle c|$

- If $|\angle 1| + |\angle 2| = 180°$, then $\angle 1$ and $\angle 2$ are called **supplementary** angles.

- **A theorem** is a statement obtained by logical argument from an axiom (or other theorem).

- **Theorem 1:** Vertically opposite angles are equal in size.

- **Axiom 4:**

  a. Two triangles are congruent if all three corresponding sides in each are equal (SSS).

  b. Two triangles are congruent if two sides and the included angle in each are equal (SAS).

  c. Two triangles are congruent if two angles and the side between them are equal in each (ASA).

- A **theorem** is a statement obtained by logical argument from an axiom (or other theorem).

- **Theorem 1:** Vertically opposite angles are equal in size.

- **Theorem 2:** (i) In an isosceles triangle, the angles opposite the equal sides are equal.

  (ii) Conversely, if two angles are equal, then the triangle is isosceles.

- Alternate and corresponding angles are made when two lines m and n meet a third line t, called the transversal.

- **Theorem 3:** If m and n are parallel, then alternate angles are equal.

- **Theorem 5:** If m and n are parallel, then corresponding angles are equal.

- **Theorem 4:** The three angles in a triangle sum to 180°.

- **Theorem 6:** Each exterior angle of a triangle is equal to the sum of the two interior opposite angles.

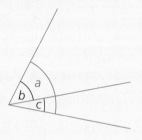

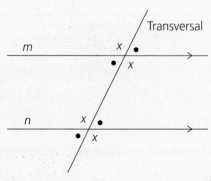

Geometry 3

You will need...

- a pencil
- a ruler
- a geometry set

Introduction

In this chapter we continue our investigations of geometry by various constructions. If you have a sharp pencil and a geometry set you will find this relaxing and enjoyable. Always be on the lookout for reasons why the constructions work. For example, you will find that in some constructions you are in fact making congruent triangles.

Connections

The connection between constructions and theorems is very important. Sometimes the constructions help us to understand the theorems, and sometimes the theorems tell us how to do the constructions.

Section 16A Starting Constructions

These are formal constructions and must be done as accurately as possible.

Construction 8

Example: Draw a line segment of length 5 cm on a ray [AB.

1. Draw a line segment [PQ] of length 5 cm using a ruler.

2. Draw a ray [AB.

3. Using A as the centre and a radius equal to |PQ|, draw an arc with your compass to cut [AB and label the intersection C.

4. |AC| = 5 cm and is the required line segment.

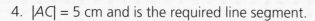
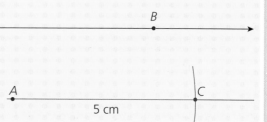

Construction 9

Example: Construct an angle of 70°.

1. Draw a ray [AB.

2. Place the centre of your protractor on the point A.

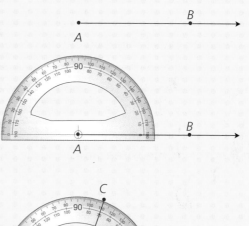

3. Mark a point C on the circumference of the protractor at the angle required (70° in this example).

4. Remove the protractor and join A to C.

5. ∠BAC is the required angle.

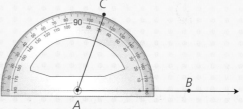

Activity 16.1

1 (i) Draw a ray [AM.

   (ii) Construct the line segment [AB] on [AM such that |AB| = 7 cm.

2 (i) Draw a ray [PQ.

   (ii) Construct ∠APC with [PQ as one arm, where |∠APC| = 50°.

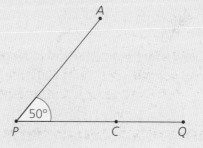

3 (i) Draw a ray [AM.

   (ii) Construct the line segment [AB] on [AM such that |AB| = 85 mm.

4 (i) Draw a ray [PR.

   (ii) Construct ∠APR with [PR as one arm, where |∠APR| = 120°.

5 (i) Draw a ray [PR.

   (ii) Construct the line segment [PQ] on [PR such that |PQ| = 65 mm.

   (iii) On the same diagram, construct ∠APR with [PR as one arm, where |∠APR| = 90°.

6 (i) Draw a ray [MN.

   (ii) Construct ∠AMN with [MN as one arm, where |∠AMN| = 200°.

Section 16B Construction of a Triangle Given Three Sides (SSS)

In this section, we will learn how to construct a triangle using a ruler and compass.

Remember that all six parts of a triangle may be different in size:

- The three sides might all be different in length.
- The three angles might be different sizes as well.

Usually we will not know all six measurements. In fact, we will see that we can often draw a triangle when we know only three measurements.

Our first triangle construction is when we are given the **lengths of the three sides** (usually called **SSS**). Notice that there are no angle sizes given.

Hints

> Always draw a small rough freehand sketch first. You will find the construction much easier if you do this.

> Be sure to use a sharp pencil.

> Always strive to be as accurate as possible.

Construction 10

(i) Construct a triangle ABC where |AB| = 6 cm, |BC| = 8 cm and |CA| = 7 cm.

(ii) Use your protractor to measure all the angles in the triangle and write them into your diagram.

(iii) Put this triangle into two categories.

Solution

(i) 1. Draw a rough sketch to help you to see what the triangle will look like.

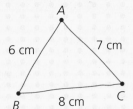

6 cm   7 cm

B   8 cm   C

   2. Draw a line segment 8 cm in length. Label the end points B and C and mark the length.

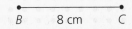

B   8 cm   C

3. Using a compass with *B* as centre, draw an arc of length 6 cm.

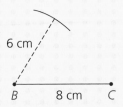

4. With *C* as centre, draw another arc of length 7 cm. Point *A* is where the two arcs intersect.

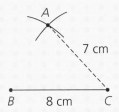

5. Join *A* to *B* and *A* to *C* to complete the triangle.

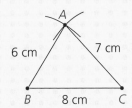

(ii) Using a protractor the angles are approximately as shown.

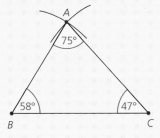

(iii) *ABC* is a scalene, acute-angled triangle.

Activity 16.2

In the following activities, remember to:

- Label your drawing and mark in all the dimensions.
- Check your construction using a ruler.
- Use your protractor to measure all the angles in the triangle.

1. (i) Construct the triangle *PQR* where |*PQ*| = 8 cm, |*QR*| = 10 cm and |*RP*| = 9 cm.

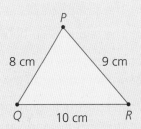

(ii) Find all the angles using your protractor.

(iii) What is the total of all the angles?

(iv) Can you see where the biggest angle is in relation to the longest side?

(v) What about the smallest angle and the shortest side?

(vi) Put this triangle into two of these categories: scalene, isosceles, equilateral, right-angled, acute-angled, obtuse-angled.

2. (i) Construct the triangle *TUV* where |*TU*| = 6 cm, |*UV*| = 8 cm and |*VT*| = 10 cm.

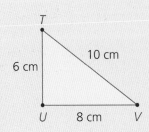

(ii) Find all the angles using your protractor.

(iii) Add the three angle measurements.

(iv) Put this triangle into two of these categories: scalene, isosceles, equilateral, right-angled, acute-angled, obtuse-angled.

3 (i) Construct the triangle *ABC* where |*AB*| = 6 cm, |*BC*| = 6 cm and |*CA*| = 11 cm. (Draw a freehand sketch first.)

   (ii) Find all the angles using your protractor.

   (iii) Add the three angle measurements.

   (iv) What do you notice about the angles opposite the equal sides?

   (v) What type of triangle is this?

4 (i) Construct the triangle *ABC* where |*AB*| = 8 cm, |*BC*| = 8 cm and |*CA*| = 8 cm.

   (ii) What type of triangle is this?

   (iii) What do you notice about the three angles?

   (iv) Add the three angle measurements.

5 (i) Construct the triangle *ABC* where |*AB*| = 7 cm, |*BC*| = 7 cm and |*CA*| = 8 cm. (Draw a freehand sketch first.)

   (ii) Find all the angles using your protractor.

   (iii) Add the three angle measurements.

   (iv) What do you notice about the angles opposite the equal sides?

   (v) What type of triangle is this?

6 Try this task: 'Construct the triangle *PQR* where |*PQ*| = 6 cm, |*QR*| = 3 cm and |*RP*| = 10 cm'. You will find it impossible. Why?

Class Activity/Discussion

In doing Activity 16.2, you did a lot of measuring of angles and sides. What do these measurements lead you to think about the following?

  (i) The sum of the angles in a triangle – What did you notice?

  (ii) The size of angles in an isosceles triangle – Are two of them always equal?

 (iii) The relationship between the size of the angles and the sides in a scalene triangle.

Remember that we learned in Geometry 1 that we can assume that triangles are congruent (identical) if we have any of the three conditions SSS, SAS or ASA.

When constructing triangles, you can see this by comparing your triangles with those of the students in your class.

Section 16C Construction of a Triangle Given Two Sides and the Included Angle (SAS)

We will now learn how to construct a triangle where we are given **two sides and the included angle** (**SAS** for short).

Construction 11

Example: Construct a triangle ABC where |AB| = 6 cm, |BC| = 8 cm and |∠ABC| = 40°. (Draw a rough sketch first.)

Solution

1. Draw a rough sketch.

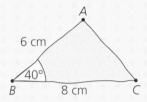

2. Draw a line segment 8 cm in length. Label the end points B and C and mark the length.

3. Use your protractor to construct an angle of 40° with [BC] as one arm.

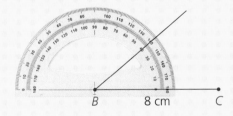

4. Using a compass with B as the centre, draw an arc of length 6 cm.

   Label point A where the arc cuts the second arm of the angle.

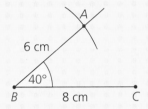

5. Join A to C to complete the triangle.

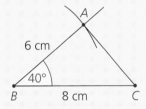

Activity 16.3

In the following activities, remember to:

- Label your drawing and mark in all the dimensions.
- Check your construction using a ruler.
- Use your protractor to measure the remaining angles in the triangle and mark them in on the diagram.
- Measure the third side with your ruler. Write these measurements into your diagram.

Geometry 3

Construct the following triangles:

1 Triangle *PQR* where |*PQ*| = 5 cm, |*QR*| = 8 cm and |∠*PQR*| = 50°.

  (i) Add up the three angles of the triangle. Is this what you expected?

  (ii) Which side is opposite the biggest angle?

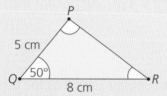

  (iii) Which side is opposite the smallest angle?

2 Triangle *ABC* where |*AC*| = 6 cm, |*BC*| = 8 cm and |∠*ACB*| = 40°.

  (i) Add up the three angles of the triangle. Is this exactly what you expected or slightly bigger or smaller?

  (ii) Which side is opposite the biggest angle?

  (iii) Which side is opposite the smallest angle?

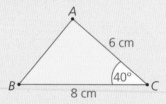

3 Triangle *GHK* where |*GH*| = 5.5 cm, |*HK*| = 10 cm and |∠*GHK*| = 135°.

  (i) Add up the three angles of the triangle.

  (ii) Which side is opposite the biggest angle? Try to see a pattern in your results.

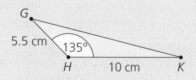

  (iii) Which side is opposite the smallest angle? Try to see a pattern in your results.

4 Triangle *LIJ* where |*LI*| = 4.5 cm, |*IJ*| = 7.5 cm and |∠*LIJ*| = 90°.

  (i) Add up the three angles of the triangle. Is this what you expected?

  (ii) Which side is opposite the biggest angle?

  (iii) Which side is opposite the smallest angle?

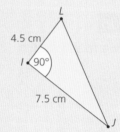

5 Triangle *MNO* where |*MN*| = 8.5 cm, |*NO*| = 5 cm and |∠*MNO*| = 130°.

  (i) Add up the three angles of the triangle.

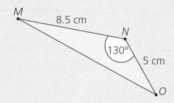

  (ii) Which side is opposite the biggest angle? Write a rule for this in your own words.

  (iii) Which side is opposite the smallest angle? Write a rule for this in your own words.

6 Triangle *GHK* where |*GH*| = 7.5 cm, |*HK*| = 10 cm and |∠*GHK*| = 120°.

7 Triangle *MNO* where |*MN*| = 9 cm, |*NO*| = 9 cm and |∠*MNO*| = 80°.

  (i) What type of triangle is this?

  (ii) Use your protractor to measure the other two angles.

  (iii) What do you notice about the two angles which are opposite the equal sides?

Section 16D **Construction of a Triangle Given Two Angles and the Included Side (ASA)**

The last triangle construction in this chapter shows how to draw a triangle where we are given **two angles and the included side** (**ASA** for short).

Construction 12

Construct a triangle *ABC* where
$|\angle ABC| = 60°$, $|BC| = 8$ cm and $|\angle BCA| = 40°$.
(Draw a rough sketch first.)

Solution

1. Draw a rough sketch.

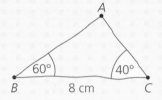

2. Draw a line segment 8 cm in length. Label the end points *B* and *C* and mark the length.

3. Use your protractor to construct an angle of 60° with vertex *B*, and [*BC*] as one arm.

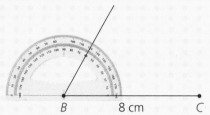

4. Use your protractor to construct an angle of 40° with vertex *C*, and [*CB*] as one arm.

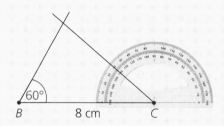

5. Label the point where the two line segments meet as point *A*. Triangle *ABC* is now complete.

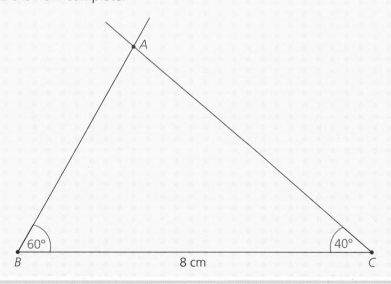

Construct the following triangles. Label each drawing and mark in all the dimensions. When finished, check your construction using a ruler and protractor.

In each case, measure the lengths of the remaining two sides and the size of the remaining angle.

1 Triangle *ABC* where |∠*ABC*| = 50°, |*BC*| = 7 cm and |∠*ACB*| = 70°.

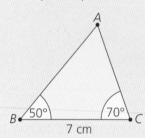

2 Triangle *DEF* where |∠*DEF*| = 80°, |*EF*| = 6 cm and |∠*DFE*| = 60°.

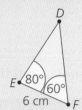

3 Triangle *TPR* where |∠*TPR*| = 30°, |*PR*| = 6 cm and |∠*TRP*| = 120°. Remember to draw a rough sketch first.

4 Triangle *TUV* where |∠*TUV*| = 50°, |*UV*| = 7 cm and |∠*TVU*| = 80°.

5 Triangle *ABC* where |∠*ABC*| = 60°, |*BC*| = 7 cm and |∠*ACB*| = 60°.

6 Triangle *TPR* where |∠*TPR*| = 90°, |*PR*| = 6 cm and |∠*TRP*| = 60°. Remember to draw a rough sketch first.

Section 16E Construction: To Bisect an Angle

To **bisect an angle** means to draw a line which will divide it into two equal (smaller) angles.

The following is the sequence for this construction.

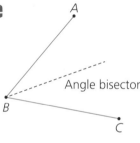

Angle bisector

Construction 1

Example: Bisect angle *ABC*.

1. With *B* as the centre and any radius, use your compass to draw an arc cutting [*AB*] at *P* and [*BC*] at *Q*.

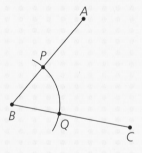

2. With *P* and *Q* as centres and using the same radius, draw two more arcs and mark the intersection as *R*.

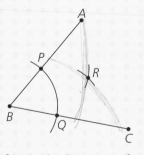

3. Join *BR*. [*BR* is the bisector of ∠*ABC*.

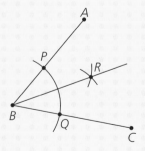

Geometry 3

As always, try to be as accurate as possible with these constructions. You must use only a compass and straight-edge.

1 Construct the following angles accurately in your copybook. You can make the arms of the angles as long as you like. Then draw the bisector of each angle. Use your protractor to check your work.

(i)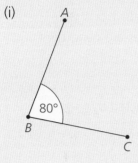

(iii)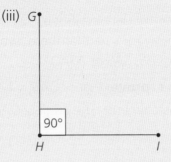

(v)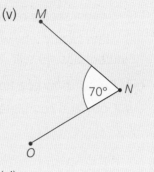

(ii)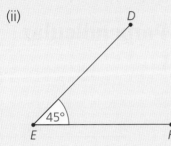

(iv)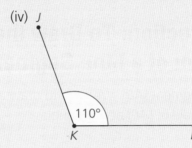

(vi)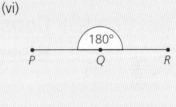

2 Michael was bisecting an angle in class. He said, 'When I am drawing the second set of arcs, it makes no difference whether or not I use a different compass width than the one I used for the first arc'. Was he right? Use a diagram to explain your reasoning.

3 (i) Construct the isosceles triangle *ABC* where |*AB*| = 8 cm, |*AC*| = 8 cm and |*BC*| = 5 cm.

(ii) Construct [*AM*], the bisector of ∠*BAC*, meeting [*BC*] at *M*.

(iii) Show that the triangles *ABM* and *ACM* are congruent.

(iv) What can you conclude about the relationship between ∠*ABC* and ∠*ACB*? Would this be true if |*AB*| and |*AC*| were not equal? Explain your answer.

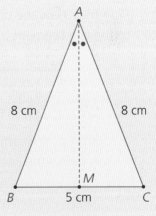

4 The two triangles below share a common side [AB].

The equal parts of the triangles are indicated by similar markings.

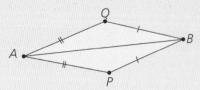

(i) Draw a sketch of the two triangles separately.

(ii) State clearly why we can say for sure that these two triangles are congruent. (Your answer will contain SSS, SAS or ASA.)

(iii) Explain how you know (i.e. **prove**) that $|\angle QAB| = |\angle BAP|$.

(iv) Copy and complete this statement: 'The angle $\angle QAP$ is bisected by ____.'

Section 16F Construction: To Draw the Perpendicular Bisector of a Line Segment

Suppose that we have a line segment [AB]. We wish to draw a line which will cut through the middle of [AB] at right angles (i.e. perpendicular) to it.

The following is the sequence for this construction.

Construction 2

Example: Draw the perpendicular bisector of the line segment [AB].

1. Set your compass radius to more than half the length of [AB].

2. With A as the centre, draw arcs above and below the line segment [AB].

3. With B as the centre and the same radius, draw two more arcs above and below [AB], intersecting the first arcs at P and Q.

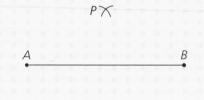

4. Join P and Q. [PQ] is the perpendicular bisector of [AB].

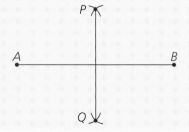

Section 16G Construction: A Line Perpendicular to a Given Line Through a Point on it

Suppose that we have a line *l* with a specified point *P* on it.
We wish to draw another line through *P* which is perpendicular to *l*.

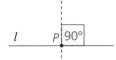

Construction 4

Example: Draw a line perpendicular to line *l*, through the point *P* on *l*.

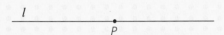

Method 1 Using ruler and compass

1. With *P* as the centre and any radius, draw two arcs intersecting the line *l* at *X* and *Y*.

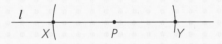

2. Set your compass to draw an arc longer than |*PX*|.

3. With *X* and *Y* as centres, draw two more arcs intersecting at *Q* (above or below the line *l*).

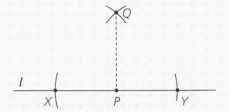

4. Join *Q* to *P*. [*QP*] is perpendicular to *l*.

Method 2 Using ruler and set-square

1. Place a set-square at the point *P* so that one edge of the set-square is along the line *l*.

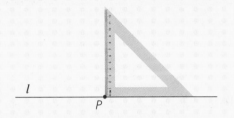

2. Use the vertical edge of the set-square to draw a line segment from *P*.

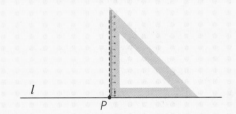

3. [*PQ*] is the required perpendicular to *l*.

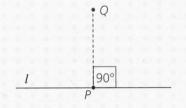

1 Accurately construct the following line segments using your ruler. Then draw the perpendicular bisector of each, using only a compass and straight-edge. Use your protractor and ruler to check your work.

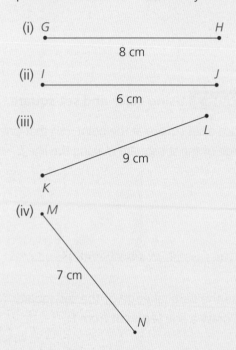

(i) *G* ————————————— *H*
8 cm

(ii) *I* ————————— *J*
6 cm

(iii)
L
9 cm
K

(iv) *M*

7 cm

N

2 Accurately construct the following line segments using your ruler. Then draw the perpendicular bisector of each using only a compass and straight-edge. Use your protractor and ruler to check your work.

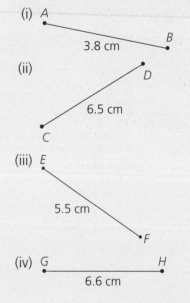

(i) *A*
3.8 cm   *B*

(ii)
D
6.5 cm
C

(iii) *E*
5.5 cm
F

(iv) *G* ————————— *H*
6.6 cm

3 (i) Using only a ruler and compass, accurately construct the triangle *OPQ* shown below.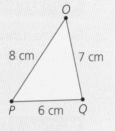

(ii) Draw the perpendicular bisector of [*OP*].

(iii) Draw the perpendicular bisector of [*OQ*].

(iv) Mark the point *M* where the bisectors meet.

(v) Can you draw a circle with centre at *M* which passes through *O*, *P* and *Q*?

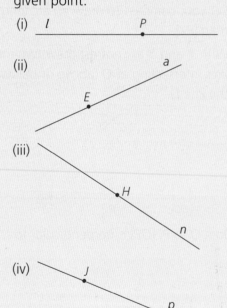

O
8 cm   7 cm
P   6 cm   *Q*

4 Copy the following lines into your copybook. Use two methods to construct a second line perpendicular to the given line passing through the given point.

(i) *l* ————————•———————— *P*

(ii)
a
E

(iii)
H
n

(iv)
J
p

5 Copy the following lines into your copybook. Construct a second line perpendicular to the given line passing through the given point.

(i)
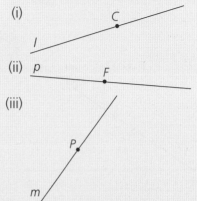

(ii)

(iii)

6 Mary constructed the bisector of a straight angle, shown below.

She said, 'This is another way of drawing a line perpendicular to another through a given point. I have two constructions in one here'.

Was she correct? Explain your answer.

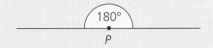

Section 16H Constructions 5 and 6

In this section, we use our growing knowledge of geometry to do two further constructions. Here, we have our last axiom:

AXIOM 5

Given any line *l* and a point *P*, there is exactly one line through *P* that is parallel to *l*.

P Parallel line

l

Construction 5

Example: Draw a line parallel to the line *k*, through the point *P*.

P

k

1. Place a set-square with one side along the line *k*. Place a ruler along the other side and hold the ruler firmly.

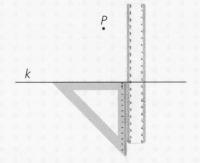

2. Slide the set-square along the ruler until the edge is at the point *P*.

Using this edge of the set-square, draw a line through *P*.

This is the required line.

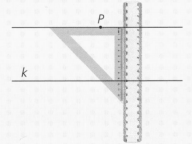

Construction 6

Example: Divide the line segment [AB] into three equal segments.

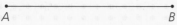

1. Draw a ray from the point A, making an acute angle with [AB].

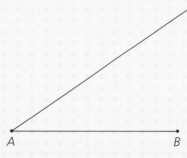

2. With A as the centre and any radius, draw an arc crossing the ray at P.

   With P as the centre and the **same** radius, draw a second arc crossing the ray at Q.

With Q as the centre and the **same** radius, draw a third arc crossing the ray at R.

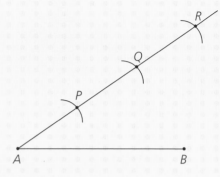

3. Join B to R.

   Use a set square and ruler to draw [QL] and [PM] parallel to [RB].

   [AB] is now divided into three equal segments.

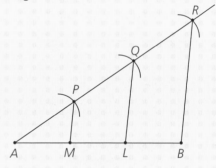

Activity 16.7

1 (i) Copy this diagram into your copybook.

   (ii) Construct a line m through C which is parallel to l.

   (iii) How many such lines are possible?

2 (i) Copy this diagram into your copybook.

   (ii) Construct a line through P which is parallel to m.

3 (i) Copy this diagram into your copybook.

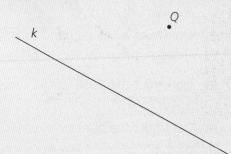

(ii) Construct a line through *Q* which is parallel to *k*.

4 (i) Construct a line segment [*AB*] of any length.

A ●————————————————● B

(ii) Using a ruler and compass, and without measuring, divide the line segment [*AB*] into three equal segments.

(iii) Check your construction by measuring.

5 (i) Construct a line segment [*PQ*] where |*PQ*| = 8 cm.

(ii) Using a ruler and compass, and without measuring, divide the line segment [*PQ*] into three equal segments.

(iii) Check your construction by measuring.

6 (i) Construct a line segment [*MN*] where |*MN*| = 7 cm.

(ii) Using a ruler and compass, and without measuring, divide the line segment [*MN*] into two equal segments.

(iii) Check your construction by measuring.

7 (i) Construct a line segment [*RS*] where |*RS*| = 10 cm.

(ii) Using a ruler and compass, and without measuring, divide the line segment [*RS*] into three equal segments.

(iii) Check your construction by measuring.

8 (i) Copy the diagram below into your copybook.

(ii) Construct a line through *Q* which is parallel to *AB*.

(iii) Construct a line through *Q* which is parallel to *DC*.

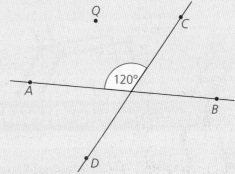

Revision Activity 16

1 (a) Construct a ray [*AB*.

(b) On the ray [*AB*, construct a line segment of length 9 cm.

2 (a) Construct a ray [*PQ*.

(b) Using the ray [*PQ* as one arm, construct ∠*RPQ* where |∠*RPQ*| = 65°.

3 (a) Triangle *ABC* has three equal sides. Write down the size of each angle in this triangle.

(b) *EFG* is a right-angled triangle which has two equal sides.

(i) Write down the size of each angle in this triangle.

(ii) If |*EF*| = |*FG*| = 6 cm, accurately construct the triangle *EFG*. Show clearly your construction marks.

4 The triangle *ABC* is an isosceles triangle where |*AB*| = |*AC*|, |∠*BAC*| = 36°, and |*AB*| = 7 cm.

 (a) Construct the triangle accurately. Show all your construction marks.

 (b) Calculate |∠*ACB*|.

 (c) On your diagram, construct the bisector of ∠*ABC*. Show all construction lines clearly.

 (d) Mark in the point *D* where the bisector meets the line *AC*.

 (e) Calculate all the angles in the triangle *BDC* and write them into your diagram.

 (f) Can you conclude that triangle *BDC* is also isosceles? Give a reason for your answer.

5 (a) Construct a line segment [*PQ*] such that |*PQ*| = 8.5 cm.

 (b) Construct the perpendicular bisector of [*PQ*].

6 (a) Construct a line *m* and mark a point *P* anywhere on it.

 (b) Construct a line perpendicular to *m* through the point *P*.

7 (a) Construct the angle ∠*ABC* where |∠*ABC*| = 70°.

 (b) Construct the bisector of ∠*ABC*.

8 Construct the triangle *ABC* where |*AB*| = 10 cm, |*BC*| = 6 cm and |*CA*| = 8 cm.

 Draw a rough sketch first and show all your construction marks.

9 Construct the triangle *PQR* where |*QR*| = 6 cm, |∠*QRP*| = 120° and |*PR*| = 7 cm.

 Draw a rough sketch first and show all your construction marks.

10 Construct the triangle *XYZ* where |∠*XYZ*| = 30°, |*YZ*| = 5 cm and |∠*YZX*| = 130°.

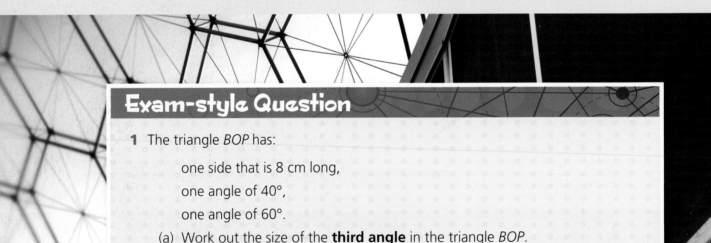

Exam-style Question

1 The triangle *BOP* has:

 one side that is 8 cm long,

 one angle of 40°,

 one angle of 60°.

 (a) Work out the size of the **third angle** in the triangle *BOP*.

 (b) Draw a **sketch** of one such triangle *BOP*.

 On your sketch, **write in** the size of **all** 3 angles, and the length of one of the sides.

 (c) **Construct** the triangle *BOP* from your sketch.

 JCOL 2016

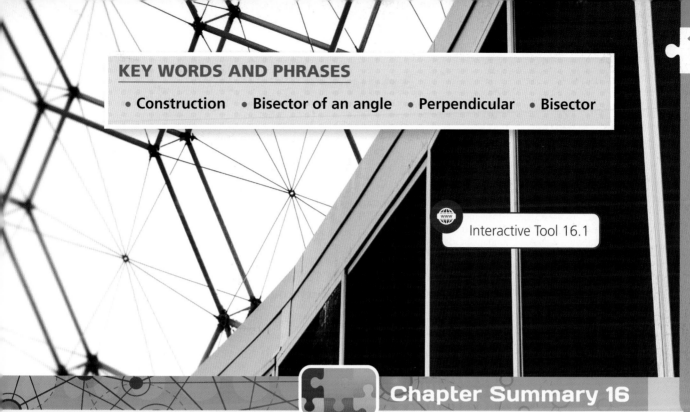

KEY WORDS AND PHRASES

- **Construction** - **Bisector of an angle** - **Perpendicular** - **Bisector**

Interactive Tool 16.1

Chapter Summary 16

- Construction 8: Construct a line segment of a given length on a given ray
- Construction 9: Construct an angle of a given number of degrees with a given ray as one arm
- Construction 10: Construct a triangle given SSS data
- Construction 11: Construct a triangle given SAS data
- Construction 12: Construct a triangle given ASA data
- Construction 1: Construct the bisector of an angle using only a straight-edge and compass
- Construction 2: Construct the perpendicular bisector of a line segment
- Construction 4: Construct a line perpendicular to a given line through a point on it
- Axiom 5: Given any line *l* and a point *P*, there is exactly one line through *P* that is parallel to *l*
- Construction 5: Construct a line parallel to a given line, through a given point
- Construction 6: Divide a line segment, without measuring, into two or three equal segments

Answers

Chapter 1

Activity 1.1
1. (i) The even numbers between 20 and 40 are a set. (ii) The small animals on a farm are not a set. (iii) The students in your maths class are a set. (iv) The members of the school basketball team are a set. (v) The good movies out this year are not a set. **2.** (i) A = {Monday, Tuesday, Wednesday, Thursday, Friday, Saturday, Sunday}; #A = 7 (ii) B = {1, 3, 5, 7, 9, 11, 13, 15, 17, 19}; #B = 10 (iii) C = {September}; #C = 1 (iv) D = {a, b, c, d, e, f}; #D = 6 (v) E = {i, o, u}; #E = 3 **3.** (i) A = {a, c, e, h, i, m, s, t}; #A = 8 (ii) B = {u, v, w, x, y, z}; #B = 6 (iii) C = {Galway, Leitrim, Mayo, Roscommon, Sligo}; #C = 5 (iv) D = {Saturday, Sunday}; #D = 2 (v) E = {1, 2, 3, 5, 8}; #E = 5 **4.** (i) 1 $\notin Q$ (ii) 2 $\in R$ (iii) 10 $\in S$ (iv) 9 $\notin S$ (v) 0 $\notin R$ (vi) u $\notin Q$ (vii) w $\notin Q$ (viii) 3 $\in R$ (ix) 2 $\in S$ (x) 3 $\notin Q$ **5.** (i) False (ii) False (iii) True (iv) True (v) False (vi) False (vii) False (viii) True (ix) True (x) False **6.** (i) The set A is the months of autumn. (ii) The set X is the first 8 letters in the alphabet. (iii) The set H is the suits in a pack of cards. (iv) The set B is a kitchen cutlery set. (v) The set Y is the days of the week beginning with "M". **7.** (i) False (ii) True (iii) False (iv) True (v) False (vi) False (vii) True (viii) True (ix) False (x) True **8.** (i) e $\notin A$ (ii) c $\in C$ (iii) x $\in B$ (iv) d $\notin C$ (v) r $\notin A$ (vi) y $\in B$ (vii) z $\in B$ (viii) l $\in C$ (ix) c $\in A$ (x) x $\notin A$ **9.** (i) #D = 5 (ii) #E = 3 (iii) #D − #E = 2 (iv) #D + #E = 8

Activity 1.2
1. (i) A: Proper subsets: {2}, {5}, Improper subsets: {2, 5}, { } (ii) B: Proper subsets: {heads}, {tails}, Improper subsets: {heads, tails}, { } (iii) C: Proper subsets: {1}, {3}, {5}, {1, 3}, {3, 5}, {1, 5}, Improper subsets: {1, 3, 5}, { } **2.** (i) True (ii) False (iii) False (iv) True (v) True (vi) False (vii) False (viii) False (ix) True (x) False **3.** { }, {a}, {b}, {c}, {a, b}, {a, c}, {b, c}, {a, b, c} **4.** { }, {w}, {x}, {y}, {z}, {w, x}, {w, y}, {w, z}, {x, y}, {x, z}, {y, z}, {w, x, y}, {w, x, z}, {w, y, z}, {x, y, z}, {w, x, y, z} **5.** (i) X = {31, 33, 35, 37, 39} Y = {30, 31, 32, 33, 34, 35, 36, 37, 38, 39, 40} (ii) (a) True (b) True (c) False (d) False (e) False

Activity 1.3
1. (i) (a) {1, 2, 3} (b) {3, 4, 5} (c) {1, 2, 3, 4, 5} (d) {3} (e) {1, 2, 3, 4, 5} (f) {3} **2.** (i) (a) {1, 2, 3, 4, 6, 9, 12} (b) {3} (ii) (a) 4 (b) 4 (c) 7 (d) 1 **3.** (ii) (a) {a, e, i, o, u, b, c, d} (b) {a} (iii) (a) 8 (b) 1 **4.** (ii) (a) {1, 2, 3, 4, 5} (b) {1, 3, 5, 7} (c) {1, 2, 3, 4, 5, 7} (d) {1, 2, 3, 4, 5, 7} (e) {1, 3, 5} (f) {1, 3, 5} (iii) (a) 5 (b) 4 (c) 6 (d) 3 **5.** (i) The students who have a dog or a cat or both. (ii) The students who have both a cat and dog. **6.** (i) True (ii) False (iii) True (iv) False (v) True (vi) False (vii) True (viii) False **7.** (i) the students who play sport **and/or** are in the school musical. (ii) the students who play sport **and** are in the school musical. **10.** (i) 3 elements (ii) 8 elements

Activity 1.4
1. (i) {1, 2, 3, 4, 5, 6, 7, 8, 9} (ii) {1, 3, 5, 8} (iii) {4, 5, 9} (iv) {1, 3, 4, 5, 8, 9} (v) {5} **2.** (ii) (a) {2, 3, 4, 5, 6, 7, 8, 10} (b) {2} **3.** (ii) (a) {s, c, i, e, n, t, f} (b) {i, e, c, n} (c) {s, e, t, n} (d) {i, e, c, n, s, t} (e) {e, n} **4.** (ii) (a) 10 (b) 7 **5.** (i) 25 (ii) 7 (iii) 44 **6.** (ii) (a) 6 (b) No members **7.** (i) 101 (ii) 64 (iii) 21 (iv) 35 **8.** (ii) 8

Revision Activity 1
1. (a) (i) {991, 993, 995, 997, 999, 1001, 1003, 1005, 1007, 1009} (ii) {e, i, o, p, r, s, t, u} (iii) { } (iv) {s, t, u, v, w, x, y, z}

(v) {50, 55, 60, 65, 70, 75, 80, 85, 90, 95, 100} (b) (i) The list of even numbers between 1 and 10 (ii) The vowels in the English alphabet. (iii) The days of the week beginning with the letter T. (iv) The Null or empty set. **2.** (b) (i) $A \cup B$ = {a, e, i, o, u, h, s} (ii) $A \cap B$ = {e, o, u} **3.** (b) 120 (c) 56 **4.** (a) (i) False (ii) True (iii) True (iv) True (v) False (vi) False (vii) True (viii) True (ix) False (b) { }, {w}, {x}, {y}, {w, x}, {w, y}, {x, y}, {w, x, y} (c) (i) The students that like Chinese food or like Italian food or like both. (ii) The students that like both Chinese and Italian food.

Exam-style Question
(b) A set with any two of I, O and A. (c) A subset of X with at most one of I, O and A.

Chapter 2

Activity 2.1
1. (i) 58 (ii) 62 (iii) 57 (iv) 16 (v) 83 (vi) 9 (vii) 108 (viii) 10 (ix) 115 (x) 32 **2.** (i) 26 (ii) 24 (iii) 7 (iv) 33 (v) 16 (vi) 37 (vii) 9 (viii) 35 (ix) 19 (x) 29 **3.** (i) 12 (ii) 4 (iii) 20 (iv) 48 (v) 42 (vi) 47 **4.** (i) 50 (ii) 5 (iii) 500 (iv) 50 000 (v) 5 000 000 (vi) 5 (vii) 50 000 (viii) 500 000 (ix) 50 000 (x) 5 000 **5.** (i) 368 < 372 < 373 < 375 < 379 < 381 (ii) 4801 < 4839 < 4845 < 4862 < 4893 (iii) 27 235 < 27 374 < 27 472 < 27 523 < 27 732 **6.** (i) 459 494 > 459 236 > 458 392 > 457 234 > 451 392 (ii) 567 234 > 563 321 > 562 349 > 560 784 > 560 344 (iii) 937 291 > 935 345 > 935 123 > 934 923 > 934 234 **7.** (i) 2 245 (ii) 13 782 (iii) 105 854 (iv) 635 899 (v) 4 523 300 (vi) 9 048 (vii) 1 182 987 **8.** (i) 857 350 > 857 349 > 856 784 > 856 440 > 856 235 (ii) 168 287 > 163 009 > 157 194 > 132 129 > 123 321 (iii) 397 238 > 391 875 > 391 238 > 382 492 > 381 201 **9.** (i) 98 (ii) 98 653 (iii) 356 (iv) 3 568 (v) 98 653 **10.** (i) 16, 17, 18 (ii) $n + 1, n + 2, n + 3$

Activity 2.2
2. (i) 21 (ii) 18 (iii) 30 (iv) 5 (v) 6 (vi) 3 (vii) 27 **3.** (i) 345 (ii) 323 (iii) 273 (iv) 384 (v) 425 (vi) 351 **4.** (i) 12 (ii) 14 (iii) 13 (iv) 12 (v) 16 **5.** (i) 405 (ii) 468 (iii) 1032 (iv) 704 **6.** (i) 345 (ii) 323 (iii) 273 (iv) 384 (v) 425 (vi) 351 **9.** (i) Addition is commutative (ii) Multiplication is commutative (iii) Multiplication is associative (iv) Addition is associative (v) Subtraction is not associative (vi) Multiplication is commutative (vii) The distributive property of multiplication over addition (viii) The distributive property of multiplication over subtraction (ix) The distributive property (x) Division is **not** commutative (xi) Subtraction is **not** commutative (xii) Division is **not** associative

Activity 2.3
1. (i) {8, 16, 24, 32, 40} (ii) {11, 22, 33, 44, 55} (iii) {15, 30, 45, 60, 75} (iv) {19, 38, 57, 76, 95} (v) {24, 48, 72, 96, 120} **2.** (i) (a) Factors of 6 = {1, 2, 3, 6} (b) Factors of 10 = {1, 2, 5, 10} (c) Factors of 15 = {1, 3, 5, 15} (d) Factors of 24 = {1, 2, 3, 4, 6, 8, 12, 24} (e) Factors of 13 = {1, 13} (ii) 13 **3.** {2, 3, 5, 7, 11, 13, 17} **4.** {10, 12, 14, 15, 16, 18, 20} **5.** (i) (a) {1, 3, 5,15} (b) {1, 5, 7, 35} (ii) 5 **6.** (i) (a) {1, 2, 4, 6, 8, 12, 24} (b) {1, 2, 3, 4, 6, 9, 12, 18, 36} (ii) HCF = 12 **7.** (i) HCF = 2 (ii) HCF = 2 (iii) HCF = 5 (iv) HCF = 11 (v) HCF = 14 (vi) HCF = 8 (vii) HCF = 28 (viii) HCF = 15 **8.** (i) (a) {4, 8, 12, 16, 20} (b) {6, 12, 18, 24, 30} (ii) LCM =12 **9.** (i) (a) {9, 18, 27, 36, 45}

(b) {12, 24, 36, 48, 60}   (ii) LCM = 36   **10.** (i) LCM = 35
(ii) LCM = 84   (iii) LCM = 99   (iv) LCM = 130   (v) LCM = 90
(vi) LCM = 80   **11.** (i) $3 \times 3 \times 5 = 45$ (ii) $2 \times 2 \times 3 \times 5 = 60$
(iii) $2 \times 2 \times 5 \times 5 = 100$ (iv) $2 \times 2 \times 59 = 236$ (v) $2 \times 191 = 382$
(vi) $2 \times 3 \times 5 \times 17 = 510$ **12.** (i) {1, 2, 5, 10, 25, 50}
(ii) {1, 2, 43, 86}   (iii) {1, 2, 61, 122}   (iv) {1, 2, 5, 10, 23, 46,
115, 230}   (v) {1, 3, 9, 27, 37, 111, 333, 999}   **13.** (i) (a) HCF = 1
(b) LCM = 12   (ii) (a) HCF = 2   (b) LCM = 24   (iii) (a) HCF = 1
(b) LCM = 30   (iv) (a) HCF = 5   (b) LCM = 20   (v) (a) HCF = 1
LCM = 70   **14.** 345, 270, 4565, 12 345, 88 885   **15.** 270,
2370, 8 764 000, 888 850   **16.** 4569, 357 942   **17.** 2007,
3528, 357 948   **18.** LCM = 24 After 24 minutes they all finish
at the same time. Kevin has done 3 laps, Paul 4 laps and Keith
6 laps.   **19.** 42 days   **20.** LCM of 12 and 16 = 48   10:00:48

Activity 2.4
1. (ii) 5^4 (iii) 5^6 (iv) $2^3 \times 5^3$ (v) $5^4 \times 7^2$ (vi) $3^2 \times 4^3$
2. (i) 13   (ii) 220   (iii) 141   (iv) 229   (v) 2276   (vi) 108
3. (i) 3^7 (ii) 3^{10} (iii) 3^7 (iv) $3^0 = 1$ (v) 3^{12} (vi) 3^9 **4.** (i) 4^3
(ii) 3^4 (iii) 5^2 (iv) 2^8 (v) 3^2 (vi) $5^0 = 1$ **5.** (i) 5^2 (ii) 5^7
(iii) 5^{11} **6.** (i) False   (ii) True   (iii) False   (iv) True   (v) False
7. (i) 5^6 (ii) 3^3 (iii) 2^2 (iv) 5^4 (v) 6^2 **8.** (i) n^3 means
$n \times n \times n$ (ii) $n^4 \times n^5 = n^9$ **9.** 4, 9, 16, 25, 36, 49, 64, 81,
100, 121, 144, 169, 196   **10.** (i) 2   (ii) 3   (iii) 11   (iv) 1
11. 28   **12.** $496 = 1 + 2 + 4 + 8 + 16 + 31 + 62 + 124 + 248$

Activity 2.5
1. (i) 11   (ii) 1   (iii) 17   (iv) 16   (v) 28   (vi) 37   (vii) 16
(viii) 30   (ix) 18   (x) 4   **2.** (i) 8   (ii) 76   (iii) 19   (iv) 54
(v) 68   (vi) 52   (vii) 1   (viii) 55   (ix) 18   (x) 48   **3.** (i) 4
(ii) 38   (iii) 9   (iv) 3   (v) 10   **4.** (i) 12   (ii) 6   (iii) 7   (iv) 2
(v) 12   (vi) 3   (vii) 5   (viii) 2   (ix) 5   (x) 5   **5.** (i) 62   (ii) 5
(iii) 35.5   (iv) 67   (v) 6   (vi) 1   (vii) 20   (viii) $\frac{25}{29}$ (ix) 11 (x) 4

Activity 2.6
1. (i) 50   (ii) 60   (iii) 60   (iv) 160   (v) 170   (vi) 170
(vii) 90   **2.** (i) 100   (ii) 200   (iii) 200   (iv) 2100   (v) 2200
(vi) 2200   (vii) 2300   **3.** (i) 42 000   (ii) 1000   (iii) 71 000
(iv) 32 000   (v) 33 000   (vi) 33 000   (vii) 11 000   **5.** Estimate =
€1000   Exact cost = € 912   **6.** Estimate = €40   Exact cost =
€ 43.12   **7.** (i) Estimate = 1000 mm   (ii) Exact Value = 1010 mm
8. (i) 37 500   (ii) 38 000   (iii) 40 000   **9.** (i) 50 700   (ii) 51 000
(iii) 50 000   **10.** (i) 57 000   (ii) 56 500   **11.** (i) 7 500   (ii) 8 499

Revision Activity 2
2. (a) 97   (b) 97 542   (c) 245   (d) 2457   (e) 97 542   (f) 5
3. (a) (i) 8, 16, 24, 32, 40   (ii) 12, 24, 36, 48, 60   (b) 24
4. (a) LCM = 77   (b) LCM = 39   **6.** (a) 1, 2, 3, 4, 5, 6, 10, 12,
15, 20, 30, 60   (b) 1, 5, 13, 65   (c) 1, 3, 41, 123
7. (a) (i) $6 = \{2 \times 3\}$, $8 = \{2 \times 2 \times 2\}$, $24 = \{2 \times 2 \times 2 \times 3\}$
(ii) $7 = \{7\}$, $21 = \{3 \times 7\}$, $84 = \{2 \times 2 \times 2 \times 7\}$ (b) 2   (ii) 7
(c) (i) 24   (ii) 84   **8.** (a) 5^7 (b) 5^8 (c) 5^3

Exam-style Question
1. (a) Factors of 10 = 1, 2, 5, 10; factors of 11 = 1, 11; factors
of 12 = 1, 2, 3, 4, 6, 12   (b) 11. It has only two factors, 1 and
itself.   (c) Any three of: 2, 3, 5, 7, 13, 17   (d) LCM of the
three numbers in (c)

Chapter 3

Activity 3.1
1. (i) A = –4, B = –1, C = 2, D = 5   (ii) A = 6, B = –4, C = 0,
D = 3   (iii) A = 5, B = –3, C = –2, D = 1   **2.** (i) 18°   (ii) 32°
(iii) 10°   **4.** (ii) (a) True   (b) True   (c) False   (d) True   (e) False
(f) False   (g) False   (h) True   (i) False   (j) False   **5.** (a) 7 > 3
(b) –1 < 0   (c) –9 < –3   (d) –4 > –5   (e) –2 > –5
(f) 4 > –3   (g) –9 < 0   (h) –11 < –10   (i) –6 < 6   (j) –1 > –4
6. (i) {–7, –1, 0, 2, 3, 5}   (ii) {–8, –5, –4, –3, 0, 2, 6}
(iii) {–9, –5, –2, 0, 2, 4, 8, 9}   (iv) {–6, –3, –1, 0, 1, 2, 4}
(v) {–8, –7, –5, –4, –3, 1, 4, 6, 9}   (vi) {–89, –78, –75, –74, 57,
76, 89}   **7.** (i) {5, 4, 3, 2, 1, –3}   (ii) {6, 2, 1, –2, –3, –4, –6}
(iii) {20, 18, 16, 14, –12, –15, –19, –20}   (iv) {61, 59, 51, –7,

–32, –40, –45, –48, –52}   (v) {22, 12, 10, 9, –1, –10, –13}
(vi) {14, 13, 9, 7, –1, –2, –8, –13, –17}   **8.** (i) 14°C
(ii) –3°C   (iii) –10°C   (iv) –5°C   (v) –10°C   (vi) –5°C
9. (i) –3, –9, –15   (ii) 5, 9, 14   (iii) 1, –2, –5   (iv) –18, 18, 27
(v) –8, 13, 20   (vi) 6, –10, –18

Activity 3.2
1. (i) 1   (ii) –1   (iii) 5   (iv) –5   (v) –7   (vi) 7   (vii) –13
(viii) 13   (ix) 4   (x) –4   **2.** (i) –15   (ii) –3   (iii) 12   (iv) 1
(v) –11   (vi) –11   (vii) 16   (viii) 0   (ix) –6   (x) –7   **3.** (i) 5
(ii) –6   (iii) 8   (iv) 8   (v) –7   (vi) 5   (vii) –14   (viii) –4
(ix) 11   (x) –4   **4.** (i) 8   (ii) –9   (iii) –1   (iv) –7   (v) 0
(vi) –12   (vii) –1   (viii) –3   **6.** (i) 3   (ii) 8   (iii) 4   (iv) 5
(v) 29   (vi) 8   (vii) 23   (viii) 4   (ix) –7   (x) –11
7. Paris 5°C, Madrid 10°C, New York –2°C, Dallas 6°C,
London –2°C, Hong Kong 18°C, Perth 28°C, Stockholm –2°C,
Moscow –7°C, Dublin –1°C   **8.** 6th floor   **9.** 3°C   **10.** –€20
12. (i) 3   (ii) –3   (iii) Subtraction is **not commutative** as the
answer is different depending on the order of subtraction.

Activity 3.3
1. (i) 1   (ii) 17   (iii) –12   (iv) 2   (v) 8   (vi) –16   (vii) 5
(viii) 10   (ix) –12   (x) 0   **2.** (i) –3   (ii) 1   (iii) 10   (iv) 4
(v) –1   (vi) 17   (vii) 10   (viii) –17   (ix) 1   (x) 1   **3.** (i) False
(ii) False   (iii) False   (iv) False   (v) True   (vi) False   (vii) True
(viii) False   (ix) False   **4.** (i) 3   (ii) –4   (iii) –7   (iv) –3   (v) –9
(vi) 8   (vii) 4   (viii) –10   (ix) –5   (x) –2   **5.** (i) –2   (ii) 0   (iii) –8
(iv) 15   (v) 1   (vi) 42   (vii) –1   (viii) –63

Activity 3.4
1. (i) 6   (ii) 6   (iii) –6   (iv) –6   (v) –16   (vi) 48   (vii) 15
(viii) –27   (ix) –21   (x) –24   **2.** (i) 6   (ii) 6   (iii) –6   (iv) 6
(v) 4   (vi) 3   (vii) 8   (viii) 3   **4.** (i) –8   (ii) 9   (iii) –15
(iv) –11   (v) 10   (vi) 9   (vii) 5   (viii) –5   (ix) –5   (x) –20
5. (i) –2   (ii) –72   (iii) 18   (iv) 6   **6.** (i) 3   (ii) 3   (iii) –2
(iv) 3   **7.** (i) –14   (ii) 55   (iii) –2   (iv) –3   (v) 10   (vi) –4
8. (i) 27   (ii) 4   (iii) –8   (iv) 16   (v) –32   **9.** (i) 8   (ii) –5
(iii) 4   **10.** (i) 4   (ii) –6   (iii) 4.5   (iv) 1   (v) –5   **11.** (i) –3
(iii) 4   **12.** –4°C

Revision Activity 3
1. (a) 8 > 4   (b) –3 < 1   (c) –8 < –5   (d) –4 > –5   (e) –2 > –5
(f) 6 > –1   (g) –4 < 0   (h) –21 < –10   (i) 3 > –3   (j) –2 > –6
2. (a) 9   (b) –10   (c) –2   (d) –5   (e) 2   (f) –15   (g) –2
(h) –6   **3.** (a) 4   (b) 15   (c) –25   (d) 10   (e) 12   (f) 11
(g) –1   (h) 6   (i) –24   (j) –24   **4.** (a) 48   (b) –16   (c) –10
(d) 3   (e) –8   (f) 4   **5.** (a) (i) –1   (ii) 1   (iii) –1   (iv) 1
(v) –1   (c) (i) –1   (ii) 1   (iii) 1   (iv) –1   (v) 1   **6.** (a) 3   (b) –3
(c) 4   (d) –7   (e) –2   **7.** (a) –2   (b) –2

Exam-style Question
(i) 3 – 2 + 5 = 6   (ii) 3 × 2 – 5 = 1

Chapter 4

Activity 4.1
1. A = 2, B = 4, C = 1, D = 3, **2.** A = 2, B = 4, C = 1, D = 3
3. (i) $\frac{2}{5}$ (ii) $\frac{3}{8}$ (iii) $\frac{5}{9}$ (iv) $\frac{9}{15}$ (v) $\frac{10}{13}$ (vi) $\frac{11}{14}$ **4.** (i) $\frac{3}{5}$ (ii) $\frac{5}{8}$
(iii) $\frac{4}{9}$ (iv) $\frac{6}{15}$ (v) $\frac{3}{13}$ (vi) $\frac{3}{14}$ **5.** (i) $\frac{2}{5}$ (ii) $\frac{6}{15}$ (iii) $\frac{11}{15}$
(iv) $\frac{3}{25}$ (v) $\frac{6}{9}$ (vi) $\frac{6}{17}$ **8.** (i) A = $\frac{1}{5}$ B = $\frac{2}{5}$ C = $\frac{3}{5}$ D = $\frac{4}{5}$
(ii) A = $\frac{2}{6} = \frac{1}{3}$ B = $\frac{1}{6}$ C = $\frac{4}{6} = \frac{2}{3}$ D = $\frac{5}{6}$ (iii) A = $\frac{3}{12}$ B = $\frac{5}{12}$
C = $\frac{10}{12} = \frac{5}{6}$ D = $\frac{11}{12}$

Activity 4.2
3. (i) Proper   (ii) Improper   (iii) Improper   (iv) Proper
(v) Improper   (vi) Improper   (vii) Proper   **4.** (i) (a) $2\frac{1}{4}$ (b) $3\frac{1}{3}$
(c) $4\frac{3}{5}$ (d) $5\frac{1}{2}$ (e) $3\frac{1}{2}$ (f) $4\frac{4}{5}$ (ii) (a) $\frac{9}{4}$ (b) $\frac{10}{3}$ (c) $\frac{23}{5}$
(d) $\frac{11}{2}$ (e) $\frac{7}{2}$ (f) $\frac{24}{5}$ **5.** (i) (a) $\frac{4}{3}$ (b) $\frac{23}{9}$ (c) $\frac{13}{10}$ (d) $\frac{33}{7}$

(e) $\frac{25}{8}$ (f) $\frac{27}{5}$ (g) $\frac{8}{3}$ 6. (i) (a) $1\frac{1}{2}$ (b) $2\frac{1}{4}$ (c) $3\frac{1}{6}$ (d) $5\frac{2}{3}$
(e) $2\frac{4}{5}$ (f) $4\frac{3}{4}$ (g) $8\frac{1}{6}$ 7. (i) 12 sweets (ii) $\frac{2}{50}$ sweets = $\frac{1}{25}$

Activity 4.3
1. (a) (i) $\frac{1}{2} = \frac{2}{4} = \frac{4}{8} = \frac{8}{16}$ (ii) $\frac{2}{3} = \frac{4}{6} = \frac{6}{9}$ (iii) $\frac{1}{4} = \frac{2}{8}$ (iv) $\frac{2}{5} = \frac{4}{10}$
2. (i) $\frac{3}{8}, \frac{5}{12}, \frac{7}{16}$ and $\frac{11}{24}$ (ii) $\frac{5}{7}, \frac{11}{16}, \frac{23}{32}$ and $\frac{7}{10}$ 3. (i) $\frac{3}{6}$ (ii) $\frac{2}{10}$
(iii) $\frac{1}{6}$ (iv) $\frac{3}{7}$ (v) $\frac{9}{15}$ (vi) $\frac{14}{18}$ 4. (i) $\frac{12}{36}$ (ii) $\frac{28}{77}$ (iii) $\frac{12}{16}$
(iv) $\frac{11}{15}$ (v) $\frac{7}{12}$ (vi) $\frac{8}{56}$ (vii) $\frac{25}{30}$ (viii) $\frac{32}{48}$ 5. (i) $\frac{12}{15}$
(ii) $\frac{3}{4}$ (iii) $\frac{6}{8}$ (iv) $\frac{3}{6}$ (v) $\frac{3}{6}$ (vi) $\frac{55}{88}$ (vii) $\frac{18}{81}$ (viii) $\frac{4}{16}$
(ix) $\frac{21}{24} = \frac{56}{64}$ 7. (i) 2 slices (ii) 2 slices (iii) 9 slices
(iv) Each person will get $\frac{1}{3}$ of cake 8. (i) $\frac{2}{3}$ (ii) $\frac{3}{10}$ (iii) $\frac{2}{3}$
(iv) $\frac{5}{6}$ (v) $\frac{2}{5}$ (vi) $\frac{123}{250}$ (vii) $\frac{17}{30}$ (viii) $\frac{23}{50}$ (ix) $\frac{14}{25}$ (x) $\frac{31}{50}$
9. (i) $\frac{1}{4} = \frac{2}{8} = \frac{3}{12} = \frac{4}{16} = \frac{5}{20} = \frac{6}{24}, \frac{1}{6} = \frac{2}{12} = \frac{3}{18} = \frac{4}{24} = \frac{5}{30} = \frac{6}{36}$
(ii) $\frac{5}{24}$ 10. $\frac{3}{11}$ and $\frac{4}{15}$

Activity 4.4
5. (i) $\frac{4}{5}$ is larger (ii) $\frac{7}{12}$ is larger (iii) $\frac{2}{3}$ is larger (iv) $\frac{3}{7}$ is
larger 6. (i) = (ii) > (iii) > (iv) > (v) = 7. $\frac{1}{9}, \frac{2}{9}, \frac{3}{9}, \frac{5}{9}, \frac{9}{9}$
8. $\frac{1}{3}$ 9. $\frac{1}{4}$ 10. $\frac{5}{5}$ 11. (i) $\frac{2}{15}, \frac{6}{15}, \frac{7}{15}, \frac{8}{15}, \frac{12}{15}, \frac{13}{15}$ (ii) $\frac{1}{23}, \frac{1}{17}, \frac{1}{15}$,
$\frac{1}{13}, \frac{1}{9}, \frac{1}{5}, \frac{1}{2}$ (iii) $\frac{1}{2}, \frac{3}{5}, \frac{2}{3}, \frac{7}{10}, \frac{5}{6}$ (iv) $\frac{2}{30}, \frac{9}{30}, \frac{15}{30}, \frac{19}{30}, \frac{21}{30}, \frac{27}{30}$
(v) $\frac{3}{13}, \frac{3}{11}, \frac{1}{3}, \frac{3}{7}, \frac{1}{2}, \frac{3}{5}$

Activity 4.5
1. (ii) (a) $\frac{2}{3}$ (b) $\frac{29}{35}$ (c) $\frac{9}{14}$ 2. (ii) (a) $\frac{11}{12}$ (b) $\frac{9}{20}$ (c) $\frac{19}{21}$
(d) $1\frac{1}{18}$ (e) $1\frac{1}{10}$ 3. (i) $\frac{1}{2}$ (ii) $\frac{5}{14}$ (iii) $1\frac{1}{12}$ (iv) $\frac{2}{3}$ (v) $1\frac{1}{6}$
4. (i) $\frac{14}{15}$ (ii) $\frac{5}{18}$ (iii) $\frac{27}{35}$ (iv) $\frac{1}{6}$ (v) $\frac{8}{15}$ 5. (i) $1\frac{3}{20}$ (ii) $\frac{13}{45}$
(iii) $\frac{25}{21}$ (iv) $\frac{3}{14}$ (v) $\frac{5}{8}$ 6. (i) False (ii) True (iii) False
(iv) True (v) False 7. 1 and $\frac{7}{20}$ kilometres 8. 1 and $\frac{3}{4}$ kilometres
9. $\frac{13}{20}$ of his book 10. $\frac{17}{20}$ kg 11. $\frac{1}{12}$ 12. $\frac{4}{9}$ m

Activity 4.6
1. (i) $\frac{12}{7}$ (ii) $\frac{4}{21}$ (iii) $\frac{4}{15}$ (iv) $\frac{5}{6}$ (v) $\frac{4}{9}$ 2. $\frac{1}{7}$
3. (i) $\frac{7}{4}$ (ii) $\frac{5}{2}$ (iii) $\frac{14}{3}$ (iv) $\frac{9}{4}$ (v) $\frac{18}{5}$ 4. 3 hours
5. (i) $\frac{5}{9}$ (ii) $\frac{3}{10}$ (iii) $\frac{1}{5}$ (iv) $\frac{1}{6}$ (v) $\frac{1}{8}$ (vi) $\frac{7}{60}$
6. (i) $1125 (ii) 400 kg (iii) 25 km (iv) 150 (v) €508
7. (i) €24 (ii) 120 g (iii) 180 m (iv) 270 litres (v) 9 hours
8. (i) 40 tickets (ii) 75 tickets (iii) 5 9. €22 10. (i) €2.50
(ii) €3.50 11. (i) 1 hour (ii) $5\frac{1}{2}$ hours (iii) $1\frac{1}{2}$ hours

Activity 4.7
1. 12 people 2. 20 bags 3. (i) 5 (ii) $\frac{16}{3}$ (iii) 10 (iv) 16
4. (i) $\frac{26}{9}$ (ii) $\frac{357}{456} = \frac{119}{152}$ (iii) $\frac{2}{3}$ (iv) $\frac{3}{4}$ (v) $\frac{11}{10}$ (vi) $\frac{5}{7}$ 5. 30
6. (i) $\frac{1}{5}$ (ii) $6\frac{1}{8}$ (iii) 6 (iv) $\frac{21}{40}$ (v) $23\frac{1}{7}$ (vi) $4\frac{1}{2}$ 7. (i) 4
(ii) 2 (iii) $\frac{45}{2}$ (iv) 6 (v) 5 8. (i) 1 (ii) 1 (iii) $\frac{5}{2}$ (iv) $\frac{3}{7}$
9. (i) 1 (ii) 1 (iii) $\frac{9}{5}$ 10. (i) $\frac{8}{3}$ (ii) 1 11. 8 Strips
12. 3 times 13. $\frac{1}{10}$ = 1150 tonnes, so $\frac{9}{10}$ = 10350 tonnes

Revision Activity 4
1. (a) $\frac{1}{2}$ (b) $\frac{1}{21}$ (c) $\frac{1}{6}$ (d) $\frac{1}{17}$ (e) $\frac{1}{5}$ (f) $\frac{1}{24}$ (g) $\frac{1}{12}$ (h) $\frac{1}{8}$
(i) $\frac{5}{23}$ (j) $\frac{1}{13}$ 2. (a) $\frac{27}{13}$ (b) $1\frac{4}{63}$ (c) $\frac{73}{9}$ (d) $1\frac{64}{357}$
(e) $\frac{80}{7}$ (f) $4\frac{9}{20}$ (g) $\frac{73}{6}$ (h) $2\frac{2}{5}$ (i) $2\frac{1}{112}$ (j) $\frac{59}{8}$
3. (a) $\frac{1}{2}$ (b) $\frac{17}{6}$ (c) $\frac{13}{117}$ (d) $\frac{9}{15}$ (e) $\frac{11}{1}$ (f) $\frac{1}{32}$ (g) $\frac{4}{1}$
4. (a) $\frac{31}{15}$ (b) $\frac{3}{4}$ (c) $\frac{23}{18}$ (d) $\frac{31}{18}$ (e) $\frac{41}{39}$ (f) $\frac{53}{28}$ (g) $\frac{39}{38}$
(h) $\frac{43}{24}$ 5. (a) $\frac{1}{8}$ (b) $\frac{7}{12}$ (c) $\frac{1}{14}$ (d) $\frac{7}{18}$ (e) $\frac{5}{39}$ (f) $\frac{3}{14}$
(g) $\frac{16}{23}$ (h) $\frac{5}{12}$ 6. (a) $\frac{5}{14}$ (b) $\frac{18}{77}$ (c) $\frac{7}{12}$ (d) $\frac{7}{90}$ (e) $\frac{21}{32}$
(f) $\frac{11}{18}$ (g) $\frac{54}{115}$ (h) $\frac{11}{15}$ 7. (a) $\frac{1}{16}$ (b) $\frac{1}{11}$ (c) $\frac{1}{4}$ (d) $\frac{7}{4}$
(e) $\frac{45}{8}$ (f) $\frac{1}{20}$ (g) $\frac{4}{7}$ (h) $\frac{55}{3}$ 8. 10 bars 9. (a) €64
(b) €96 10. 5 plants 11. €840 12. 2000 shares
13. €600

Exam-style Questions
1. (a) $\frac{1}{3}$ (b) $\frac{2}{5}$ (c) $\frac{1}{15}$ 2. (a) $\frac{3}{4}$ (b) $\frac{5}{7}$ (c) $\frac{15}{28}$
(d) Tim's statement is wrong.

Chapter 5

Activity 5.1
1. (i) 0.07 (ii) 7 (iii) 7 000 (iv) 0.07 (v) 0.0007
(vi) 0.007 (vii) 70 (viii) 70 000 (ix) 0.7 (x) 0.00007
2. (i) 0.5 (ii) 0.005 (iii) 50 (iv) 0.05 (v) 50
(vii) 5 000 (viii) 50 000 (ix) 0.05 (x) 5 000 (xi) 5
(xii) 50 3. (i) 4.537218 (ii) 17.101603 (iii) 590.274057
4. (i) $\frac{5}{10} + \frac{3}{100}$ (ii) $\frac{1}{100} + \frac{1}{1000}$ (iii) $\frac{6}{10} + \frac{7}{100}$
(iv) $\frac{8}{100} + \frac{4}{1000}$ (v) $\frac{9}{10} + \frac{0}{100} + \frac{3}{1000}$ (vi) $\frac{8}{10} + \frac{0}{100} + \frac{8}{1000}$
(vii) $\frac{9}{10} + \frac{7}{100} + \frac{3}{1000} + \frac{5}{10000}$ (viii) $\frac{7}{10} + \frac{0}{100} + \frac{2}{1000} + \frac{1}{10000}$
(ix) $\frac{1}{10} + \frac{2}{100} + \frac{9}{1000} + \frac{3}{10000} + \frac{7}{100000}$
(x) $\frac{2}{10} + \frac{6}{100} + \frac{3}{1000} + \frac{7}{10000} + \frac{7}{100000} + \frac{3}{1000000}$
5. (i) A = 8.1, B = 8.3, C = 8.5, D = 8.7, E = 8.8 (ii) A = 2.13,
B = 2.14, C = 2.16, D = 2.18, E = 2.19 (iii) A = 1.2, B = 1.5,
C = 1.8, D = 2.3, E = 2.7 (iv) A = 6.54, B = 6.57, C = 6.62,
D = 6.65, E = 6.68 6. (i) 0.521, 0.45, 0.431, 0.398, 0.273
(ii) 0.748, 0.746, 0.743, 0.741, 0.74 (iii) 0.9829, 0.9827,
0.9826, 0.9823, 0.9822, 0.9821 (iv) 5.001, 1.5, 1.055, 1.05,
1.005 (v) 2.3223, 2.233, 1.2332, 1.23, 0.2323 7. (i) $\frac{2}{5}$
(ii) 0.4 (iii) $\frac{1}{5}$ (iv) 0.2 8. (i) (a) 0.4 (b) −0.3 (c) 0.73
(d) 0.92 (e) −0.34 (f) 0.048 (g) 0.267 (h) 0.0176
(i) 0.3267 (j) −8.99991 9. (i) (a) $\frac{1}{4}$ (b) $\frac{1}{2}$ (c) $\frac{7}{20}$ (d) $\frac{2}{5}$
(e) $\frac{31}{50}$ (f) $\frac{27}{100}$ (g) $\frac{13}{20}$ (h) $\frac{12}{25}$ (i) $\frac{41}{50}$ (j) $\frac{3}{8}$
10. fraction: $\frac{47}{100}$ 11. (a) (i) $\frac{43}{100}$ (ii) $\frac{1}{4}$ (b) (i) 0.43
(ii) 0.25 (c) (i) $\frac{57}{100}$ (ii) $\frac{3}{4}$ (d) (i) 0.57 (ii) 0.75 12. (i) $\frac{4}{5}$
(ii) $\frac{3}{10}$ (iii) $\frac{2}{5}$ (iv) $\frac{1}{2}$ (v) $\frac{3}{10}$ (vi) (i) 0.8 (ii) 0.3 (iii) 0.4
(iv) 0.5 (v) 0.3 13. (i) $\frac{1}{2}$ = 0.5 (ii) $\frac{2}{5}$ = 0.4 14. $0.\dot{2}$, $0.08\dot{3}$

Activity 5.2
1. (i) 6.168 (ii) 47.553 (iii) 0.100224 (iv) 9.09904 (v) −30.9445
(vi) −120.8384 2. (ii) (a) 4.55 (b) 7.011 (c) 1.06 (d) 12.144
(e) 29.657 (f) 17.025 (g) 6.27 (h) 21.037 (i) 24.576 (j) 19.5195

3. (ii) (a) 8.5 (b) 2.56 (c) 890 (d) 46.56 (e) 2.8925 (f) 10400
(g) 130 (h) 4.7 **4.** (i) €0.654 (ii) €0.704 (iii) 5 cent
5. (i) Simon (ii) Paul (iii) Lucy (iv) 0.34 (v) 0.41
6. 0.15 kg **7.** 15.39 km **8.** (i) €11.29 (ii) €8.71
9. (i) 4.8 kg (ii) 3.2 kg (iii) 0.5 kg (iv) 0.2 kg
10. (i) €9.20 (ii) €5.80 (iii) €1.45 (iv) 0.38 litres

Activity 5.3

1. (i) 16.85 litres (ii) €21.70 (iii) 0.03 kg
(iv) 0.60 m (v) 28.92°C (vi) 2.99 km (vii) $125.68
(viii) 19.61 ml (ix) 77.67°F **2.** (i) (a) 28 cm (b) 33 m
(c) 38°C (d) 10 minutes (e) 93 litres (f) €100 (g) 83°F
(h) 565 km (i) 99 (j) £230 (ii) (a) 27.8 cm (b) 33.2 ml
(c) 38.3°C (d) 10.0 minutes (e) 92.5 litres (f) €100.5
(g) 83.3°F (h) 564.9 km (i) 99.5 (j) £230.0
3. (i) 2 significant figures (ii) 4 significant figures (iii) 7
significant figures (iv) 5 significant figures (v) 4 significant
figures (vi) 4 significant figures (vii) 2 significant figures
(viii) 3 significant figures (ix) 4 significant figures
(x) 6 significant figures (xi) 4 significant figures
(xii) 5 significant figures **4.** (i) 270 (ii) 0.055 (iii) 350 000
(iv) 2900 (v) 0.0047 (vi) 22 000 (vii) 9800 (viii) 31
(ix) 0.028 (x) 250 000 **5.** (i) 0.289 (ii) 0.0429 (iii) 2.33
6. (i) (a) 1.6 km (b) 2.5 cm (c) 0.6 miles (d) 0.5 kg
(e) 4.5 litres (f) 3.1 (g) 340.3 m/s (h) 9.8 m/s²
(ii) (a) 1.61 km (b) 2.54 cm (c) 0.621 miles (d) 0.454 kg
(e) 4.55 litres (f) 3.14 (g) 340 m/s (h) 9.81 m/s² (iii) (a) 2 km
(b) 3 cm (c) 0.6 miles (d) 0.5 kg (e) 5 litres (f) 3
(g) 300 m/s (h) 10 m/s² **7.** (i) 6 400 000 (ii) 2 400 000
(iii) 6 100 000 (iv) 3 400 000 (v) 71 000 000 (vi) 60 000 000
(vii) 26 000 000 (viii) 25 000 000 **8.** (i) 4 (ii) 3 (iii) 2
(iv) 6 (v) 6.125 **9.** (i) (a) 2 (b) 4 (c) 8 (d) 3 (e) 2 (f) 10
(g) 35 (h) 16 (ii) (a) 3.39 (b) 4.77 (c) 7.89 (d) 3.24
(e) 2.03 (f) 11.17 (g) 43.94 (h) 14.97

Activity 5.4

1. (i) 3 out of 100 (ii) (a) €3 (b) €6 (c) €9 **2.** (i) 80%
(ii) 25% (iii) 50% (iv) 72% (v) 38% (vi) 95% (vii) 67.5%
(viii) 23% (ix) 12.5% (x) 37.5% **3.** (i) True (ii) False
(iii) True (iv) False (v) True (vi) False (vii) True (viii) False
(ix) True **4.** (i) < (ii) > (iii) < (iv) < (v) < (vi) > (vii) <
(viii) > (ix) > **5.** €316.80 **6.** €16 605 **7.** (i) $\frac{3}{20}, \frac{4}{25}$, 0.20,
21%, 25%, 0.29 (ii) 20%, $\frac{6}{25}$, 0.25, 0.28, $\frac{3}{10}$, 31%
(iii) $\frac{27}{100}, \frac{3}{4}$, 0.8, $\frac{41}{50}$, 0.83, $\frac{17}{20}$, 86% **8.** (i) $\frac{1}{4}$ = 0.25 = 25%
(ii) $\frac{1}{5}$ = 0.2 = 20% (iii) $\frac{3}{5}$ = 0.6 = 60% (iv) $\frac{1}{2}$ = 0.5 = 50%
9. (i) $\frac{3}{4}$ = 0.75 = 75% (ii) $\frac{1}{8}$ = 0.125 = 12.5% (iii) $\frac{1}{2}$ = 0.5 = 50%
(iv) $\frac{1}{4}$ = 0.25 = 25% **10.** (i) 65% (ii) 80% (iii) 70%
(iv) 56% (v) 80% (vi) 64% (vii) 55% (viii) 90%
11. 42 people **12.** (i) 148 students (ii) 37 students
13. (i) 70% (ii) 75% (iii) 35% (iv) 48% (v) 40%
(vi) 20% (vii) 7.5% (viii) 30% (ix) 32.5% (x) 30%

Revision Activity 5

1. (a) 0.5 = 50% (b) 0.33... = 33.33% (c) 0.25 = 25%
(d) 0.4 = 40% (e) 0.4375 = 43.75% (f) 0.2 = 20%
(g) 0.36 = 36% (h) 0.26 = 26% (i) 0.04 = 4%
(j) 0.73 = 73% **2.** (a) $\frac{1}{10}$ = 10% (b) $\frac{3}{10}$ = 30% (c) 25% = $\frac{1}{4}$
(d) 60% = $\frac{3}{5}$ (e) 75% = $\frac{3}{4}$ (f) $\frac{11}{50}$ = 22% (g) $\frac{14}{25}$ = 56%
(h) $\frac{81}{100}$ = 81% (i) $\frac{3}{8}$ = 37.5% (j) $\frac{123}{200}$ = 61.5%
3. (a) $\frac{1}{20}$ = 0.05 (b) $\frac{1}{10}$ = 0.1 (c) $\frac{1}{2}$ = 0.5 (d) $\frac{11}{100}$ = 0.11
(e) $\frac{7}{20}$ = 0.35 (f) $\frac{47}{100}$ = 0.47 (g) $\frac{63}{100}$ = 0.63
(h) $\frac{19}{25}$ = 0.76 (i) $\frac{21}{25}$ = 0.84 (j) $\frac{99}{100}$ = 0.99

4. (a) 5.1978 (b) 10.709 (c) 0.033 (d) 2.738 (e) 0.893
(f) 8.88638 (g) 4.031 (h) 339.111 (i) 5.832181 (j) 8.229
5. 330 kg **6.** 4 litres of water **7.** €147.60 **8.** (a) 3
(b) 2.846 **9.** (a) 0.125, 0.2125 order $\frac{1}{8}$, 0.1525, $\frac{17}{80}$ (b) 132.48

Exam-style Question
1. (a) 0.375

Chapter 6

Activity 6.1
1. 27 **2.** 30 **3.** 24 **4.** 60 **5.** 16 **6.** 18
7. (i) {1, 2, 3, 4, 5, 6} (ii) 6 possible outcomes
8. (i) 2 possible outcomes (ii) (H, T) **9.** (i) 12 **10.** (ii) 36
11. 10 000 **12.** (ii) 4

Activity 6.2
5. (i) D (ii) A (iii) C (iv) E (v) B

Activity 6.3
1. 0.46 **2.** 0.116 **3.** 0.53 **4.** (ii) 0.28 (iii) 0.36 (iv) 0.36
6. (i) 120 (ii) 0.23 (iii) 0.65 **7.** (i) 56 (ii) 0.44 **8.** (i) 0.325
(ii) red 8, blue 13, green 12, yellow 7

Activity 6.5
1. 30 **2.** 10 red and 10 green **3.** 30 **4.** (ii) $\frac{3}{4}$ (iii) 2
6. (i) 52 (ii) 4 suits: spades, clubs, hearts, diamonds. (iii) 13
(iv) 4 (v) 12 (vi) 4 (vii) 26 (viii) 2 **7.** (i) $\frac{1}{2}$ (ii) $\frac{1}{4}$
(iii) $\frac{1}{13}$ (iv) $\frac{1}{52}$ (v) $\frac{3}{13}$ (vi) $\frac{1}{26}$ (vii) $\frac{1}{52}$ (viii) $\frac{1}{13}$ (ix) $\frac{2}{13}$
(x) $\frac{3}{4}$ **8.** (i) $\frac{1}{2}$ (ii) $\frac{1}{3}$ (iii) $\frac{1}{2}$ (iv) $\frac{2}{3}$ **9.** (i) $\frac{1}{7}$ (ii) $\frac{3}{7}$ (iii) $\frac{4}{7}$
(iv) $\frac{2}{7}$ **10.** (i) $\frac{2}{11}$ (ii) $\frac{2}{11}$ (iii) $\frac{4}{11}$ (iv) $\frac{7}{11}$ **11.** (i) $\frac{1}{2}$ (ii) $\frac{1}{3}$
(iii) $\frac{1}{6}$ (iv) $\frac{5}{6}$ **12.** 500 **13.** 100 **14.** (i) $\frac{1}{3}$ (ii) $\frac{1}{2} = \frac{2}{4} = \frac{3}{6}$
= $\frac{4}{8} = \frac{5}{10}$ **15.** (i) $\frac{1}{4}$ (ii) $\frac{1}{3} = \frac{2}{6} = \frac{3}{9} = \frac{4}{12} = \frac{5}{15}$ **16.** (ii) $\frac{1}{36}$

Revision Activity 6
1. (a) $\frac{1}{4}$ (b) $\frac{2}{5}$ (c) $\frac{3}{5}$ (d) $\frac{17}{20}$ **2.** (a) 15 **3.** 200 **4.** (a) $\frac{3}{5}$
(b) $\frac{6}{8} = \frac{9}{12} = \frac{12}{16} = \frac{15}{20} = \frac{18}{24} = \frac{21}{28}$ etc

Exam-style Question
1. (a) (i) Grey = 90°, Black = 120°, White = 150°
(ii) $\frac{90}{360} \times 60 = \frac{1}{4} \times 60$ = 15 times (b) (i) B 50%; C 0.4; D $\frac{1}{50}$, 0.02

Chapter 7

Activity 7.1
1. (i) 2 medals, position 62 (ii) 55 (iii) 67 (iv) The table is
ranked by number of gold medals won; GB won 27 gold while
China won 26. (v) 12 **2.** (ii) 13 (iv) 290

Activity 7.2
1. (i) secondary (ii) primary (iii) primary (iv) secondary
(v) primary **2.** 1E, 2G, 3A, 4C, 5I, 6H, 7B, 8D, 9F
3. D, B, A, C **5.** First row = Numerical discrete; second row =
Categorical Ordinal; third row = Categorical Nominal
10. A: Numerical continuous data, B: Numerical discrete data,
C: Numerical continuous data, D: Categorical nominal data,
E: Numerical continuous data, F: Numerical discrete data,
G: Categorical ordinal data **13.** (i) 30 (ii) 17 male and
13 female (iii) September and June (iv) 180 (v) 190
(vi) 16 cm (vii) 9 (viii) Baton twirling (ix) He was born in
December and sometimes watches reality TV.

Activity 7.3
1. (i) Mode = 4, mean = 5 (ii) Mode = 23, mean = 23
(iii) Mode = 158, mean = 157 **2.** No number occurs most often.
3. (i) Median = 7, mean = 6.7 (ii) Median = 174, mean = 174.1

(iii) Median = 6.5, mean = 6.2　**4.** (i) Median = 163 cm
(ii) Mode = 175 cm　(iii) Mean = 161.7 cm　**5.** Median = 5.5
6. (i) Median = 8　(ii) Median = 177.5　(iii) Median = €141
7. (i) Mean = 8, median = 8, mode = 8　(ii) Mean = 12,
median = 12, mode = 12　(iii) Mean = 9.5, median = 6.5,
mode = 6　**8.** (i) 16 minutes　(ii) 12.5 minutes　(iii) 44 minutes
9. (i) 163 cm　(ii) 163 cm　(iii) 30 cm　(iv) 163 cm
10. (i) 162 cm　(ii) 164 cm　(iii) 50 cm　(iv) 162 cm
11. (i) 4.8　(ii) 4　(iii) 6　**13.** (i) Seán　(ii) The person who
leaves is called Seán and the person who joins is called Emily.

Activity 7.4
1. (i) Numeric discrete data　**3.** (i) Numeric discrete data
5. (i) 20　(ii) 15　(iii) 5　(iv) 5

Activity 7.5
1. (i) 20　(ii) 90　(iii) $\frac{4}{9}$　(iv) 33.3%　**2.** (i) 150 cars
(ii) 75 cars　(iv) 725 cars　(v) Mean = 60.4 cars　**3.** (i) Monday
(ii) 16　(iii) $\frac{1}{8}$　**4.** (i) 12 students had no days absent.
(ii) 50　(iii) 38%　**5.** (i) 2 hours　(ii) Friday　(iii) 3.5 hours /
Tuesday　(iv) Mean = 2.4 hours　(v) 25%　**6.** (ii) Mode = 4
text messages　**10.** (i) 1741　(ii) 49%　(iii) 51%　(iv) 2%

Activity 7.6
1. (i) 55　(ii) 100　(iii) 45　(iv) 67　**2.** (ii) 62　(iii) 60
3. (i) (a) 142 cm (b) 200 cm (c) 58 cm (d) 168 cm　(ii) (b) 165 cm
5. (i) (a) 140 cm (b) 190 cm (c) 50 cm (d) 163 cm　(ii) (b) 164 cm
6. (ii) 15%　**7.** (ii) 71 km　(iii) 163 km　(iv) 167 km

Revision Activity 7
2. (c) Mean = 25.27 ≈ 25 cm, median = 24 cm, mode = 24 cm
(d) 16 cm (e) 21 cm and 27 cm.　**3.** (a) 21 (b) 50 seconds
(c) 45 seconds (d) 46 seconds

Exam-style Question
1. (a) 198 cm　(b) 12　(c) 32%　(d) 184.5　(f) (i) Tallest: 198:201
(ii) Shortest: 177:176　(g) Tallest: 0.99, Shortest: 1.01　(h) 170 cm

Chapter 8

Activity 8.1
(iv) No　(vii) Point *H*.　(xii) Yes　(xiii) The distance |*EF*| is never
negative

Activity 8.2
1. |*MQ*|　**2.** |*PR*|　**5.** Yes　**12.** (i) True　(ii) False　(iii) True
(iv) False　(v) False　(vi) True　(vii) False
(viii) True　(ix) True

Activity 8.3
2. (i) 50°, 85°, 45°　**6.** (i) Right angle　(ii) Straight angle
(iii) Right angle　**7.** (i) 180°　(ii) 120°　(iii) 240°　(iv) 270°
8. 90° or 270°　**9.** 180°　**10.** 45°　**11.** 360°

Activity 8.4
11. (A1, B10, C8), (A2, B4, C1, C10), (A3, B1, C9), (A4, B5, C4),
(A5, B6, C7), (A6, B3, C5), (A7, B7, C1, C2, C5, C10),
(A8, B9, C3), (A9, B8, C6), (A10, B2, C2)

Revision Activity 8
3. (a) |∠*ABC*| = 49° and |∠*DEF*| = 114°　(b) *O, N, M, P*
4. (a) A　(b) E　(c) D　(d) Shape B is the only shape with four
equal sides　(e) Shape C could be formed by joining together
two copies of shape B.　**5.** $\frac{1}{2}$ = 180°, $\frac{1}{4}$ = 90°, $\frac{1}{3}$ = 120°,
$\frac{1}{6}$ = 60°, $\frac{1}{12}$ = 30°

Exam-style Question
1. (a) 40°　(b) 140°　(c) 180°　(d) |∠*A*| = |∠*C*| …. vertically
opposite angles.

Chapter 9

Activity 9.1
1. *A*(1, 2), *B*(4, 1), *C*(4, 4), *D*(2, 0), *E*(−1, 4), *F*(−3, 2), *G*(−2, 0),
H(−2, −2), *I*(0, −3), *J*(1, −3), *K*(4, −2)　**3.** A square　**4.** Cogito
ergo sum　**8.** (i) Happy ending　(ii) I love maths　(iii) Seize the
day　(iv) Carpe diem　**9.** (i) *A*(−2, 2), *B*(7, 5), *C*(1, 0),
D(7, 7), *E*(2, 6)　**10.** (a) *B*(2, 7), *S*(2, 1), *R*(6, 4), *P*(7, 1), *T*(9, 5)
(b) 121 m²　(c) The ring　(d) 6 metres　**11.** (a) *B*(3, 1), *H*(8, 5)
(b) 45 kilometres　(c) 242.55 kilometres

Activity 9.2
1. (i) $\frac{1}{4}$　(ii) $\frac{3}{4}$　(iii) $\frac{1}{2}$　(iv) 1　**2.** (i) $\frac{4}{3}$　(ii) $\frac{1}{4}$　(iii) $\frac{1}{5}$
(iv) 0　**3.** (i) $-\frac{1}{2}$　(ii) −1　(iii) $-\frac{1}{4}$　(iv) $-\frac{1}{2}$　**4.** Slope of *AB* = $\frac{1}{6}$;
slope of *CD* = −1　**5.** Slope of *EF* = $-\frac{2}{7}$; slope of *GH* = $\frac{3}{5}$
6. Slope of *PQ* = $-\frac{1}{7}$; slope of *RS* = 1　**8.** (i) Slope of *l* = $-\frac{2}{3}$;
slope of *m* = $-\frac{2}{3}$; slope of *n* = 1　(ii) The slopes are the same
(iii) They are parallel　**10.** (i) $\frac{1}{10}$　(iii) not very steep
11. (i) $-\frac{1}{4}$　**13.** $\frac{1}{2}$　**14.** Slope of *m* = 2; slope of *n* = $\frac{1}{5}$;
slope of *p* = 0; slope of *s* = $-\frac{1}{4}$

Revision Activity 9
1. *A*(2, 1), *B*(4, 0), *C*(4, 4), *D*(1, 6), *E*(0, 5), *F*(−2, 2), *G*(−4, 0),
H(−5, 3), *I*(−3, −2), *J*(−5, −3), *K*(−3, 0), *L*(0, 0), *M*(3, −2), *N*(5, −3)
3. (a) −1　(b) $\frac{2}{3}$　(c) $\frac{1}{3}$　(d) $-\frac{2}{3}$　**4.** *E*(5, 3), *D*(4, 4), *A*(1, 1), *B*(3, 3)

Exam-style Question
1. (i) (3, 4)　(ii) *E*(6, 7)　(iii) Bee 2

Chapter 10

Activity 10.1
4. (ii) *B* = (−1, 5), *C* = (−2, 3)　(iii) *A′* = (4, 1), *B′* = (1, 5),
C′ = (2, 3)　**6.** (i) 1　(ii) 2　(iii) No axes of symmetry.　(iv) 1
(v) 1　(vi) None　**7.** F, G, J, L, N, P, Q, R, S, Z

Activity 10.2
1. (ii) The lines *MN* and *M′N′* are parallel.　**2.** (ii) The lines *RS*
and *R′S′* are parallel.　**4.** (i) Image 2　(ii) Image 4　(iii) Image 1
(iv) Image 1　**9.** (i) (a) Nine of diamonds (b) Ace of hearts (c)
Jack of clubs (d) Two of diamonds (e) Two of clubs
(f) King of hearts　(ii) (a) Yes　(b) No　(c) Yes　(d) Yes
(e) Yes　(f) Yes　**10.** H, I, N, O, S, X and Z

Activity 10.3
1. (i) Image 2　(ii) Image 1　**2.** **c** maps to **d** by moving 3 units
up and 5 units to the right, **e** maps to **f** by moving 3 units up
and 8 units to the right, **g** maps to **h** by moving 6 units down
and 0 units to the right, **i** maps to **j** by moving 6 units down
and 3 units to the right　**3.** (iii) *A′* = (6, 2) *B′* = (8, 5)
4. (iii) *D′* = (7, 7) , *E′* = (5, 4), *F′* = (9, 4)　**5.** (ii) *A* = (−4, −1),
B = (−2, −3), *C* = (−5, −4)　(iv) *A′* = (1,1), *B* = (3, −1), *C* = (0, −2)
6. (ii) *A* = (−1, 4), *B* = (−4, 3), *C* = (2, 1)　(iii) *A′* = (4, 1),
B′ = (1, 0), *C′* = (7, −2)

Revision Activity 10
1. (a) Image A central symmetry, Image B axial symmetry, Image
C translation　(b) Image A axial symmetry, Image B translation,
Image C central symmetry　(c) Image A axial symmetry, Image
B central symmetry, Image C translation　**4.** (a) Image
A = translation, Image B = central symmetry, Image C = axial
symmetry　(b) Image A = axial symmetry, Image B = translation,
Image C = central symmetry　(c) Image A = translation,
Image B = axial symmetry, Image C = central symmetry
5. (a) Rotation 90° (anti-clockwise) or 270° (clockwise)
(b) Central symmetry or rotation of 180°　(c) Axial symmetry.

Exam-style Question
1. Axial symmetry in the *y*-axis: (1, 1), (4, 3), (2, 5);
Central symmetry in the point (0, 0): (1, –1), (4, –3), (2, –5);
Axial symmetry in the *x*-axis: (–1, –1), (–4, –3), (–2, –5)

Chapter 11

Activity 11.1
1. (i) 16.30 (ii) 02.45 (iii) 20.15 (iv) 00.20 (v) 21.25
(vi) 01.46 (vii) 23.55 (viii) 10.59 **2.** (i) 1.25 pm
(ii) 6.40 am (iii) 11.30 am (iv) 5.50 pm (v) 8.15 am
(vi) 11.45 pm (vii) 12.10 am (viii) 6.29 am **3.** (i) 140 mins
(ii) 30 mins (iii) 45 mins (iv) 132 mins (v) 235 mins
(vi) 10 mins (vii) 84 mins (viii) 150 mins **4.** (i) 8 hrs
(ii) €76.00 **5.** (i) 3 hrs 9 mins, 3 hrs 5 mins, 3 hrs 5 mins,
3 hrs 1 min, 3 hrs 9 mins, 3 hrs 1 min, 3 hrs 4 mins (ii) 5
(iii) 1 (iv) 1 hr 10 minutes (v) (a) 11.16 am (b) 46 minutes

6. 17.50 **7.** (i) Monday – Thursday $6\frac{3}{4}$ hours,   Friday 5 hrs
40 mins (ii) 12 (iii) Maths 5, Geography 4, Irish 5, History 4,
Science 4, English 5, Art 4, C.S.P.E. 1, Woodwork 4, French 4,
S.P.H.E. 1, P.E. 2 (iv) 10 mins (v) 3 hrs 10 mins
8. (i) 1 000 000 (ii) 11 days 14 hours **9.** 1 000 000 000
(ii) 31 yrs 259 days

Activity 11.2
3. (i) 30 cm (ii) 120 cm (iii) 1.9 cm (iv) 235 cm
(v) 100 000 cm (vi) 3400 cm (vii) 200 cm (viii) 50 cm
4. (i) km (ii) metres (iii) cm (iv) mm (v) cm (vi) mm
5. (i) 2.4 m (ii) 1500 m (iii) 3 m (iv) 70 m (v) 2800 m
(vi) 750 m (vii) 350 m (viii) 0.99 m **6.** (i) 2.3 km (ii) 0.5 km
(iii) 4.2 km (iv) $\frac{3}{10}$ km (v) 10 km (vi) 0.25 km (vii) 3.6 km
(viii) 9 km **7.** 16 **8.** (i) 3300 m (ii) 3.3 km **9.** 1800 km
10. 186 lengths, 187 stakes **11.** 150 **12.** 240 km

Activity 11.3
2. (i) Grams (ii) Tonnes (iii) Kg (iv) Tonnes (v) Kg
(vi) Grams (vii) Grams (viii) Tonnes (ix) Grams
3. 4 runs and 3 runs **4.** 312.5 g **5.** (i) Add 450 g on the left
(ii) Add 500 g on the left (iii) Add 1150 g on the left
(iv) Add 1.475 kg on the left **6.** 670.5 bags **7.** 1312.5 g
flour, 1050 g butter, 937.5 g sugar, 15 eggs **8.** (i) 2.25 kg
(ii) 0.155 kg (iii) 2.55 kg (iv) 0.786 kg **9.** 14.30

Activity 11.4
1. (i) Perimeter 28 cm, Area 49 cm² (ii) Perimeter 50 cm,
Area 150 cm² (iii) Perimeter 18 cm, Area 19.25 cm²
(iv) Perimeter 16 cm, Area 15.96 cm² **2.** (i) Perimeter 16 cm,
Area 13 cm² (ii) Perimeter 46 cm, Area 80 cm²
(iii) Perimeter 46 cm, Area 90 cm² (iv) Perimeter 120 cm,
Area 540 cm² **3.** (i) Perimeter 38 cm, Area 60 cm²
(ii) Perimeter 48 cm, Area 44 cm² (iii) Perimeter 40 cm,
Area 84 cm² (iv) Perimeter 46 cm, Area 62 cm² **4.** (i) 34 cm²
(ii) 59 cm² (iii) 148 cm² (iv) 184 cm² **5.** (i) 136 cm²
(ii) 171 cm² **6.** (i) (a) 9 cm (b) 11 cm (c) 12 m (d) 23 cm
(ii) (a) 54 cm² (b) 99 cm² (c) 120 m² (d) 345 cm²
7. 229 m² **8.** (i) 1012 mm (ii) 62160 mm² (iii) There is no
difference **9.** 52 m² **10.** (i) 6.2 m² (ii) 0.04 m² (iii) 155
11. (ii) 576 cm² **12.** (ii) 320 m² **13.** (ii) 24 m
14. (ii) 100 mm² **15.** (i) 100 cm × 100 cm (ii) 10 000 cm²

Activity 11.5
1. (i) 424 cm² (ii) 91.5 cm² (iii) 13.5 m² (iv) 302 cm²
(v) 208 cm² **2.** (a) 90 cm² (b) 360 cm² (c) 59 cm²
(d) 148.5 cm² **3.** (i) 96 cm² **4.** (i) 76 m² (ii) 766 cm²
(iii) 13.375 m² (iv) 4550 cm² (v) 19900 mm² (vi) 4.5 m²
5. 1528 cm², 1042 cm² (iii) 461900 cm² or 46.19 m²
6. (i) *F* (ii) *B* ↔ *D* and *C* ↔ *E*. **7.** (i) *C* (ii) *E* (iii) *F*
9. (i) (a) and (c) **10.** (i) 5 cm (ii) 7 cm (iii) 1 m (iv) 3 cm
11. Box A 272 cm²   Box B 410 cm²   Box C 138 cm²
(iii) 246 000 cm² Or 24.6 m²

Revision Activity 11
1. (a) 36 mins, 45 mins, 49 mins, 46 mins, 42 mins (b) 4
(c) 62 mins (d) 06.44 (e) 06.42 **2.** (a) 3 (b) 3 pieces each
of length 4 cm **3.** (a) 240 m² (b) 3 m (c) 306 m²
4. (a) 3 hrs 36 mins (b) 70 km/hr (c) €63 **5** (a) 856 cm²
(b) 52 cm² (c) 1550 cm² (d) 1860 cm²

Exam-style Question
1. (a) 2.5 m (b) 25 m (c) 28.5 m² (d) 114 (e) No

Chapter 12

Activity 12.1
1. (i) 5 – 3 (ii) 5*q* – 3*r* (iii) 9 + 7 (iv) 9*a* + 7 (v) 21 – 11
(vi) 21*b* – 11 (vii) 4 × 2 (viii) (4*d*)(2*d*) (ix) (7*x*)(16)
(x) 7 × *k* × *k* (or 7*k*²) (xi) *mnp* **2.** (i) 5 (ii) 1 (iii) 10
(iv) 10 (v) 7 (vi) 6 (vii) 18 (viii) 12 (ix) 5 (x) 6
3. (i) 10 (ii) 2 (iii) 25 (iv) 11 (v) 7 (vi) 10 (vii) 15
(viii) 0 (ix) 5 (x) –3 **4.** (i) 6 (ii) 13 (iii) 2 (iv) 11
5. (ii) 2 **6.** (ii) An even number **7.** (ii) An odd number
8. (ii) 49, 64, 81, 100 **10.** (i) 6 (ii) 14 (iii) 8 (iv) 7
(v) 4 (vi) 20 (vii) 8 (viii) 17 **11.** (i) 17 (ii) 4 (iii) –4
(iv) –1 (v) 57 (vi) 144 **12.** (i) 10 (ii) 3 (iii) 1 (iv) 7
(v) 2 (vi) 12 **13.** (i) 3 (ii) 14 (iii) –18 (iv) 1 (v) 0
(vi) 39 (vii) –6 (viii) 16 (ix) –2 **15.** (i) –60 (ii) 4 (iii) 14
(iv) –17 **16.** (i) –30 (ii) –6 (iii) 45 (iv) $-\frac{15}{4}$ (v) $\frac{7}{9}$ (vi) 2
17. (i) –24 (ii) 36 (iii) 59 (iv) –91 (v) –15 (vi) –37
18. (i) 1 (ii) –8 (iii) 14 (iv) 4 (v) 108 (vi) 14 **19.** (i) 28
(ii) 23 (iii) 29 (iv) –10 **20.** (i) $\frac{1}{5}$ (ii) 0 (iii) $\frac{3}{80}$ (iv) $\frac{62}{69}$

Activity 12.2
1. (i) 11*x* (ii) 9*a* (iii) 7*x* + 9 (iv) 4*a* + 7 (v) 7*a* + 7*b*
(vi) 9*a* + 11*y* **2.** (i) 2*x* (ii) 5*a* (iii) 4*x* (iv) 4*a* – 1
(v) 3*x* – 2*y* (vi) –3*y* + 6 **3.** (i) 7*a* (ii) 17*x* (iii) 4*x* (iv) 2*y*
(v) 9*p* (vi) 3*m* (vii) 8*p* (viii) 4*t* (ix) 11*x*² (x) 5*xy*
4. (i) 11*x* (ii) 7*ab* + *a* (iii) 3*x*² (iv) 2*a*² + 9 (v) 3*y* – 4*xy*
(vi) 12*y*³ – 4*y* + 6 **5.** (i) 8*x*² (ii) –2*x* (iii) 7*a* + 7*b* (iv) 5*x*² + 9*x*
(v) 8*x*³ + 6*x*² (vi) 6*w* – 3*v* (vii) 8*ab* + 2*xy* (viii) 5*a* + 3*b* + 2*c*
(ix) *x* + *y* (x) *ab* + 3*cd* **7.** (i) 2*x*² – 2*x* + 1 (ii) 9*a*² + 4*a* – 3
(iii) 2*x*³ + 2*x*² – 15 (iv) 10*a*² – 3*a* + 5 (v) 3*xy* – 4*y*
(vi) 7*y*³ – 10*y*² + 4*y* – 2 **8.** (i) 11*a* – 4 (ii) 9*a* – 3 (iii) 13*a* + 3

Activity 12.3
1. (i) 15*x* (ii) 12*a* (iii) 18*m*² (iv) 20*x*² (v) 6*ax* (vi) 15*m*⁴
2. (i) –15*x* (ii) –12*m* (iii) 24*m*² (iv) –90*x*² (v) –10*ax*
(vi) –21*m*⁵ **3.** (i) *x*²*y* (ii) 12*ab*² (iii) 18*m*²*n*² (iv) 20*x*²
(v) 28*ax* (vi) 16*m*⁵ **4.** (i) –20*ab* (ii) –8*m*²*n*² (iii) 24*x*³*y*
(iv) –10*m*³*n*² (v) –15*a*³*b*³ (vi) –60*m*⁶ **5.** (i) *x*⁵ (ii) *x*¹¹
(iii) *a*¹⁵ (iv) *a*⁴ (v) 15*a*³ **6.** (i) 10*x*⁵ (ii) 12*b*⁸ (iii) 24*y*⁵
(iv) *x*³ (v) *x*²*y*² **7.** (i) 18*x* (ii) 27*y* (iii) 12*y*² (iv) 12*x*²*y*²
(v) –12*x* **8.** (i) 15*a*⁴ (ii) 36*y*⁵ (iii) 15*x*² (iv) –36*m*²
(v) –40*p*² **9.** (i) –24*t*² (ii) 12*t*² (iii) –6*w*⁵ (iv) 15*x*⁴ (v) 10*b*⁸
10. (i) 16*x*² (ii) 9*x*⁴*y*² (iii) –8*x*³ (iv) 25*m*⁴*y*⁶ (v) 100*a*⁴*b*⁴
11. (i) –16*x*³ (ii) 36*x*²*y* (iii) –12*x*²*y* (iv) –4*x*²*y*² (v) –72*x*³*y*³
12. (i) 7*xy* (ii) 12*x*²*y*² (iii) –*xy* (iv) 5*p* + 6*q* (v) 30*pq*
(vi) 5*p* – 6*q* (vii) 10*a*²*b* (viii) 24*a*⁴*b*² (ix) –2*a*²*b* (x) 5*x*² + 6*x*
(xi) 30*x*³ (xii) 5*x*² – 6*x* (xiii) 7*x*³ (xiv) 6*x*⁶ (xv) 5*x*³

Activity 12.4
1. (i) 3*x* + 6 (ii) 10*a* + 15*b* – 30 (iii) 20*x* – 4*y* – 24
(iv) 6*x*³ + 15*x*² – 18*x* (v) –24*x*³ + 30*x*² + 6*x* (vi) –4*x*³ + *x*² + *x*
2. (i) 3*x* + 12 (ii) 5*a* – 30 (iii) 4*p* – 12 (iv) 8*x* – 64
(v) 8*x* + 20 (vi) 24*x* – 8 (vii) 18*x* – 15 (viii) 6*x* – 24
3. (i) –5*x* – 15 (ii) –2*a* + 10 (iii) –6*p* – 24 (iv) –8*a*² + 8*a*
(v) –3*x* + 3 (vi) –5*x* + 5 (vii) –24*x* + 8 (viii) –10 + 6*y*
4. (i) 15*x* – 10*y* – 5 (ii) 12*x*³ – 28*x*² – 8*x* (iii) 3*x* – 3*y* – 6
(iv) 12*x*³ + 21*x*² (v) –42*x*² + 12*x* (vi) 18*x*³ + 12*x*² + 60*x*
(vii) –*x*² + *xy* + *x* (viii) 9*x*² + 6*xy* – 21*x* **5.** (i) 13*x* + 21
(ii) 14*x* + 4 (iii) 17*p* – 17 (iv) –*m* – 32 (v) 7*x* + 4*y* – 11
(vi) 5*a* – 10*b* + 31 (vii) 12*p* + 16*q* – 3 (viii) –15*y* + 6
6. (i) –3*x*² – 13*x* + 20 (ii) 9*x*² + 25*x* + 17 (iii) 4*x*³ – 5*x*² – 6*x* – 6

(iv) $3x^3 - x^2 - 3x - 2$ (v) $-3x^2 - 2x + 12$ (vi) $3m^2 - 13m + 12$
(vii) $p^3 - 1$ (viii) $8a^3 - 3$

Activity 12.5
1. (i) $x^2 - x - 6$ (ii) $2x^2 + 3x - 5$ (iii) $2a^2 + 9a - 5$
(iv) $p^2 + p - 42$ (v) $3m^2 + 7m - 6$ (vi) $y^2 - 3y - 18$
2. (i) $x^2 + 6x + 5$ (ii) $a^2 + 5a + 6$ (iii) $b^2 + 12b + 35$
(iv) $y^2 + 11y + 30$ (v) $p^2 + 8p + 16$ (vi) $x^2 + 14x + 48$
3. (i) $x^2 - 3x - 4$ (ii) $a^2 + 5a - 14$ (iii) $b^2 - 6b + 8$
(iv) $y^2 + y - 2$ (v) $p^2 - 8p - 20$ (vi) $x^2 - 9x + 18$
4. (i) $6x^2 - 10x - 4$ (ii) $15a^2 + 19a - 10$ (iii) $20b^2 - 26b + 8$
(iv) $6y^2 - 8y - 8$ (v) $2p^2 - 10p - 12$ (vi) $8x^2 - 20x + 12$
5. (i) $10p^2 + 29p + 10$ (ii) $6x^2 - 31x + 35$ (iii) $21x^2 + 22x - 8$
(iv) $2p^2 + 11p + 12$ (v) $8a^2 + 10a + 3$ (vi) $8y^2 - 2y - 15$
(vii) $2a^2 - 9a - 5$ (viii) $x^2 - 10x + 24$ **6.** (i) 10 (ii) $x^2 + 7x + 10$
7. (i) $x - 2$ (ii) $3x^2 - 11x - 4$ (iii) $3a^2 + 7a + 2$
(iv) $5a^2 + 9a - 2$ **8.** $2x^2 + 7x + 3$ **9.** $3x^2 - 7x - 6$
10. (i) $x^2 + 4x + 4$ (ii) $b^2 - 8b + 16$ (iii) $4m^2 + 4m + 1$
(iv) $9n^2 - 24n + 16$ **11.** $4x^2 - 12x + 9$ **12.** $(x + 4)$ **13.** $a = 7$
14. $a = 3$

Revision Activity 12
1. (a) $9ab$ (b) $14x^2$ (c) x^9 (d) $15y^2$ (e) $-4x^2$ (f) $4x^2$ (g) a
2. (a) $-2x^2 - 4x + 4$ (b) $-5a + 20b$ (c) $3x + y + z$
(d) $2x^2 - 7x - 21$ (e) $-x^2 - x + 7$ (f) $12d - 3e$
(g) $-8x^2 - 2x + 11$ (h) $-5x^2 - x + 7$ **3.** (a) -28 (b) -7
(c) -80 (d) -383 **4.** (a) 59 (b) 295 (c) 135 (d) 347
5. (a) a^2 (b) $-36a - 3$ (c) $4x$ (d) $-14a - 18y$
(e) $-11d + 12e + 2$ (f) $6x^3 - 5x^2 + 7x + 2$ (g) $6y^3 - 7y - 3$
6. (a) $3x + y$ (b) $20y + 4$ (c) $12m + 4n$ (d) $83 + 4f$
(e) Perimeter $= 12x - 16$; Area $= 9x^2 - 24x + 16$
7. (a) $2x^2 + 13x + 20$ (b) $y^2 - 4y + 3$ (c) $10a^2 - 13a - 3$
(d) $6z^2 - 27z + 30$ **8.** (a) $20x^2 + 7x - 6$ (b) $6a^2 + ab - 2b^2$
(c) $4x^2 - 25y^2$

Exam-style Questions
1. (a) 13 (b) 9 **2.** $-3x^2 + 17x - 22$ **3.** $a = 16$, $b = 63$

Chapter 13

Activity 13.1
1. (i) 18, 22, 26 (ii) peach, banana, pear (iii) Jack, Katie,
Conor (iv) ⌐⌐ ⌐ ⌐ (v) 4, 6, 8 (vi) purple, blue,
pink (vii) b, d, a (viii) horse, cow, pig (ix)
(x) sun, moon, star **2.** (i) Yellow crescent moon, yellow star,
yellow circle, yellow triangle (ii) yellow crescent moon
(iii) yellow triangle (iv) yellow crescent moon (v) yellow star
3. (i) Lilac arrow pointing East, pink arrow pointing South,
yellow arrow pointing West (ii) yellow arrow pointing West
(iii) pink arrow pointing South (iv) lilac arrow pointing East
(v) yellow arrow pointing West **4.** (i) yellow lightning bolt,
pink smiley face, red heart, yellow sun (ii) yellow lightning
bolt (iii) yellow sun (iv) pink smiley face (v) red heart
(vi) red heart **5.** (i) grey arrow (ii) green arrow (iii) red
arrow (iv) blue arrow (v) grey arrow **6.** (ii) 6, 12, 18, 24,
30, 36, 42, 48, 54, 60, 66, 72, 78, 84, 90, 96 (iii) The blue
squares are all multiples of 6. (iv) Blue (v) Blue (vi) White
7. (a) 15, 18, 21 (b) 11, 13, 15 (c) 17, 20, 23 (d) 16, 19,
22 **8.** (a) 13, 15, 17 (b) 27, 32, 37 (c) 35, 32, 29
(d) 20, 23, 26 (e) 16, 18, 20 (f) 15, 14, 13 (g) 17, 11, 5
(h) $-3, -6, -9$ (i) $-5, -1, 3$ **9.** (a) 10 (b) 11 (c) 62
(d) 19 (e) 21 (f) 55 (g) -36

Activity 13.2
1. (i) 15, 18, 21, 24, 27 (ii) Starting at 3, add 3 each time.
(iii) These numbers are all divisible by 3. They are also multiples
of 3. **2.** (ii) (a) 1, 3, 5, 7, 9, 11, 13, 15, 17, 19 (b) They are
all odd numbers (c) 2, 4, 6, 8, 10, 12, 14, 16, 18, 20
(d) They are all even numbers. (e) Green (f) Red (g) 200
(h) 199 (iv) This does work. **3.** (ii) (a) $3n - 2$, where n is the
number of the red block (b) $3n - 1$, where n is the number
of the yellow block (c) $3n$, where n is the number of the

green block (d) Green (e) Green (f) Green (g) Red
(h) Yellow (i) Red (j) Red **4.** (vi) (a) 4 is the number of blue
squares. (b) $3n$ is the number of red squares. (vii) (a) 34
(b) 30 (viii) (a) 8th (b) 24 (ix) (a) 14 (b) 46

Activity 13.3
1. (iii) 2 (iv) 4 (v) number of squares $= 2 \times$ stage number $+ 4$
(vi) $T_n = 2S + 4$ (vii) 24 **2.** (iii) The number of stars is increasing
by 2 in each stage (iv) $T_n = 2S - 1$ (v) 23 **3.** (iii) The yellow
squares are increasing by 1 in each stage. (iv) The blue squares
are increasing by 4 in each stage. (v) The number of yellow
squares in each stage equals the stage number. (vi) The
number of blue squares in each stage equals '4 times the stage
number' plus 1. (vii) The total number of squares in each
stage equals '5 times the stage number' plus 2. **4.** (iii) The
triangles are increasing by 1 in each stage. (iv) The squares are
increasing by 1 in each stage. (v) The matches are increasing
by 5 in each stage. (vi) The number of triangles in each stage
equals the stage number. (vii) The number of squares in each
stage equals the stage number. (viii) The number of matches
in each stage equals '5 times the stage number' plus 1.
(ix) 51 **5.** (iii) The number of yellow squares remains constant.
(iv) The number of green squares increases by 3 in each stage.
(v) For all stages, the number of yellow squares is 2.
(vi) The number of green squares is 3 times the stage number.
(vii) The total number of squares is '3 times the stage number'
$+ 2$. **6.** (iii) The number of red squares is increasing by 3 in
each stage. (iv) The number of blue squares is constant.
(v) The number of red squares is 3 times the stage number.
(vi) The number of blue squares is always 6. (vii) The total
number of squares is '3 times the stage number' $+ 6$.

Revision Activity 13
1. (iii) The number of tiles in increasing by 3 in each stage.
(iv) The number of tiles in each stage is '3 times the stage
number' $- 2$. **2.** (iii) The number of squares is increasing by 4
in each stage. (iv) The number of squares in each stage is '4
times the stage number' $+ 1$. **3.** (ii) 18 (iii) $2n + 6$
4. (ii) $T_n = 5S + 1$ (iii) 41 (iv) 10th

Exam-style Question
1. (iii) 9 (iv) White discs $=$ '2 times the number of shaded
discs' $+ 3$.

Chapter 14

Activity 14.1
1. $a = 5$ **2.** $x = -1$ **3.** $d = -10$ **4.** $y = 3$ **5.** $b = 4$
6. $h = 3$ **7.** $h = 0$ **8.** $y = 5$ **9.** $c = -7$ **10.** $b = 11$
11. $d = 8$ **12.** $s = 7$ **13.** $m = -13$ **14.** $g = 3$ **15.** $x = -8$
16. $x = -10$ **17.** $x = 6$ **18.** $w = -8$ **19.** $c = 3$ **20.** $x = 6$
21. $n = 3$ **22.** $x = -7$ **23.** $a = -4$ **24.** $d = -5$ **25.** $k = 5$
26. $y = -7$ **27.** $x = 12$ **28.** $h = 3$ **29.** $m = -4$ **30.** $b = -4$
31. $h = -22$ **32.** $x = 120$ **33.** $n = -12$ **34.** $p = 36$
35. $d = -42$ **36.** $x = 16$ **37.** $m = -20$ **38.** $y = 40$
39. $k = 3$ **40.** $a = -21$

Activity 14.2
1. $a = 8$ **2.** $y = 3$ **3.** $a = -7$ **4.** $b = 33$ **5.** $d = -9$
6. $t = 11$ **7.** $z = 60$ **8.** $y = 2$ **9.** $k = 7$ **10.** $x = 10$
11. $p = -22$ **12.** $m = 2$ **13.** $q = -11$ **14.** $h = 30$ **15.** $x = 14$
16. $p = 45$ **17.** $h = 7$ **18.** $w = -5$ **19.** $c = 19$ **20.** $n = 5$

Activity 14.3
1. $a = 7$ **2.** $h = 2$ **3.** $x = 2$ **4.** $d = 3$ **5.** $t = 1$ **6.** $y = -7$
7. $s = 1$ **8.** $x = -3$ **9.** $x = 5$ **10.** $q = 2$ **11.** $y = 8$
12. $b = 5$ **13.** $x = -2$ **14.** $g = 2$ **15.** $b = 1$ **16.** $h = -70$
17. $x = -5$ **18.** $w = 2$ **19.** $x = 7$ **20.** $r = 2$

Activity 14.4
1. $y = -3$ **2.** $s = 5$ **3.** $x = 2$ **4.** $d = 5$ **5.** $x = 10$ **6.** $a = 5$
7. $h = 3$ **8.** $y = 2$ **9.** $b = 2$ **10.** $c = 9$ **11.** $s = 62$

12. $y = 25$ **13.** $g = 7$ **14.** $w = 4$ **15.** $k = 1$ **16.** $b = -1$
17. $x = 6$ **18.** $y = -8$ **19.** $m = 11$ **20.** $n = 2$

Activity 14. 5
1. (i) $x = 11$ (ii) $x = 75$ (iii) $x = 63$ (iv) $x = 6$ (v) $x = -5$
(vi) 1st number = 26, 2nd number = 33 **2.** (i) $(y - 6)$ years
(ii) $y - 6 = 14$, $\rightarrow y = 14 + 6$, $\rightarrow y = 20$ **3.** $y = 9$ cm,
$y + 3 = 12$ cm, $y + 6 = 15$ cm **4.** (i) $(y + 13)$ years
(ii) $y + 13 = 42$, so $y = 29$ **5.** $4x + 13 = 7x - 20$, so $x = 11$
6. 4 m **7.** 33, 34 and 35 **8.** Jack = 6 sweets, DJ = 6 sweets,
Rachel = 8 sweets, Katie = 7 sweets and Conor = 9 sweets
9. 49 **10.** Length = 8 m, Width = 4 m **11.** (i) $y + 1$
(ii) the numbers are 43 and 44 **12.** Tom is 8 years old.
13. 5 goals **14.** (i) $(21 - x)$ hens (ii) 5 sheep, 16 hens

Revision Activity 14
1. (a) (i) $y = 2$ (ii) $x = -14$ (b) $n = 5$ (c) $d = -1$
(d) Child ticket = €6, Adult ticket = €9 **2.** (a) (i) $h = 10$
(ii) $k = 3$ (b) $f = -1$ (c) $m = 1$ (d) 5 cm, 6 cm and 7 cm
3. (a) (i) $y = -11$ (ii) $b = 13$ (b) $m = 3$ (c) $h = 2$ (d) 52

Exam-style Question
1. $x = -3$

Chapter 15

Activity 15.1
1. Three sides and three angles **2.** (iii) SSS, ASA, SAS
3. (iii) $|\angle HGI| = |\angle LJK|$, $|\angle HIG| = |\angle LKJ|$, $|\angle GHI| = |\angle JLK|$
4. (iii) $|\angle MAN| = |\angle EGD|$, $|\angle ANM| = |\angle GDE|$, $|AN| = |GD|$
5. (iii) $|BC| = |LK|$, $|BF| = |LJ|$, $|\angle CBF| = |\angle KLJ|$
6. (iii) $|FC| = |MK|$, $|\angle ACF| = |\angle LKM|$, $|\angle AFC| = |\angle LMK|$
7. (iii) $|\angle JKN| = |\angle GED|$, $|\angle JNK| = |\angle GDE|$, $|KN| = |ED|$

Activity 15.2
1. (ii) (a) 140° (b) 110° (c) 45° (d) 130° **2.** (i) 50°
(ii) 60° (iii) 60° **4.** (i) $\alpha = 30°$, $\beta = 120°$ (ii) $\theta = 70°$,
$\alpha = 110°$, $\beta = 110°$ (iii) $\alpha = 50°$, $\beta = 70°$ (iv) $\theta = 130°$
(v) $x = 60°$ (vi) $x = 310°$ (vii) $A = 60°$, $B = 30°$ (viii) $X = 30°$,
$Y = 90°$ **5.** (i) AB and AC (ii) JM and KM (iii) RT and ST
(iv) OQ and LQ (v) IU and UV (vi) XY and XZ **6.** α
7. $\angle HIJ = \angle HJI$, $\angle KIJ = \angle KJI$ **8.** $\angle TPS = \angle TSP$, $\angle TPQ = \angle TQP$,
$\angle TQR = \angle TRQ$, $\angle TRS = \angle TSR$

Activity 15.3
2. (v) 3, 4, 5, 6 **4.** (i) $A = 50°$, $B = 130°$, $C = 130°$, $D = 130°$,
$E = 50°$, $F = 130°$, $G = 50°$ **5.** (i) $A = 70°$, $B = 110°$, $C = 70°$,
$D = 110°$, $E = 70°$, $F = 70°$, $G = 110°$

Activity 15.4
1. (i) $\alpha = 50°$ (ii) $\beta = 50°$ (iii) $\theta = 50°$ **2.** (i) $A = 130°$,
$B = 50°$, $C = 130°$, $D = 50°$, $E = 130°$, $F = 50°$, $G = 130°$
3. $A = 70°$, $B = 110°$, $C = 70°$, $D = 110°$, $E = 70°$, $F = 110°$,
$G = 70°$ **4.** $A = 59°$, $B = 60°$ **5.** $A = 125°$, $B = 55°$,
$C = 125°$, $D = 55°$, $E = 125°$, $F = 55°$, $G = 125°$, $H = 55°$,
$J = 125°$, $K = 55°$, $L = 125°$, $R = 55°$, $S = 125°$, $T = 55°$,

$U = 125°$ **6.** $A = 115°$, $B = 65°$, $C = 115°$, $D = 115°$, $E = 65°$,
$F = 65°$, $G = 115°$, $H = 115°$, $J = 115°$, $K = 65°$, $L = 115°$,
$R = 65°$, $S = 65°$, $T = 65°$, $U = 115°$ **7.** $A = B = C = D = 37°$
9. (iii) $\angle BPS = 36°$, $\angle PSF = 36°$ **10.** (i) $\alpha = 45°$ (ii) $\beta = 30°$
(iii) $\theta = 45°$ **11.** (i) $\theta = 80°$ (ii) $\alpha = 60°$ (iii) $\beta = 40°$
12. (i) $|\angle 1| + |\angle 2| + |\angle 3| = 180°$ (ii) $|\angle 1| = |\angle 4|$, $|\angle 3| = |\angle 5|$

Activity 15.5
1. (i) 70° (ii) 60° (iii) 50° (iv) 29° (v) 113° **2.** (i) $A = 90°$,
$B = 69°$ (ii) $A = 109°$, $B = 37°$ **3.** 76° **4.** (i) 60° (ii) 70°
(iii) $\angle QPT$ and $\angle PQT$ **5.** (i) 65° (ii) 135° (iii) $\angle CAB$ and
$\angle CBA$ **6.** (i) $A + B + C = 180°$ (ii) $C + D = 180°$

Activity 15.6
1. (i) $A = 123°$ (ii) $B = 72°$ (iii) $C = 43°$ (iv) $D = 68°$
(v) $E = 45°$ (vi) $F = 126°$, $G = 119°$ **2.** $A = 38°$, $B = 142°$,
$C = 63°$ **3.** $|\angle NRT| = 40°$, $|\angle NTR| = 100°$, $|\angle NTP| = 118°$,
$|\angle TNP| = 31°$, $|\angle TPN| = 31°$ **4.** $X = 70°$, $Y = 110°$, $Z = 250°$
5. $|\angle 1| = 72°$, $|\angle 2| = 135°$, $|\angle 3| = 45°$, $|\angle 4| = 72°$, $|\angle 5| = 45°$
6. (iii) $A = 145°$, $C = 45°$, $D = 100°$, $E = 35°$, $G = 45°$
7. $\theta = 25°$, $\alpha = 25°$, $\beta = 73°$

Revision Activity 15
1. $x = 135°$ **3.** $A = 56°$, $B = 124°$, $C = 124°$, $D = 45°$, $E = 45°$,
$F = 78°$ **6.** Acute angles are 18° and 72° **7.** $A = 110°$,
$B = 70°$, $C = 50°$, $D = 130°$

Exam-style Question
1. (d) 77° (e) $|\angle CAB| = 60°$, $|BAC| = 77°$

Chapter 16

Activity 16.2
1. (ii) $|\angle PQR| = 59°$, $|\angle QRP| = 49°$, $|\angle RPQ| = 72°$ (iii) 180°
(vi) scalene, acute-angled **2.** (ii) $|\angle UTV| = 53°$, $|\angle TVU| = 37°$,
$|\angle VUT| = 90°$ (iii) 180° (iv) scalene, right-angled
3. (ii) $|\angle ABC| = 133°$, $|\angle BAC| = 23.5°$, $|\angle BCA| = 23.5°$
(iii) 180° (v) isosceles, obtuse-angled **4.** (i) equilateral
(ii) They all equal 60°. (iv) 180° **5.** (ii) $|\angle ABC| = 70°$,
$|\angle BAC| = 55°$, $|\angle BCA| = 55°$ (iii) 180° (v) isosceles,
acute-angled **6.** The two shorter sides add up to less than
the length of the longest side.

Activity 16.3
1. (ii) QR (iii) QP **2.** (ii) BC (iii) AB **3.** (ii) GK (iii) GH
4. (ii) LJ (iii) IL **5.** (ii) MO (iii) NO **7.** (i) isosceles
(ii) They are both 50°. (iii) The sides are equal.

Activity 16.4
1. $|AB| = 7.6$, $|AC| = 6.2$, $|\angle BAC| = 60°$ **2.** $|DE| = 8.1$,
$|DF| = 9.2$, $|\angle EDF| = 40°$ **3.** $|PT| = 10.4$, $|RT| = 6$, $|\angle PTR| = 30°$
4. $|UT| = 9$, $|VT| = 7$, $|\angle UTV| = 50°$ **5.** $|AB| = 7$, $|AC| = 7$,
$|\angle BAC| = 60°$ **6.** $|TP| = 10.4$, $|TR| = 12$, $|\angle PTR| = 30°$

Exam-style Question
1. (a) $180° - (40° + 60°) = 80°$

Workings

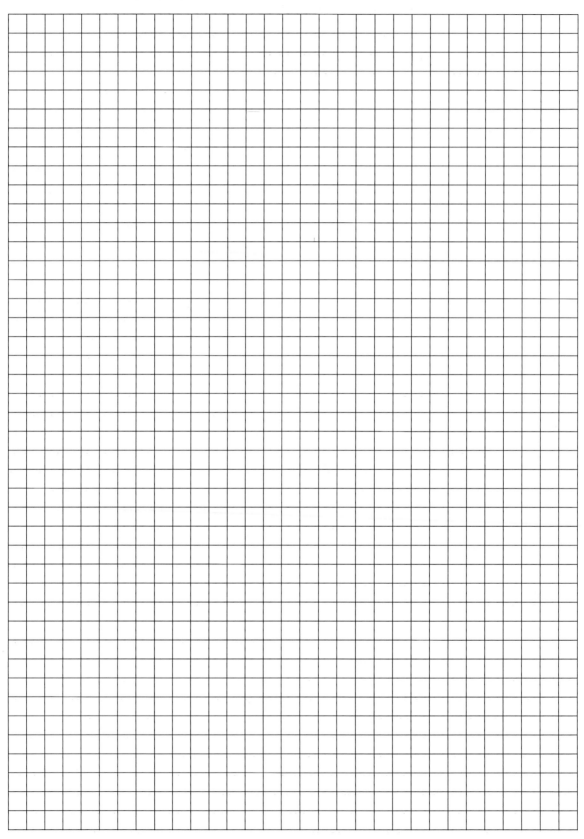

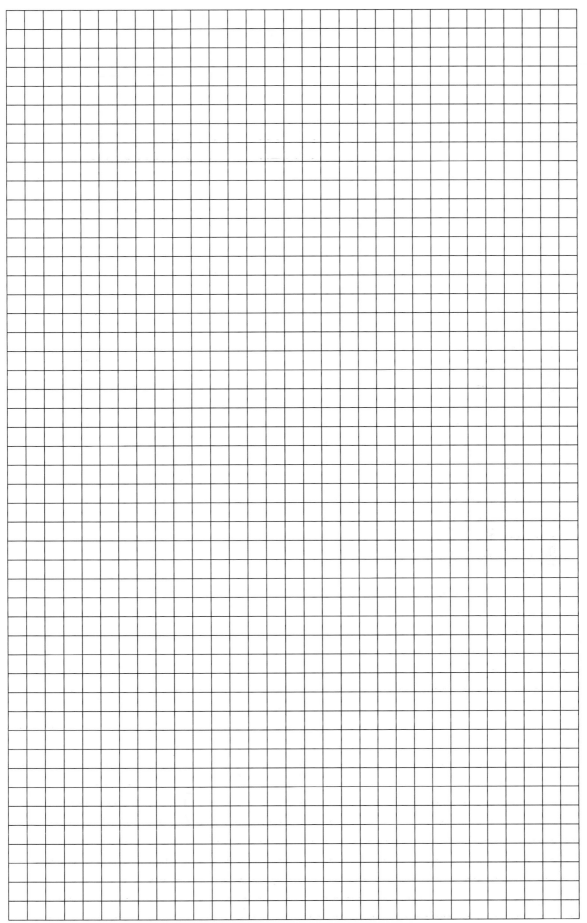

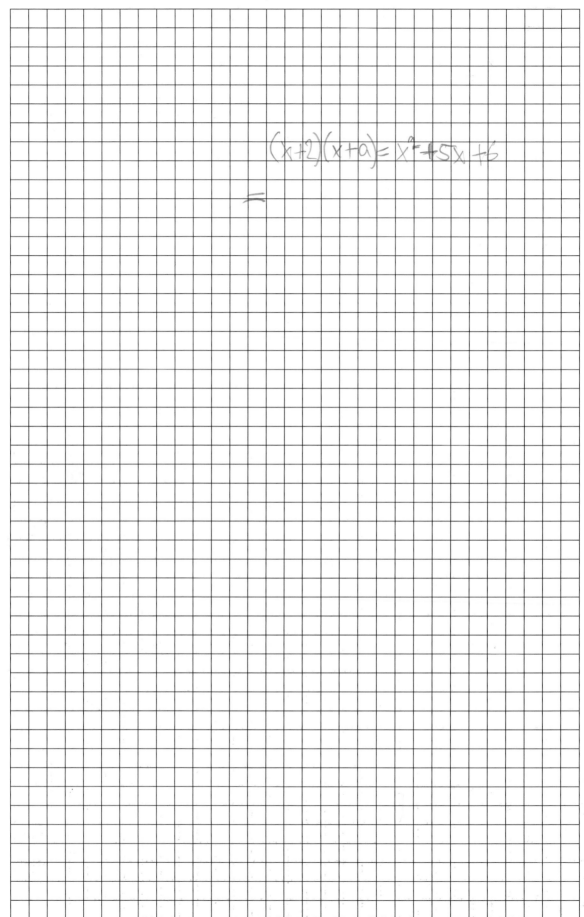

$$(x+2)(x+a) = x^2 + 5x + 6$$

$$=$$

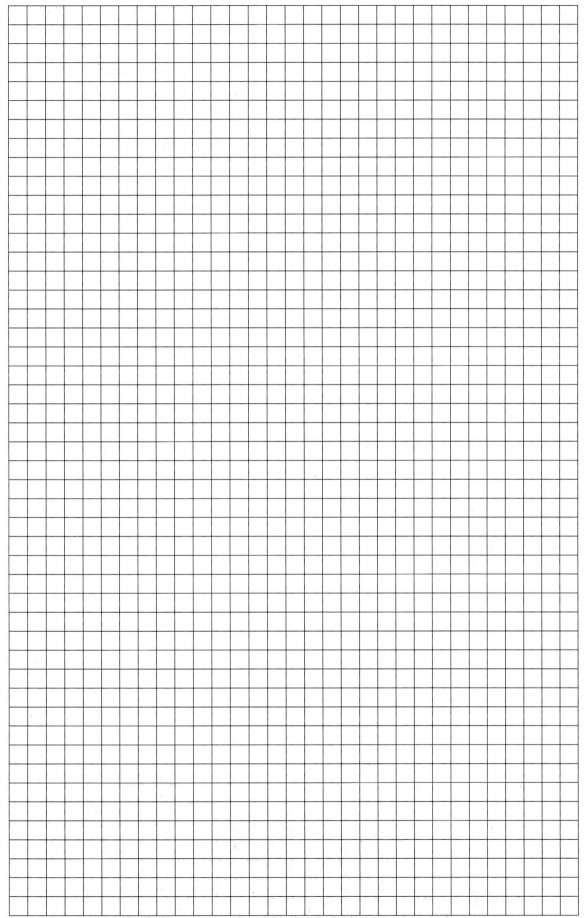

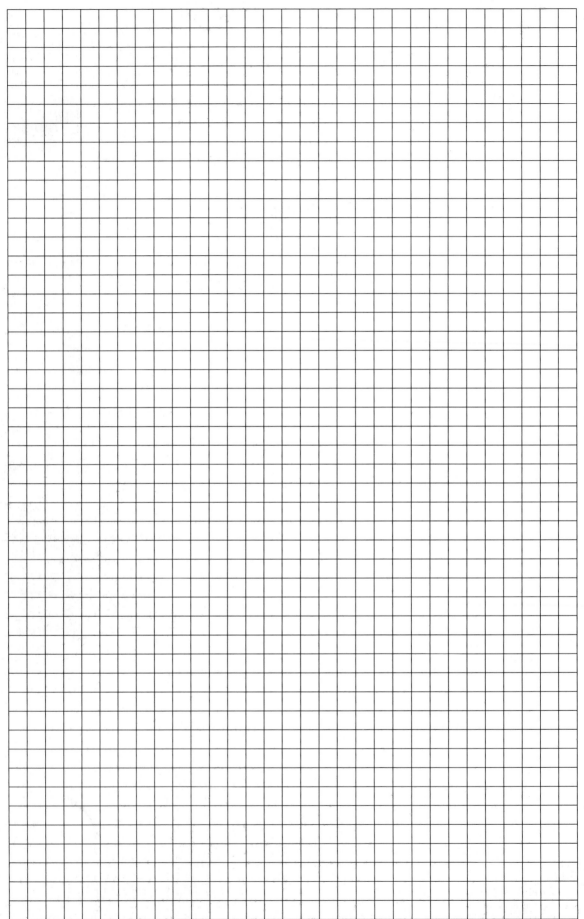